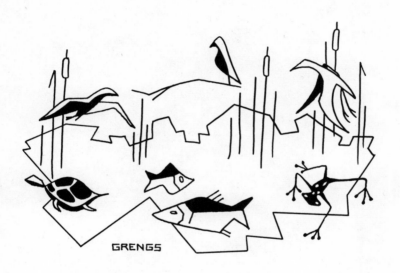

GRENGS

Minnesota Conservation Department

Spring burning of game habitat

An Ecological Approach to

CONSERVATION

RUSSELL L. HAMM

Coordinator of Curriculum and Instruction
Roseville Schools

LARRY NASON

Science Department, Fairview Junior High School
Roseville Schools

Illustrations

JOHN GRENGS

Art Department, Capitol View Junior High School
Roseville Schools

Edited by

LAURENCE S. FLAUM

Burgess Publishing Company

426 South 6th Street • Minneapolis, Minn. 55415

Burgess

EDUCATION SERIES

Consulting Editor — LAURENCE S. FLAUM

Library of Congress Catalog Card Number 64-7544

Printed in the United States of America

Foreword

One of the urgent educational tasks of our times is that of alerting the American public to the problems of conservation. This task must, in large part, be accomplished through our schools. To be effective, conservation education must permeate all levels of learning, must arouse genuine concerns for the future, and must capture the imagination of youth. It must be accorded more consideration than can be given in the classroom; it must include actual experiences that involve the student personally.

An ecological approach to conservation problems is essential to achieve real understanding. No natural resource ~Ecosystem~ can be isolated; it is related to all other aspects of the environment. Man's own place in his ecological community must be constantly borne in mind in any search for a long-term solution to serious conservation problems.

Conservation has taken on new importance as a result of the tremendous expansion of human population. For the first time, the human species has overrun the earth. Conservation today is an essential vehicle in the race to provide, in a world of limited size, not only enough space and food for the prolific family of man but also enough room for other inhabitants of the earth--both plant and animal--and for man's own spiritual requirements.

The problems of air and water pollution and chemical poisoning, although not new, have become increasingly difficult with our growth of population, industry, and inventive genius.

The role of nuclear science in a program of conservation is a new consideration, one which may help in the understanding of certain problems of resource use and life processes, as well as suggesting possible new sources of energy to relieve the drain on non-renewable resources.

All of these aspects of conservation education, considered in this publication, were either barely touched upon or omitted in earlier conservation publications. They are important today, and they will of necessity receive increasing attention in coming years. The approach to conservation in this book is therefore both pertinent and timely.

Several devices assist the reader in making practical application of the information contained in these pages. The objectives stated at the beginning of each chapter clarify the presentation for the user and make him aware of the materials and other things needed in teaching that chapter. The teacher using this book as a text or reference will find particular value in the designation of materials, activities, literature, and audio-visual aids according to their suitability for various educational groups--elementary, secondary, and college. Many materials are suggested for planning educational experiences. Useful ideas are offered for integrating conservation education into various courses in the school curriculum. The glossary at the end of the book is convenient and enlightening.

In philosophy sound, in subject matter timely, in style clear, and in presentation practical, the authors have given us a book which should contribute to effective education in an area of vital importance.

Reynold E. Carlson
Chairman
Department of Recreation
Indiana University

Acknowledgments

In compiling this book the following organizations were most helpful: Corps of Engineers, U. S. Army Engineer District, St. Paul, Minnesota; Erie Mining Company, Hoyt Lakes, Minnesota, (Pickands Mather & Company, agents, Duluth, Minnesota); Watershed Management Division, United States Forest Service, Washington, D.C.; Minnesota State Department of Conservation, St. Paul, Minnesota; United States Steel Corporation, Duluth, Minnesota; Minnesota Department of Business Development, St. Paul, Minnesota; Minnesota Department of Health, St. Paul, Minnesota; Rural Cooperative Power Association, Elk River, Minnesota; United States Soil Conservation Service, St. Paul, Minnesota; Minnesota Historical Society, St. Paul, Minnesota; and the Roseville School District (Library and Audio-Visual Departments), Roseville, Minnesota.

Special credit: Mrs. Jacqueline Jambor and Mrs. Lorraine Thunstedt in preparing the manuscript; Mrs. Edythe Fawkes in reading the manuscript to improve the English; Dr. Harry A. Robinson of General Beadle State Teachers College in scientific criticism and reading; and Dr. Laurence S. Flaum, President of General Beadle State Teachers College as editor.

Table of Contents

GRENGS

The waste of plenty is
the resource of scarcity.

T. L. Peacock

Chapter I   INTRODUCTION

OBJECTIVES

   I. To achieve a broader understanding of the nature and meaning of conservation.

  II. To point to the significance and ramifications of the conservation movement.

 III. To highlight the major developments of the conservation movement in the United States.

 IV. To note the interrelationships of conservation in the many subject matter fields -- and the value of conservation to people in all walks of life.

Man's very survival depends on the wise use of resources. The importance of conservation is symbolized by the daily headlines: The controversy over insecticides was initiated by Rachel Carson's *Silent Spring*, and for days Minnesota newspapers were filled with news stories and articles about ducks dying on the Mississippi River because of stream pollution. The Supreme Court decision over Colorado water rights made the headlines in California and Arizona newspapers. *Conservation is important today!*

     This book is an attempt to present an overview to the whole area of conservation -- as a resource for teachers, for elementary, secondary, and college students, and for laymen. Future chapters of the book will be concerned with the following topics: *Conservation and Ecology* will develop the community concept to show how various biotic and environmental factors interact in nature to maintain a relatively "dynamic" stability in plant and animal communities; *Water Conservation* will emphasize the importance of water to community life -- watershed management, hydrological cycle, etc.; *Soil Conservation* will discuss the formation, properties of soil, as well as the erosion problem, the role of irrigation, and the importance of soil in world ecology; *Air Pollution* will point to the progress made in reducing contaminants as well as the unsolved problems that still remain with nuclear contamination, dust storms, smog; *Mineral Conservation* will present the basic kinds of mineral structure and formation, with its influence on soil formation vegetative development, and economic development; *Forest Conservation* will deal primarily with the ecology, management, and economy; *Grassland Conservation* will include ecological application to the biota, and management for economic use; *Wildlife Conservation* will emphasize ecological and aesthetic values as well as the economic values; the importance of recreation in developing the health and economy of a nation will be stressed in *Recreational Resource Values;* the controversial subject of *Chemical Pollution* will show the beneficial and detrimental effects of chemical use in controlling plant and animal pests; the *Role of Nuclear Science in Conservation* will evaluate the alternatives and the philosophical questionings of nuclear power; the "exploding" world population will be the topic of *Population Dynamics; Home and Yard Conservation* will illustrate conservation as a "living" subject -- landscaping and its various aspects. And finally, *Agriculture Conservation* will highlight the economic, political and technological changes as they relate to conservation.

Conservation means the wise use of human and natural resources. Essentially conservation does not mean saving resources. In fact, the new emphasis in conservation is upon *multiple use.* The multiple use of federal and state forests, for example, for the production of wood crops, for slowing down run-off of water, for wildlife habitat and protection, and for outdoor recreation increases the overall total conservation of the forests. (See Figures 1 and 2) "The goal of conservation should be the achievement of a harmonious, perpetual adjustment of the American society to the total resource base." [1]

Sometimes conservation involves the replacement of resources that have been used. The tree farmer, for example, sets out seedlings to replace the trees he cuts. The dirt farmer adds fertilizer and minerals to his soil to replace the ingredients taken from the soil by the crops. Sometimes new resources must be found. The development and use of synthetics can reduce the pressure of depletion on scarce resources, but all synthetic products require natural resources for materials and production energy. Chemical industries, for example,

[1]Richard M. Highsmith, Jr., J. Granville Jensen, Robert D. Rudd, Conservation in the United States (Chicago: Rand McNally and Company, 1962), p. 4.

Minnesota Department of Business Development

Figure 1. For Outdoor Recreation

which produce synthetics require water of suitable quantity
and quality which in turn depends on sound management of
grazing, agricultural, and forest lands, and upon reduction
of water pollution.[2] Atomic energy is one example of a substitute which is being used to take the place of scarce resources. It must be made clear to the public that certain
natural resources (fuels and minerals) are limited and can
never be replaced once they are used. "Atomic farms" are
located throughout the country. On these farms, scientists

---

[2]Byron L. Ashbaugh and Muriel Beuschlein, Things to Do in Science and Conservation (Danville, Ill.: Interstate Printers and Publishers, Inc., 1960), p. 146

Minnesota Department of Business Development

Figure 2. Gooseberry Falls -- For Wildlife Habitat and Protection

are working to produce better strains of plants, discover better
methods of using fertilizers, rid crops of insect pests and learn
more about the ways plants make food.[3] "Scientists have said
that radioisotopes are the most important new tool of research
they have had since the microscope."[4] By tagging atoms with
radioactivity, scientists can trace their journeys through life
processes and learn more about the events which occur inside
living cells.

[3]Margaret O. Hyde, Atoms: Today and Tomorrow (New York: Whittlesey House-
McGraw Hill, 1955) p. 92.
    [4]Laura Fermie, The Story of Atomic Energy (Eau Claire, Wisc.: E. M. Hale and
Company, 1961), p. 163.

Today, more than ever before, conservation is of the utmost importance. First of all, the human population is increasing on the earth at an almost explosive rate. The world's population is nearly three billion and is increasing by about 135,000 a day. The spaces on the earth's surface where human beings may live are extremely limited by oceans, by mountains, and by deserts. Also, the need for conservation for a long time was recognized by only a few people. As a result, serious mistakes were made; forests were burned, grasslands were plowed, wildlife was killed in great numbers. In conservation, each generation cannot start with a clean slate. The passenger pigeon cannot be brought back; erosion ditches cut in a few brief years may take decades to fill, or they may never fill. In conservation, errors accumulate and act like a chain reaction. Trees cut on a steep hillside foster erosion, erosion facilitates flood conditions and damages watershed, flood conditions destroy wildlife, soil, and habitat. (See Figure 3).

One of the big problems in conservation is man's own limited life span. He cannot always see the wasting away of resources, so gradual is the disintegration that it may be inconspicuous to him; or, he may see the dangers of the wasting away of resources and, in his own selfishness, not care. It is unfortunate that posterity matters little to some men. It is in these terms that the late Richard T. Neuberger defined conservation: "The disaster which Americans must continually patrol against is the reckless and speedy consumption of our natural resources by our waste and profligacy. We could use up most of these resources and leave future generations comparatively destitute. The prevention of such a catastrophe has come to be known as conservation."[5]

W. C. Lowdermilk indicates in a United States Department of Agriculture bulletin that poor conservation practices have caused the demise of once great civilizations.[6] In Mesopotamia, for example, at least eleven empires have risen and fallen in 7,000 years. It is a story, he says, of a precarious agriculture practiced by people who lived and grew up under the threat of raids and invasions from the denizens of grasslands and the desert, and of the failure of their irrigation canals because of silt.

[5]Richard L. Neuberger, Our Natural Resources -- And Their Conservation (Public Affairs Pamphlet No. 230, January, 1956), p. 2.

[6]W. C. Lowdermilk, Conquest of the Land Through 7,000 Years (Washington, D.C.: Agriculture Information Bulletin No. 99, U. S. Department of Agriculture, 1953), p. 4.

Minnesota Conservation Department

Figure 3. Minnesota River Flood -- 1962

Conservation is not a science, although conservation makes use of the knowledge discovered by science. Conservation is essentially a branch of the social studies; it is essentially a political and economic term. Conservation is concerned with getting the maximum use of natural resources so as to secure the greatest good for the greatest number of people over the longest period of time.

It is too bad that many men are not able to see that conservation is everybody's business, that what affects one man affects all men, that this is an interdependent world, that no man is an island. Conservation concerns the fire warden, the teacher, the social worker, the farmer, the doctor, and the layman -- "every man, U. S. A. " Conservation is the concern of the local, state, and national government.

The first conservationists in America were Indians. Before the white man changed their habits, the Indians used only what was needed. Most of the early settlers of the United States were not concerned with conservation. The Swiss and the Pennsylvania Dutch settlers were the notable exceptions as they were interested in conservation.

Rapid depletion of forests initiated early conservation efforts. William Penn in 1681 proclaimed by ordinance that for every five acres of land cleared, one acre was to be left in forest. In 1691, the English government ruled that white pines, over twenty-four inches in diameter, were to be marked with a broad arrow and reserved for the Royal Navy. The Broad Arrow Edict came to apply to all New England, New York, and New Jersey.

George Washington was a conservationist. He believed in the rotation of crops, the use of clover, rye, and timothy to enrich the soil. He imported trees and shrubs from all parts of the world, and corresponded with experimenters in agriculture both far and near.

Like Washington, Thomas Jefferson was an agriculturist and a conservationist. He also believed in crop rotation and was one of the first Americans to employ contour plowing. He invented a mold board plow that was used widely for many years.

The first official conservation act of the United States government came during the administration of John Quincy Adams. In 1828, he set aside 30, 000 acres of oak forest near Pensacola, Florida, for building ships for the navy. This was the Santa Rosa project. Part of the area was planted in oaks, but the experiment failed -- and the station was abandoned.

The Department of Interior was established in 1849. Its principal function is to develop and conserve the natural resources of the United States and its territories. The department sponsors scientific investigation and research relating to natural resources. The department operates fish hatcheries and wildlife sanctuaries. It administers the national park system; it supervises the management and disposition of public land and resources.

The Department of Agriculture was established in 1862, but it was not made an executive department until 1889. The department collaborates with state agriculture colleges and experiment stations in research, soil conservation, and forestry. The department also administers the national forests and aids in flood control.

The real need for conservation grew out of defects in the land policy after the War between the States. Land speculators, lumber companies, and mining companies had taken over vast areas, paying practically nothing for them.

In 1873, Franklin B. Hough read a paper before the American Association for the Advancement of Science stressing the importance of retaining large areas of public forests. In 1875, the American Forestry Association was organized, and its major purpose was forest conservation. In 1876 Congress enacted legislation authorizing a forestry agent in the Department of Agriculture, and Mr. Hough was appointed to the position.

In 1879, Major John Wesley Powell published *Report on the Lands of the Arid Region of the United States.* He wrote of the problems of flood control and irrigation. In 1886 he was appointed director of the geological survey, a post he occupied until 1894. He worked for conservation until his death in 1902.

In 1891 Congress passed one of the most significant laws dealing with conservation. The law authorized the President of the United States to withdraw land from the public domain and to create forest reserves. That same year, the first forest reserve was acquired. President Benjamin Harrison set aside 15,000,000 acres as forest reservations, and President Grover Cleveland withdrew 21,000,000 additional acres and placed them in reserve.

Theodore Roosevelt is the president who is most noted for his efforts in conservation. A national policy of conservation was begun during his administration. Growing out of a suggestion made by the Inland Water Commission (1907), appointed by Theodore Roosevelt, was the recommendation that the President call a governors' conference. This group declared the problem of conservation to be truly a national problem. Acting on this suggestion, the President called a conference on May 13, 1908. Not only governors, but also congressmen, scientists, and other national leaders were invited. This conference was extremely important for three reasons. First, it led to the establishment of the National Conservation Commission (1908), which made the first inventory of national resources in the United States. Second, a further conference was held, i.e., the North American Conservation Conference which was held on February 18, 1909, and to which the President invited interested representatives from Canada, Newfoundland, and Mexico. Third, the governors' conference resulted in the establishment of state conservation commissions by governors in forty-one states.

Theodore Roosevelt started the construction of the Roosevelt Dam on the Salt River in Arizona as a means of bringing moisture to arid soils in that area. In 1902, the Reclamation Act (Newlands Act) became law. It was the beginning of the modern reclamation policy and established the Reclamation Service. In 1894 Congress had passed the Carey Act, a law which turned over to the states certain arid public lands on condition that they be reclaimed. They could be irrigated by private enterprise.

Theodore Roosevelt in his *Autobiography* said that Gifford Pinchot is the man to whom the nation owes most for what has been accomplished as regards the preservation of the national resources of this country. Pinchot had gone to France to obtain his training in forestry; and when he returned to this country, he was hired by George W. Vanderbilt to make working plans for the management of the forests on the Biltmore estate in North Carolina. This effort resulted in the first successful forest management work in the United States. [7] Later, in 1898, Pinchot became the Head of the Division of Forestry in the United States Department of Agriculture. In 1901 Theodore Roosevelt became President of the United States. Being vitally interested in the conservation of all national resources, he formed a team with Gifford Pinchot to bring about the most spectacular conservation era in this country. [8] Incidentally, Gifford Pinchot also acted as chairman of the National Conservation Commission which grew out of the White House Conference of Governors in May, 1908.

During Taft's administration there arose the Ballinger-Pinchot controversy. Gifford Pinchot, a personal friend of Roosevelt and a conservation expert, was instrumental in organizing the National Conservation Association and served as its president. Richard Ballinger, Secretary of Interior under William Howard Taft, cancelled a Roosevelt order as illegal. Ballinger claimed that public land was valuable for water

[7]Dale White, Gifford Pinchot: The Man Who Saved the Forests (New York: Julian Messner, Inc., 1957), p. 91.

[8]A. F. Gustafson, C. H. Guise, W. J. Hamilton, Jr., and H. Ries, Conservation in the United States (Ithaca, New York: Comstock Publishing Company, 1933), p. 18.

power, and he claimed the President's authority extended only
to timber lands.   Pinchot protested Ballinger's act and further
accused him of permitting valuable coal lands in Alaska to fall
into private hands.   The House of Representatives supported
Ballinger, and the President removed Pinchot from his job as
Chief Forester.   Ardent conservationists charged Taft with
allying himself to private interests.   It is to be noted, however,
that Ballinger recommended that Congress pass a series of
acts to compel future presidents to continue the policy of conservation, and that nine separate laws were passed which gave
conservation a solid legal basis for the future.

Federal cooperation with the states in forest conservation was really started by Senator John Weeks in 1911.   From
that time on, the federal government steadily enlarged its
holdings of national forests.   The Clarke-McNary Act of 1924
made available funds to assist states in their efforts to prevent and to control forest fires.   The funds available for this
cooperation were increased in amount over the years, and at
the present time the annual federal authorization amounts to
over $9,000,000.   Now purchases of land could be made at
the headwaters of navigable streams for inclusion in the national forest system.   Prior to that time, all national forests
had been established in the West.

It was not until 1916 that the National Park Service, as
it presently operates, was established.   It now protects nearly
thirty large parks and almost one hundred and fifty other areas
of scenic and historical interest in every state in the Union.

Franklin D. Roosevelt established a significant record
in conservation -- second only to that of Theodore Roosevelt.
The Civilian Conservation Corps, one of his earliest conservation projects, provided work for unemployed young men.   At
one time, there were 2,652 camps in operation.   The CCC boys
planted trees, fought forest fires, terraced land, cleared
stream channels, constructed picnic areas, built fish rearing
ponds -- a multitude of jobs that essentially had to do with conserving the natural resources of the country. [9]

The Tennessee Valley Authority also was established
during Roosevelt's administration.   The Tennessee River and
its tributaries with all its resources were to be brought to a
high degree of development through unified and integrated governmental control.   The various purposes of T.V.A. were

[9]Charles N. Elliott, Conservation of American Resources (Atlanta: Turner E. Smith
and Company, 1956), p. 39

many: Supply cheap power, improve navigation, reduce flood damage, restore the forests, halt erosion, relieve unemployment -- and in all ways improve the social and economic conditions of the citizens of the Tennessee Valley.

Prior to the Taylor Grazing Act (1934), the public lands were relatively free to stockmen. There was over-grazing and, as a result, there was deterioration of the range resources. The Taylor Grazing Act was to stabilize the livestock industry's using the public range and to provide for the improvement and development of the public range.

The great dust storms of the Southwest in 1934 made the public aware of the great need for soil conservation. In 1935 the Soil Conservation Act was passed to deal with the problem of soil erosion and other forms of soil deterioration.

The Wildlife Restoration Act of 1937 gave federal aid to states for acquiring and developing lands under state control for conserving wildlife. A further Migratory Bird Conservation Agreement was made with Mexico in 1936.

Franklin Roosevelt also established the National Resources Board with Harold L. Ickes, Secretary of Interior, as chairman. The board submitted a report containing an inventory of all natural resources and recommendations for future action -- the first such report since 1908.

The first comprehensive study of our known mineral resources and needs appeared in 1947 as a joint report by the United States Geological Survey and the United States Bureau of Mines to the Committee on Public Lands of the United States Senate. Later reports by individual mining associations brought the situation with respect to certain minerals more nearly up-to-date; and in June, 1952, the President's Minerals Policy Commission published a voluminous report entitled "Resources for Freedom" -- commonly known as the Paley Report. This report calls the attention of the public to the progressive depletion of our known resources. It brought together available information concerning known resources and showed the probable production and consumption trends in this country for the next quarter of a century. [10]

Also, during the Eisenhower administration, further important conservation measures were passed by Congress. The Watershed Protection and Flood Prevention Act (1954) encouraged the efforts of local citizen groups to protect water-

[10]P. E. McNall, Our National Resources (Danville, Ill.: Interstate Printers and Publishers, 1954), p. 235.

sheds "from the top down. " Specific attention was focused on the range states by the Great Plains Conservation program of 1956. The Soil Bank Act of 1956 also included features that contributed to soil and water conservation. Payments to help defray costs of establishing conservation were made to participants in the program. The act specified that land retired from crop production must be planted to trees or grass, or be used for water storage facilities such as lakes and ponds.

More recently in the Kennedy administration, under the leadership of Stewart Udall, Secretary of Interior, further progress has been made in conservation. A report by scientists has backed Rachel Carson's stand on pesticides as presented in her book *Silent Spring*. New legislation is sure to be forth-coming.

In summary, even the definition of conservation has undergone change, and at last the great significance of the conservation movement has been communicated to people in all walks of life. The above paragraphs are but a precis of conservation history, but positively speaking, it is also a prologue of conservation history in the making.

ACTIVITIES

E = Elementary   *S* = Secondary   *C* = College

1. Construct a resource unit which would compare and contrast the conservation movement in the United States with that of another country such as India or Sweden. *C*
2. Write a summary of the history of the conservation movement in your state which may be duplicated and used as a reading resource for your students. *C*
3. Prepare a list of local personnel who could be used by your school as resource people in teaching about conservation. *C*
4. Make a bulletin board display of great men in conservation. *C–S*
5. Make a survey to discover the most important area of concern in conservation in the school or local community. (The survey instrument must be carefully constructed.)
6. Make an electrical quiz board to be used in the classroom. (If famous conservationists are used in the first unit, mammals, birds, fish, etc. , may later replace the famous men.) *C–S*

7. Write a short biography of outstanding conservationists such as John Muir, Carl Schurz, and John Burroughs. *C-S*

8. Keeping up-to-date: Report on the Dixon-Yates Contract, cancelled in July, 1955, by President Eisenhower. What are the implications? What was the significance of the contract? *C-S*

9. Make a chart showing the significant acts of Congress (or the state legislature) in the areas of conservation. *C-S*

10. Clip all articles from the local newspaper over a two-week period that are directly or indirectly related to conservation. What does this prove about the significance of conservation? *E-S*

11. Organize a conservation club and write a constitution. *E-S*

12. Prepare a bibliography of conservation materials available in your own school library and/or community library. *S-C*

13. Have a committee report to the class concerning the career opportunities in conservation. (See Jean Smith's book, *Find a Career in Conservation.*) *S*

14. Make posters pointing to the need for conservation. *E*

15. Write an essay about the importance of conservation. *E--S*

16. Let's imagine: What would happen if all the grass were removed from the school yard. (Discussion) *E*

17. Make a scrapbook of clippings, drawings, and pictures about conservation. *E-S*

18. Debate: One day the earth will be unable to produce enough food and raw materials for all the people who crowd its continents. *S*

19. Library Research: Identify youth, non-governmental organizations that make significant contributions to the field of conservation. *S*

20. Collect various definitions of conservation by people such as William Howard Taft, H. G. Wells, etc. *S-C*

21. An exercise in observation: Take the class on a field trip around the school yard. Point out the differences in color and texture in the grass. Ask why? Is it shade, soil, moisture, traffic, etc. ? *E*

22. Let students bring their collections of rocks, soils, leaves, etc. for display in the classroom. These displays can be related to conservation. *E*

23. Take photographs to illustrate poor conservation in the community. *S-C*

24. Discussion: Modern man controls the environment vs.
    Man is controlled by the environment. *S-C*
25. Begin collecting resource materials of conservation --
    flat pictures, free bulletins, books. A wooden box can be
    used in lieu of a file cabinet. *C*

BIBLIOGRAPHY

Allen, Shirley W. *Conserving Natural Resources: Principles
    and Practices in a Democracy.* New York: McGraw-Hill,
    1955. pp. 1-17. *S-C*
Ashbaugh, Byron L. and Muriel Beuschlein. *Things To Do In
    Science and Conservation.* Danville, Illinois: Interstate
    Printers and Publishers, Inc. , 1960. *C*
Bathurst, Effie and Wilhelmina Hill. *Conservation Experiences
    for Children.* U. S. Department of Health, Education, and
    Welfare, Bulletin No. 16. Washington: Government Print-
    ing Office, 1957. *C*
Beuschlein, Muriel. *Free and Inexpensive Materials for Con-
    servation Education.* National Association of Biology
    Teachers. Danville, Illinois: Interstate Printers and
    Publishers, Inc. *C*
Bronson, Wilfred S. *Freedom and Plenty: Ours to Save.*
    New York: Harcourt Brace & Company, 1953. *E*
Callison, Charles H. *America's Natural Resources.* New
    York: Ronald Press Company, 1957. *S-C*
Chase, Stuart. *Rich Land, Poor Land.* New York: Whittlesey
    House (McGraw-Hill), 1936. *C*
Clawson, Marion. *Uncle Sam's Acres.* New York: Dodd,
    Mead and Company, 1951. *S-C*
Elliott, Charles N. *Conservation of American Resources.*
    Atlanta: Turner E. Smith and Company, 1956. pp. 3-48.
    S-C
Fermie, Laura. *The Story of Atomic Energy.* Eau Claire,
    Wisconsin: E. M. Hale and Company, 1961. *S-C*
Gustafson, A. F. , C. H. Guise, W. J. Hamilton, Jr. , and
    H. Ries. *Conservation in the United States.* Ithaca, New
    York: Comstock Publishing Company, 1933. pp. 8-33. *S-C*
Highsmith, Richard M. , Jr. , J. Granville Jensen, Robert D.
    Rudd. *Conservation in the United States.* Chicago: Rand
    McNally and Company, 1962. *C*
Hill, Albert F. *Economic Botany.* New York: McGraw-Hill,
    1952. pp. 1-117. *C*

Hogner, Dorothy C. *Conservation in America*. Philadelphia:
   J. B. Lippencott Company, 1958. **S–C**
Hyde, Margaret O. *Atoms: Today and Tomorrow*. New York:
   Whittlesey House (McGraw-Hill), 1955. **S–C**
Kreps, Juanita M. *Our National Resources: Their Develop-
   ment and Use.* New York: H. W. Wilson Company,
   1955. **S–C**
Lowdermilk, W. C. *Conquest of the Land Through 7,000
   Years*. U. S. Department of Agriculture, Agriculture In-
   formation Bulletin No. 99. Washington: Government
   Printing Office, 1953. **S–C**
McNall, P. E. *Our National Resources*. Danville, Illinois:
   Interstate Printers and Publishers, 1954. **S–C**
Neal, Edward H. *Nature's Guardians: Your Career in Con-
   servation*. New York: Julian Mesner, Inc. , 1956. **S**
Neuberger, Richard L. *Our Natural Resources and Conserva-
   tion*. Public Affairs Pamphlet No. 230. New York: Public
   Affairs Committee, 1956. **S**
Osborn, Fairfield, *Our Plundered Planet*. Boston: Little
   Brown and Company, 1948. **S–C**
Smith, F. C. *The First Book of Conservation*. New York:
   Franklin Watts, 1954. **E**
Smith, Jean. *Find a Career in Conservation*. New York:
   G. P. Putnam's Sons, 1959. **S**
White, Dale. *Gifford Pinchot: The Man Who Saved the
   Forests*. New York: Julian Mesner, Inc. , 1957. **S–C**
Zimmermann, Erich W. *World Resources and Industries*.
   New York: Harper and Brothers, 1951. **C**

AUDIO-VISUAL MATERIALS

16 mm. FILMS

Adventuring in Conservation

   The film features many boys and girls in an actual camp
   involved in conservation activities, such as camping,
   hiking, boating, fishing, etc. The young people discover
   many wonders of nature, as well as the need for care
   and consideration in the perpetuation of natural resources.
   E–S

Atom and Agriculture - (EBF)

This film shows how sources of radioactivity are applied to genetic and growth studies. It depicts other experiments with plants, soils, and animals -- experiments in which radioisotopes play a significant part. **S-C**

Atom and Biological Science - (EBF)

The theme deals principally with the biological effects of high energy radiations. It explains utilization of good effects of radiations on organisms and how to guard against harmful effects. **S-C**

Careers in Agriculture - (Cor)

Richard explores with his high school agriculture teacher the many careers in agriculture. He learns of career opportunities in the areas of crop and livestock farming; agricultural research, industry, conservation, and services; and agricultural communication and education. **S**

Conservation of Natural Resources - (EBF)

Early wastes in the lumbering industry and agriculture are presented. Efforts to check the abuses are outlined. There is a sequence on conservation and development of esthetic resources. **S-C**

Conservation Road - (EBF)

The conservation road has finally become a broad highway. Farmers, prospectors, oilmen, miners, lumbermen, fishermen, and men of government and industry are concerned with diminishing natural resources. **S-C**

Gift of Green - (SII)

The film indicates that all life is directly or indirectly dependent upon green plants. **S-C**

Green Gold - (UN-AssoF)

Experts of the Food and Agriculture Organization seek a lasting solution to the problems of timber shortage. **S-C**

Heritage We Guard - (UW)

It is concerned with the damage to soil and wildlife with westward migration and the current restoration plans. **S**

The Land - (CFD)

As a documentary film, it depicts drama of homeless millions, young migrants, victims of erosion, machines -- a drama of relation between human beings and the soil they cultivate. **S-C**

Look to the Land - (EBF)

This film shows dependence of our people on America's resources. It documents some of the tragic consequences of neglect of these resources and emphasizes the necessity of recognizing the relationship of things in nature to each other. **S-C**

The Meaning of Conservation - (Cor)

It shows what is being done to maintain our country's resources and natural beauty by limiting hunting and fishing, building dams to control floods, planting trees, and developing new farming methods. **S-C**

Natural Resources of the Pacific Coast - (Cor)

The necessity for conserving natural resources is presented strikingly. The film illustrates the magnitude of the lumbering, fishing, and mineral industries. **E-S**

News Magazine of the Screen: Vol. 7, No. 2, 1956 - (WPN)

This issue has several sections that relate to conservation -- the first oil well, nature on a rampage, bombs probe earth's crust, and dam dooms Indian fishing. **S**

Our Part in Conservation - (McGH)

Two children are taught the importance of conservation, as they see how it is practiced in their community and how its principles can be applied to their own lawn. **E-S**

Our Productive Land - (PDP)

Early day farming is contrasted to modern production and distribution methods. Scientific and conservation farming is emphasized. *E–S*

Rape of the Earth - (BIS)

Soil erosion has drained the earth for centuries. Remedial work has been begun, but millions of acres have been lost for all time. *S–C*

Seeds of Destruction - (EBF)

The film reveals the alarming extent to which man is depleting the resources on which his survival depends. *S*

A Strand Breaks - (EBF)

This shows the consequences of a state of unbalance in nature. Man has introduced new elements into nature's balance that cause further depletion of resources. *S–C*

T. V. A. - (TVA)

It describes the development of power and rehabilitation of the land and people of the Tennessee Valley under the Tennessee Valley Authority. Film can be used to introduce the study of long-range planning in development of physical and human resources. *S–C*

FILMSTRIPS

The Need for Conservation - (Eye-Gate House, Jamaica 35, New York) *E–S*

Story of T. V. A. - (T. V. A. Information Office)

This filmstrip presents a factual account of the operations of the T. V. A. in the fields of flood control, navigation, fertilizer-munitions research, agriculture, forestry, and electric power. It is accompanied by a written script and discussion guide. This filmstrip is free. *S*

This Land of Ours - (Eye-Gate House, Jamaica 35, New York) *S-E*

The Waste of Our Resources - (Eye-Gate House, Jamaica 35, New York) *E-S*

TAPES

Following Conservation Trails - (Order *Tape Laboratory Bulletin* to obtain information on how to order tapes and charges for services from Erwin C. Welke, Audio-Visual Extension Service, University of Minnesota, Minneapolis 14, Minnesota) Fifteen minute tapes for grades 5 through 8.

"Conservation Comes to the Land" - (FCT-601-15)

All living things, people, birds and animals depend on a thin layer of soil spread on top of the earth. Martha, Jim and Grandpa explore this "layer of life" on a farm.

"Nature's Partner" - (FCT-612-30)

The tape stresses the need to develop interest in man's role in the use and management of natural resources.

"They, Too, Shall Live" - (FCT-612-14)

The development of attitudes of concern for the welfare of wildlife and other natural resources is interwoven in this exciting story of classroom adventure.

"What Happened Here?" - (FCT-612-20)

This tape aids the development of the power of observation to interpret the cause and effect of changes and developments within the natural resources environment.

Nature, in her most dazzling
aspects or stupendous parts,
is but the background and
theatre to the tragedy of man.
John Morley

Chapter II   CONSERVATION AND ECOLOGY

OBJECTIVES

    I. To relate ecology to conservation.
   II. To point to the immediate, functional aspects of ecological "balance" and conservation.
  III. To outline the development, structure, and nature of biomes.
  IV. To vivify specific biomes and note the plant and animal relationships found therein.

      Ecology is a relatively new science which has to do with the interrelationships between living organisms and their environment. It is derived from two Greek words meaning "study of the home." The word "oecology" was coined by Ernst Haeckel, a German zoologist, in 1866, but it did not gain wide acceptance until early in the twentieth century. The ecological viewpoint is the integrated view of man's environment: There is interdependence in all its parts.

      As applied to man's practical problems, the ecological viewpoint holds that "anything so complicated as a planet inhabited by more than a million and a half species of plants and animals, all of them living together in a more or less balanced equilibrium in which they constantly use and reuse the same molecules of the soil and air, cannot be improved by aimless and uninformed tinkering."[11] The ecological approach views man in relationship to his total environment. Ecology is related to conservation in that ecology may be said to be the science from which conservation must find principles and direction.

      The ecologist collects data, makes generalizations, and predicts what will happen under a given set of circumstances. For example, an ecologist can easily predict what will happen

[11]Ralph Buchsbaum and Mildred Buchsbaum, Basic Ecology (Pittsburgh: Boxwood Press, 1957), p. 20.

to a valley farm if a nearby mountainside is deforested. A flood may rush down the valley cutting huge gullies, making the land less fertile, driving the wildlife from the region, and eventually driving the farmer off the land. The ecologist can theorize regarding the long term consequences of man's action -- or his lack of action. The ecologist can give the conservationist guidelines for action. The conservationist's questions about community may be concerned more with the *what*, while the ecologist may be more concerned with the *why*.

Obviously, plants and animals do not live in "nothingness." Trees cling to the earth and seek nourishment from the sun and the sky. Many are the creatures that live in the sea. And, varied are the animals that creep and crawl upon the face of the earth. Environment surrounds all plants and animals. (See Figures 4 and 5)

Environment is physical (non-living), which includes heat, light, gravity, the substratum, *or* environment is biotic (living), which consists of plants and animals.

In the evolutionary process, natural selection acts as a force which kills off the less able individuals and allows the more fit to survive. Through the ages, as now, living things are limited in their distribution by physical factors, as well as biotic factors. Extremes of temperatures, unusual dryness, or even the lack of a particular species of tree, will limit the ranges of animals. Bodies of water, mountains, or desert can limit the distribution of plants and animals. These organisms must adjust or adapt to the environment in order to survive. The following are examples: Frogs, although they spend much of their adult lives on land, cannot live far from the water. Plants are able to grow at only a certain depth in the ocean because of the penetration of light. Warm blooded birds and mammals are limited in their range by either high or low temperatures. The streamlined form of the fish, the woodpecker's bill, the rodent's teeth are all examples of structural adaptation of animals to the particular substratum on which they live.

Although most plants and animals become adapted to a specific kind of surface or medium and thereby are limited to that particular medium, some organisms like moles, ants, and man have changed the medium to fit their purposes. The mole tunnels beneath the surface, and this is protection against even the most agile predator. In the dry grasslands the harvester ants build mounds like ancient forts -- the like-

Minnesota Department of Business Development

Figure 4. Birds and bulrushes in a biotic community

ness even extends to the bare circle cleared of vegetation which surrounds the mound. Man, thinking organism that he is, diverts streams, tears down mountains -- and builds towering skyscrapers in his cities.

All living plants and animals also live in a biotic environment where they interact one with another -- plants with plants, animals with animals, and plants with animals. There may be competition among plants for light energy from the rays of the sun. There may be competition among animals for food, water, and habitation. In any living environment, there is a plant or animal species that is dominant, i.e., a plant that

Minnesota Department of Business Development

Figure 5.   The outdoors offers to its inhabitants and
its visitors opportunities for relaxation.

grows taller and cuts off the sunlight or an animal that is more
powerful and may even prey upon weaker animals.   The beech
tree in a woods and the lion in the grasslands are good examples.

     The community is more or less composed of closely
integrated complex agents with specialized "occupations. "
Each kind of plant and each kind of animal has its function or
niche.   The niche of an animal or plant may be defined as to
its contribution to the welfare of the whole community of which
it forms a part.   The niche expresses what the species does:

An organism *does* something, not only when it eats, grows, and multiplies, but also when it is eaten. [12]

In any community, organisms are grouped into three broad categories: The producers, the consumers, and the decomposers. [13] Generally speaking, plants can be placed in the role of the producers and animals as consumers. (There are some major exceptions: There is a group of plants called fungi which do not possess the ability to produce their own food and must depend upon other living organisms to provide it for them.) Organisms living on dead or decaying material are saprophytes. The consumers, as a group, can be divided into *herbivores,* which feed on plants; *carnivores,* which feed on other animals; and *omnivores,* which feed on both plants and animals. Organisms that live on or in a live organism or host -- at the expense of the host -- are called parasites.

Some plants are able to live together in a relationship which is mutually beneficial (mutalism); animal species may live together in a one-sided relationship (commensalism) in which one side derives benefit while the other suffers little or no harm.

All members of a community are linked together by their eating-eaten relationships, so a community can be understood to some degree by following these linkages, which are called *food chains.* Food chains follow a general pattern such as green plants → herbivores → carnivores (small) → carnivores (larger), until there are no larger predators. In a pond, the sequence would probably be more involved: Algae → protozoan → aquatic insect (small) → aquatic insect (larger) → black bass (small) → pickerel. (See Figure 6) On land, there may be only three links: Grass → sheep → man.

The diagram of the relationships in the many food chains of a community is called a *food web.* (Every predator eats a variety of foods and every kind of food is eaten by a variety of animals.) It is to be noted that the total energy requirements of the members of the food web are in dynamic equilibrium -- as much energy enters as leaves the system. All energy comes from the sun. Green plants, only, convert this energy into a form that can be used by animals. Obviously, the amount of animal life must be less than the amount of plant life on whose surplus energy the animals depend. The smallest herbivores

[12]Robert E. Coker, Streams, Lakes, and Ponds (Chapel Hill: University of North Carolina Press, 1954), p. 188.

[13]Marston Bates, The Forest and the Sea (New York: Random House, 1960), p. 147.

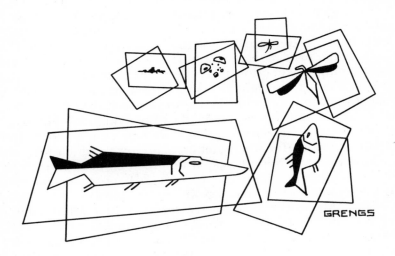

Figure 6. Food Chain

multiply very rapidly -- and to an excess number. Carnivores,
fewer in number and larger in size, feed upon these small herbivores. Other carnivores*, even fewer in number and larger
in size, feed upon the smaller carnivores -- and so on forming
a pyramid of numbers, or a *food pyramid*. The farther the
food chain progresses from the food producers, the less the
number of organisms occupying each niche. Many niches may
be occupied by several types of animals or plants. Animals
as unrelated as the hawk, the fox, the snake, for example,
may all be first level carnivores.

Food chains are vital, but not all-important, for food
alone will not keep that which lives in a forest, or maintain that
which dwells in the Mojave Desert. In the latter, we find
chains that depend on shelter, and others that involve a chance
to reproduce or spawn. What hardships and handicaps the
salmon and the eel must weather, for example, to fulfill the
ritual of reproduction. The vertical stratification of the forest displays a series in which trees protect shrubs, shrubs
cover ground plants, and the dead litter from all these hide
mice, beetles, and shrews. There is a control chain between

---

*If a carnivore eats a herbivore, it is known as a first level carnivore; if it eats a
first level carnivore, it is known as a second level carnivore, and so on.

nuthatches, harmful insects, and trees, while the one that links cedars and ferns involves both moisture and shade. [14]

Changes occur in the community from day to night and from season to season. Some animals are primarily active at night (nocturnal) as the bat and owl and may fill one of the niches occupied by a daylight (diurnal) animal. In winter some animals hibernate, some migrate, some put on a thicker coat to enable them to withstand the colder temperatures. But, the changes of night and day and the seasons are only temporary ones. There are some changes that occur in the community that are not so easy to see because they are so slow and orderly. These changes may span more years than a human lifetime.

Plants and animals that live in a community year after year modify the community little by little - by dropping leaves, holding moisture, burrowing in the earth. These subtle changes in the structure of a community are called ecological succession. When succession reaches a certain point, when a particular kind of vegetation seems best suited to survive on it, a climax is reached, and this vegetation continues to reproduce itself year after year.

A concrete example of ecological succession is presented below.

"In Minnesota, just after the last glacial period (about 7,000 years ago), there existed many small areas of water created by the filling in of pockets gouged out by the glaciers. These small ponds were fairly shallow and with rock or sandy bottoms. This is the first stage in pond succession, the *bare bottom stage*. The first life to appear in these ponds was probably microscopic: algae, protozoans, bacteria, and perhaps small crustaceans brought in on the feet of waterfowl that stopped to rest in the water. Gradually, over a period of many years, the bottom of the pond is enriched with the dead and decaying organisms, so that it may support some larger aquatic plants. These plants live entirely under the water on the bottom and this stage is known as the *submerged vegetation stage*. The pond is now capable of supporting several types of aquatic animals and as they in turn live and die, the bottom is further enriched with their remains. This also serves to make the pond more shallow as year after year the material accumu-

[14]Carroll Lane Fenton, Our Living World (Garden City, New York: Doubleday and Company, Inc., 1953), p. 273.

lates on the bottom.   The pond environment is changing
and can now support vegetation which is rooted on the
bottom, but which has its upper parts on the surface,
such as lily pads.   This stage is called the *emerging
vegetation stage*.   The emerging vegetation gradually
closes off the open areas of water, thus depleting the
supply of oxygen in the water and further modifying the
environment.   Different animals are now present; animals that can live in these changing conditions.   As the
years go by, the areas of open water are evident only
at certain times of the year, when the water is high.   This
is called the *marsh stage*.   The pond continues to fill up
and soon dries out completely in the summer.   This
means it can no longer support plants and animals that
depend on a good supply of water all of the time.   Since
it is now a pond only at certain times of the year, this
stage is called the *temporary pond stage*.   The temporary
pond, during its period of relative dryness, is invaded by
land plants and soon it develops the forms of vegetation
and animal life that are associated with the *low prairie
stage*.   Eventually, the soil is built up to a point where
it does not accumulate any appreciable amount of water
and will support the life found over all of the areas
around it. "[15]
Not only is there competition and cooperation between the
various plant and animal species; there is also competition and
cooperation within the species.   There is protection in the aggregation of bison, but an aggregation of male seals may fight
over breeding sites.   In some instances in higher animals,
there develops a social hierarchy -- as, for instance, in the
pecking order of hens or the butting order of cattle.
Biomes consist of a variety of deme (deem), which refers
to a particular population in a particular area, i.e., the black
bear in Arrowhead country or the gray squirrel in a wood lot
on a farm.   The biotic communities or biomes (by ohms) range
in size from major communities covering thousands of miles
to micro-communities no larger than the top of a boulder.
There are many kinds of biomes: forests, deserts, bogs,
prairies, and swamps.   (See Figure 7) Biomes may over-lap
or be sub-divided.   No area is static; there is always change.
A region may be in a transition zone (ecotone) -- between a

[15]Denneth Dvergsten, Biology - An Ecological Approach (St. Paul: Roseville
Schools, Independent School District 623, 1962), p. 47.

GRENGS

Figure 7. Many Kinds of Biomes

forestland and a grassland. In fact, there is rarely any dramatic beginnings or endings of biomes, be they large or small.
The hazy boundaries, the over-lappings are simply clear examples of "becoming" in the give and take of nature.

The biome is often described in terms of vegetation,
since it is impossible to classify animals in terms of environment. Plants are captives of their environment. The biomes
often are defined in terms of their dominant vegetation, as a
beech-oak biome, or a tall grass biome. However, a biome
may be identified as a lake shore biome or a pond biome.

Biomes are noted for the great degree of interdependence
of the organisms within them, whether it be a miniature biome
of algae, snail, and guppy, or whether it be the larger biome
of the savanna region of Africa with its gnu, lions, and vultures.

There is a natural balance or equilibrium operating in the
biome. If the balance is disturbed by nature (flood or earth-
quake), or by man (fire or hunting), immediately the process
of re-establishing the balance begins. However, the "balance
of nature" is never completely stable; it is always teetering
in some way so that animals vary in abundance from year to
year or millennium to millennium. [16]

There is a very definite relationship between conservation and ecology. Ecology is the balance and interaction of
living organisms in their environment; and if the delicate balance of nature gives way, trouble begins.

Example one: Suppose a bounty is offered for foxes.
Many foxes are killed. As a result, rabbits multiply in great
numbers. They begin to eat the farmers' gardens and girdle
the fruit trees.

Example two: A few beautiful birds are imported from
South Asia. They multiply rapidly because they have no natural enemies. Like the English sparrow, they drive out the
native sparrows and they become a pest.

Example three: A young lady brings a small willow home
for her back yard water garden. The willow spreads rapidly.
Other trees and plants are not able to get sunlight. They soon
die out, and even the small pond is soon filled with roots and
silt.

A clipping from the *Minneapolis Sunday Tribune* illustrating the relationship that exists between conservation and
ecology is as follows:

[16]Marston Bates, The Forest and the Sea (New York: Random House, 1960), p. 155.

... ELM DISEASE CONTROL MAY HARM WILD-LIFE

"As Dutch elm disease spreads into Minnesota, wild-life experts are increasingly concerned that efforts to save the elms might destroy birds and useful insects.

"The disease, which has been moving slowly west-ward, is a fungus infestation spread by a beetle. The beetle is attracted to dead elm branches and twigs, on which it feeds.

"Heavy spraying with DDT to kill the beetles has been the chief weapon used in eastern communities, but it has been accompanied by serious loss of songbirds, small mammals, insect-eating frogs, fish and beneficial bugs.

"' Protecting the elm trees with DDT will kill an awful lot of wildlife, ' said Walter J. Breckenridge, di-rector of the Minnesota Museum of Natural History. 'It will have to continue for years and will kill off many other insects, the value of which we do not know. '

"Breckenridge said it is possible we will have 'an explosive development of some entirely different problem which a present insect balance may be holding in check. '

" 'I even question the value of spraying for Dutch elm disease, ' he added, citing correspondence with the city forester of Toledo, Ohio, who reports heavy spraying for five years without checking the death of trees.

" 'Even if you don't spray you won't lose all the elms; but if you do, you won't save them all either, ' he said. 'It might be wisest to start planting hackberries, maples and other resistant trees so we can have a gradual re-placement of lost elms. '

"Breckenridge said that although a city might spray all its elms, the rural woods surrounding it would con-tinue to harbor the beetles and the disease.

"He emphasized how little knowledge man has of ecology, which is the balance and interaction of living things in nature.

" 'This spring, the University of Minnesota had to spray campus trees which were being attacked by a scale disease. This was being spread by scale insects, which had multiplied because mosquito spraying in the Twin Cities has killed other insects which normally prey on the scale bugs, ' he pointed out.

" 'Fish, which are extremely susceptible to DDT,
would surely be affected by water drainage from areas
heavily sprayed, ' he continued. 'Frogs, toads and liz-
ards, which destroy vast quantities of harmful insects,
likewise would be eliminated. '

"Although small mammals are more resistant to the
chemical, all the wood-chucks, rabbits and other wild
animals were killed off in a test area heavily sprayed
with DDT by Illinois scientist... ' "[17]

A description of a biome is a description of the biome at
a particular stage. A biome has a history, it passes through
several stages. Certain prerequisite conditions must exist
prior to the establishment of more or less stable or permanent
biomes. (The more or less permanent biomes are called
climax biomes.) The soil, for example, has to be favorable;
the climate must be right.

A part of any biotic community is change. The plants
and animals of the habitat change; the relationships change;
the laboratory of ecology and conservation forever changes.

A biome, obviously, consists of more organisms than
the dominant descriptive deme, as beech-maple, or sassafras-
poplar biome. Biomes have transitional and marginal areas;
and it is difficult to pinpoint specific biomes. For example,
a beech-hickory biome or a willow-cattail biome would be
described as follows:

A Beech-Hickory Biome: There are old beeches, hollow
and topless and young beeches with wide-spreading branches.
Interspersed with the beeches are tall-boled hickory trees.
These two demes dominate the biome, but there are a few
ironwood, maple, and oak trees. A small wet-weather stream
cuts through the middle of the biome. At the fringe of the biome
are blackberry briars and sassafrass bushes. On the forest
floor, which is covered by a mat of dry leaves, are patches
of May apples, crowfoot, and adder's tongue. Chipmunks
scurry through the leaves, and fox squirrels rain down scraps
of nuts. In the late evening, a raccoon leaves his hiding in the
beech to investigate the pools in the stream. A red-tailed hawk
circles above the woods. Flickers swoop from tree to tree in
raucous manner. A blue-racer negotiates his way up the almost perpendicular trunk of a beech.

A Willow-Cattail Biome: Willows line the south bank of
the pond, and cattails complete the encirclement of the pond.

[17]Don Morrison, Minneapolis Sunday Tribune, July 9, 1961.

A variety of dragon flies hover and dart over the surface of the pond. Three box turtles sun themselves on a half-submerged log. In the shallows, finger-sized bluegills travel in schools; near the middle of the pond, a large-mouth bass breaks the water. A water snake wiggles away from the shoreline, while a band of bullfrogs leap into the water to find some secret hiding. A green heron springs into the air and finds refuge in a high willow. The red-winged blackbird, with beating of wings and loud crying, drowns out the song sparrow perched on a dead branch of the far shore.

Although everyone agrees that a biome (or life zone) is the region occupied by a large and interdependent group of living things, no one has been able to say just how big those groups shall be nor just how much territory each one should occupy. Specialists disagree as to numbers and kinds of these biomes or regions. This uncertainty explains why some are content with seven zones (or biomes) for the North American Continent, while others will recognize a dozen or more in the United States alone. [18]

In summary, conservation looks to ecology for principles and guidelines. In ecology is found the structure and framework for the operational undertaking, which is called conservation. An understanding of the physical and biotic community is basic to the understanding of other facets of ecology -- food chains, ecological succession, and the wider ramifications of regional and world biomes.

ACTIVITIES

1. Keep a log of the animals (Chordata) in a specific area over a period of time. The chart below is an example. *S–C*

Date Seen	Number	Common Name	Particulars
11/7/63 9:00 a. m.	1	Robin	wind high, very cold single male on wing

2. List and/or classify all the trees and shrubs in a nearby park, woodlot, or school area. *S–C*

[18]C. L. Fenton, Our Living World (New York: Doubleday and Company, 1953), p. 241.

3. Make a series of charts showing a cross-section of a pos-
    sible pond succession: Bare bottom state, submerged veg-
    etation stage, emerging vegetation stage, almost a marsh,
    low prairie stage, shrub stage, and climax vegetation
    stage. *S*
4. Observational Technique: The students are assigned to
    bring in several live houseflies in a clear jar with a small
    amount of sugar in it. The following observations should
    be made: *S*
    a. Describe color, shape, size, and other distinctive
        characteristics of houseflies.
    b. How is the fly able to walk around the jar and up the
        walls? What possibility seems most logical -- and
        correct?
    c. How does the fly eat? Does the way the fly eats limit
        the type of food it can eat?
    d. Do the eyes of the fly have any advantages?
5. On an outline map of the world distinguish the major cli-
    matic regions of the world: Tropical rain forest, tropical
    savanna, steppe, desert, Mediterranean, humid sub-
    tropical, marine, humid continental, taiga, tundra, and
    polar ice cap. *E-S*
6. Make a mural showing the vertical climate near the equator.
    Ice-capped mountains would be in the background and in the
    foreground would be the tropical lowlands. In the middle
    altitude would be mining, cattle raising, etc. *E*
7. Visit a nearby zoo and discover the importance of ecology
    in maintaining a zoo. Notice what animal species are
    placed together. You may wish to interview the zoo direc-
    tor and report back to class. *E-S*
8. Place a variety of animals in an aquarium or terrarium and
    keep a log of your observations. You may wish to change
    the environmental conditions (temperature, sunlight, vege-
    tation) to discover if there is any change in behavior. *E-S*
9. Debate: A bounty should (or should not) be offered on any
    kind of wildlife. (This can be formal or informal debate.)
    S-C
10. Discuss how pests such as starlings, English sparrows,
    Norway rats came to be pests. How would you recommend
    they be controlled? (Library research is important.) *E-S*
11. Read two or three articles like those listed below and re-
    port to the class concerning them and/or write a summary

for your scrapbook or notebook. (Be on the look-out for other magazines that have conservation articles.) **S-C**

   a. Bellrose, Frank "Wood Duck Dilemma, " *Naturalist,* Spring, 1958.

   b. Craighead, John, "Too Many and Too Few, " *Naturalist,* Special Issue, 1958.

   c. Moyle, John B. , 'Insecticides and Wildlife Survival,'' *The Conservation Volunteer,* May-June, 1958.

12. Set up an experimental situation involving: **S-C**
   a. Peck order in chickens
   b. Migration of birds
   c. Social behavior of ants or bees
   d. Family life of racoons.

13. Just for Fun: Read one of the many books that have an underlying love of nature and a concern for ecology and conservation. **S-C**
   a. Carrighar, Sally, *Icebound Summer* (New York: Alfred A. Knopf, 1954).
   b. Carson, Rachel L. , *The Sea Around Us* (New York: Oxford University Press, 1951).
   c. Olson, Sigurd F. , *Listening Point* (New York: Alfred A Knopf, 1958).
   d. Peattie, Donald Curlross, *Flowering Earth* (New York: G. P. Putnam's Company, 1939).
   e. Peterson, Roger T. and James Fisher, *Wild America* (Boston: Houghton-Mifflin, 1955).
   f. Rowlands, John J. , *Cache Lake Country: Life in the North Woods* (New York: W. W. Norton and Company, 1947).

14. Questions for research and experimentation: **E-S**
   a. Why will a philodendron turn yellow when placed in the sunlight?
   b. How does a tree growing alone in a field differ from a tree of the same species which grows in the deep forest?
   c. How is a biome similar to the human organism?

15. Make a cross-word puzzle or a matching exercise to "match wits" with the rest of the class. **E-S**

   Match the following organisms with biomes:

a. lianas	1. coniferous forest
b. muskox	2. desert
c. moose	3. tundra
d. horned toad	4. deciduous forest
e. bison	5. tropical rainforest
f. white-tailed deer	6. prairie grassland

16. Graphically illustrate a food web, food pyramid, sand dune succession, etc. *S-C*

17. Have an old-fashioned spell down using new words of conservation and ecology like the following: Biome, tundra, zonation, successions, equilibrium, interdependence, etc.

18. Study several species in depth in a specific community: In a study of the pond, for example, the cattail, the crayfish, great pond snail, the sunfish, arrowhead, dragonfly, and the muskrat. The student may be required to write a brief summary about the species, keep a field report, pose questions and attempt to answer the questions regarding the species (sample questions: How do cattails propagate? How does the arrowhead adjust to wet and dry times? Do sunfish and bluegill ever mate?), and compile a bibliography of helpful sources. *S-C*

19. Obtain a guest speaker from the Conservation Department or a nearby college to talk with the class on "Ecology and the Local Community." *S-C*

20. Read the short story "Leinengen Versus the Ants" by Carl Stephenson as a class or as an individual. How is the theme or moral appropriate? *S*

21. Attend a local village or city council meeting and report back to class the number of instances a remark directly or indirectly referred to conservation. Note the wide-ranging implications of discussions about water, sewers, parks, etc. *S-C*

22. Make a salt-flour miniature of a woodlot or pond community. Miniature plants and animals should be a part of the structure. *E*

23. Make a topographical map of a woodlot or pond locale. (Topograph maps may be obtained from the U. S. Geological Survey, Denver District Secretary, Federal Center Building, Denver, Colorado.) *S-C*

24. Draw a woodlot or pond community to scale and locate various kinds of higher plants by the use of numbers. Numbers can refer to descriptions, pictures, or drawings displayed on a bulletin board and/or pictured in a scrapbook. *S-C*

25. Report on the Mormons and "grasshoppers." Is there a Biblical reference to the plague of locusts? *E-S*

BIBLIOGRAPHY

Allee, W. C., A. E. Emerson, O. Park, T. Park, and K. P. Schmidt. *Principles of Animal Ecology*. Philadelphia: Saunders Company, 1949. **S-C**

Bates, Marston. *The Forest and the Sea*. New York: Random House, 1960. **S-C**

Benton, Allen H. and William E. Werner, Jr. *Workbook for Field Biology and Ecology*. Minneapolis: Burgess Publishing Company, 1958. pp. 1-38, 49-50. **S-C**

Buchsbaum, Ralph, and Mildred Buchsbaum. *Basic Ecology*. Pittsburgh: Boxwood Press, 1957. **S-C**

Clarke, G. L. *Elements of Ecology*. New York: John Wiley and Sons, 1954. **S-C**

Clements, F. E. and V. C. Shelford. *Bio-ecology*. New York: John Wiley and Sons, 1939. **S-C**

Coker, Robert E. *Streams, Lakes, Ponds*. Chapel Hill: University of North Carolina Press, 1954. **C**

Daubenmire, R. F. *Plants and Environment*. New York: John Wiley and Sons, 1947. **S-C**

Dvergsten, Denneth. *Biology - An Ecological Approach*. St. Paul: Roseville Schools, Independent District 623, 1962. **S-C**

Elton, C. *Animal Ecology*. New York: Macmillan Company, 1927. **S-C**

————. *The Ecology of Animals*. New York: John Wiley and Sons, 1950. **S-C**

Fenton, Carroll Love. *Our Living World*. New York: Doubleday and Company, 1953. **S-C**

Gaul, Albro. *The Pond Book*. New York: Coward-McCann, Inc., 1955. **E**

Iowa Conservation Education Council. *Conservation Source Book*. Ames: Iowa State University Press, 1962. **C**

Moon, Truman J., Paul V. Mann, and James H. Otto. *Modern Biology*. New York: Henry Holt and Company, Inc., 1956. pp. 65-102. **S**

Odum, E. P. *Fundamentals of Ecology*. Philadelphia: Saunders Company, 1953. **S-C**

Odum, Howard T. "Ten Classroom Sessions in Ecology," reprinted from *American Biology Teacher*, Vol. 22, No. 2, February, 1960. **C**

Oosting, Henry J. *Plant Communities*. San Francisco:
    W. H. Freeman and Sons, 1948. *S–C*
    _____. *The Study of Plant Communities*. Second
    Edition. San Francisco: W. H. Freeman and Sons, 1956.
    S–C
Peterson, Roger T. *Field Guide to the Birds*. Boston:
    Houghton-Mifflin Company, 1947. *S–C*
Storer, John H. *A First Book of Ecology: The Web of Life*.
    New York: The Devin-Adair Company, 1954. *S*
Wallace, Bruce and Adrian Sub. *Adaptation*. Englewood
    Cliffs: Prentice-Hall, Inc., 1961. *S–C*
Weaver, J. E. and F. E. Clements. *Plant Ecology*. New
    York: McGraw-Hill Company, 1929. *S–C*
Weaver, Richard L. *Manual for Outdoor Laboratories*.
    Danville: Interstate Printers. *S–C*
Woodbury, A. M. *General Ecology*. Philadelphia: Blakiston,
    1954. *S–C*

AUDIO-VISUAL MATERIALS

16 mm. FILMS

Balanced Aquarium - (EBF)

This film shows the step-by-step procedure in building
a balanced aquarium. *E–S*

Beneath Our Feet - (TFC)

A sand cricket struggles with a trap-door spider, then
with a centipede whose poisonous bite kills him. There
are shots of aphids being eaten by lady-bird larvae, and
of bees on flowers. *S*

The Community - (EBF)

This film introduces the concept of the ecological community. Food chains and food webs of the typical biotic
communities are illustrated. *S–C*

How Animals Defend Themselves - (YA)

This film shows how animals are adapted for protection
against other animals and nature. Many examples of

protection by defense mechanisms are shown -- speed and agility, tough shells and hides, sharp claws and beaks, camouflage, and mimicry. *E*

How Living Things Change - (Cor)

The major evolutionary theories are examined, illustrated, and compared. Man is able to effect changes in plants and animals, but living things themselves have been changing for millions of years. *S*

Life Along the Waterways - (EBF)

All along its bank, the stream provides life to plants and animals which look to it for support. *E-S-C*

Life in a Drop of Water - (Cor)

The various single-celled forms are shown in relation to their environment. They meet the minimum problems of all life. The advantages of colonial over individual existence are pointed out. *S-C*

Life on a Dead Tree - (FA)

As boys explore a dead tree in the woods, they discover many different plants and animals -- fungus, plants, crickets, slugs, ants, etc. *E-S*

Nature's Half Acre - (WDP)

Millions of inhabitants of the tiny grass-roots world and how the balance of nature is maintained are shown. *E-S-C*

Our Animal Neighbors - (Cor)

Only by knowing their habits can small mammals like the mole, shrew, rabbit be seen. *E*

Partnership Among Plants and Animals - (Cor)

Partnerships between animals, between plants, and between plants and animals are explored. *E-S*

The Spruce Bog - (McG)

The conditions under which a spruce bog is formed, with details of the plant types found at successive stages of development from open water to mature spruce forest is illustrated. **S–C**

Succession - From Sand Dune to Forest - (EBF)

Photographed in the dunes at the southern end of Lake Michigan, the film shows one of the earliest and most thoroughly studied examples of the process. **S–C**

This Vital Earth - (EBF)

This film portrays both the beauty and logic of the balance in nature and the organization of the living community. **S**

What is Ecology? - (EBF)

The study of ecology is introduced by illustrating the wide variety of interrelationships between plants, animals, and their environment. The major biomes of the world are presented. **S–C**

World of Little Things - (MIOS)

A variety of microscopic plants and animals in fresh and salt water live together and establish a delicate balance of life. **S–C**

The Temperate Deciduous Forest - (EBF)

S–C

The Tropical Rain Forest - (EBF)

S–C

TAPES *

Conservation Nature Study Series

A series of programs broadcast by Radio Station WSUI, University of Iowa, entitled "Uncle Dan from Foggy

*See Tapes for Teaching in the Schools of Minnesota, State Department of Education.

Hollow Farm, " is about nature for the middle elementary grades. Written and produced by G. A. Burrow of Atlanta, Georgia, Board of Education. These tapes are fifteen minutes in length. Among many titles are the following:

"Living Pastures: The Aphid" - (CNS-4)

How its enemies keep it under control.

"Lawbreakers: Mrs. Quail and Mr. Blacksnake" - (CNS-5)

"Is the Crow a Villain?" - (CNS-12)

FILMSTRIPS

The African Lion - (EBF)

Six filmstrips from the Walt Disney Filmstrip Series. *E-S*

The Arctic Wilderness - (EBF)

Six filmstrips from the Walt Disney Filmstrip Series. *E-S*

Forests of Tropical America - (EBF)

Six filmstrips from the Walt Disney Filmstrip Series. *E-S*

The Living Desert - (EBF)

Six filmstrips from the Walt Disney Filmstrip Series. *E-S*

True-Life Adventures - (EBF)

Eight filmstrips from the Walt Disney Filmstrip Series. *E-S*

The Vanishing Prairie - (EBF)

Six filmstrips from the Walt Disney Filmstrip Series. *E-S*

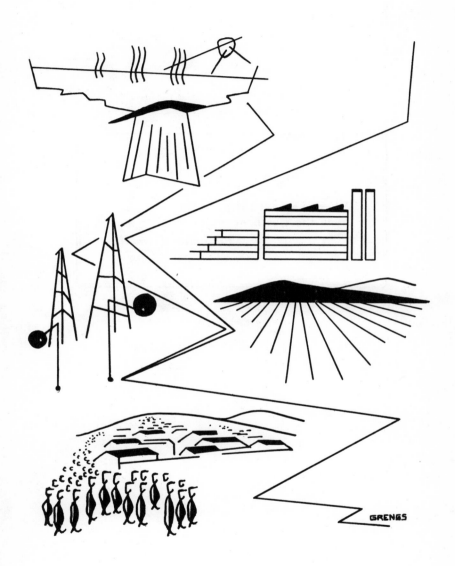

When the well's dry, we
know the worth of water.

Benjamin Franklin

Chapter III

WATER CONSERVATION

OBJECTIVES

    I. To understand man's dependence on water.

    II. To appreciate the balance of nature which is nourished by an adequate supply of water.

    III. To investigate the various sources of our water supply.

    IV. To realize the destruction that has resulted from man's poor use of this vital resource and the corrective measures that are being taken.

Like air, water is bound up with man's evolution -- and doubtless his destiny -- in many ways. One of the constant factors for life on earth is that water be available in the liquid state.

The origin of all life on earth is believed to be the sea, and today, after millions of years of evolution, modern man's tissues are still bathed in a saline solution closely related to that of the sea when the earlier forms of life first left it to dwell on the land.

"Every organic process can occur only in the watery medium. The embryo abides in a liquid from conception to birth."[19] Heat dissipation, breathing, digestion, glandular activities, and secretion can be performed only in the presence of watery solutions. Water acts as a lubricant, helps protect certain tissues from external injury, and gives flexibility to the muscles, tendons, cartilage, and bones.

The role of water in metabolism, in regulating body temperature, and in nourishing the tissues, explains why we could not long survive without adequate amounts of water. Yet our direct body needs for water are relatively small in terms of our total body weight, which is approximately seventy-one per cent water by weight, and is extremely small in relation to the

---

[19]Water: The Yearbook of Agriculture 1955, United States Department of Agriculture (Washington: Government Printing Office, 1955), p. 3.

total demands upon water by human societies, even among
primitive cultures. [20]

The average person in the temperate zone can get along
with about five and one-half pints of water a day, if he is moderately active. Slightly more than two pints are taken in with
a normal mixed diet or created in the body by the oxidation of
food, especially sugars, starches, and fats. Another three
pints are taken in as fluids. Altogether, it takes five or six
pints to replace the daily losses in perspiration, exhalation,
and excretion. [21]

The amount of water needed for a given individual varies
with his weight, age, activity, health, and other factors, but
basic needs must be met if life is to be sustained. The consumption of lesser amounts than those needed to replace losses
will lead to a diminished appetite and eventually to under-
nutrition. A man in good health might be able to survive
without water for a few days in a desert, if he is only slightly
active. If he tried to be more active, he might not last a single day, because of the loss of water -- as much as ten pints
an hour -- from the body would greatly exceed the losses in-
curred under the minimum activity. Unless water was prompt-
ly available, the losses would cause dehydration, incapacitation, and painful death. By contrast, in the parts of the tropics
where high temperature and humidity prevail, high rates of
activity could not be maintained even if abundant water were
accessible, since the body would be unable to dissipate heat
and rid itself of waste products fast enough to prevent a break-
down in body functions.

The water which we can currently use and/or see is a
phase of the *hydrologic cycle*. (See Figure 8) The water which
flows so profusely from our faucet may last year have been
part of a tumbling stream, a mountain glacier of snow and ice,
or an underground stream. But, regardless of its source,
there seems to be no end; for the rivers run into the sea, yet
the sea is not full, and high in the sky clouds form only to dissolve in rain. A never ending cycle is maintained from sea
to cloud to earth, as it has for millions of years in the past,
the endless cycle -- sea to cloud to earth -- will continue to
be maintained as far as man can see into the future. But, our

[20]Ibid.
[21]Ibid.

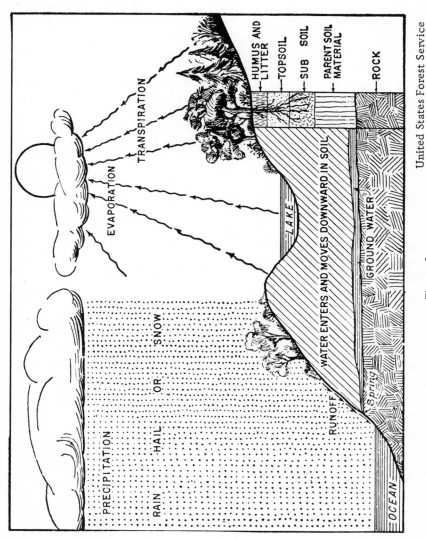

PRECIPITATION

RAIN HAIL OR SNOW

TRANSPIRATION

EVAPORATION

RUNOFF

HUMUS AND LITTER

TOPSOIL

SUB SOIL

PARENT SOIL MATERIAL

ROCK

LAKE

WATER ENTERS AND MOVES DOWNWARD IN SOIL

GROUND WATER

Spring

OCEAN

United States Forest Service

Figure 8

problem lies not with the hydrologic cycle as a whole, but with
a portion of the cycle and its distribution.

The balance between plant and animal is closely related
with the world's water supply and the conservation of matter
may be applied: "Matter can neither be created nor destroyed."
The total number of water molecules present at the earth's
formation is relatively unchanged. Water may be decomposed
into its component parts, hydrogen and oxygen gas, by elec-
trolysis in the laboratory, but nature has no means except by
an occasional bolt of lightning. We can therefore state that
the total amount of water on earth is stable. However, is our
concern with the total amount of water, or is it the amount of
usable water available to us? Plant and animal, except those
who survive in a saline environment, must have an ample supply of usable water which is fresh and clean.

Various phases of the hydrologic cycle may be taken
separately to show its relationship to all living things. The
oceans and seas might be thought of as large wholesale sup-
pliers, the atmosphere as the distributor, and the continents
as the consumers. The ocean allows vast surface areas which
in turn contribute to the enormous evaporation. Evaporation
is directly proportional to the surface area involved and quan-
titatively regulated by the relative humidity in the area. [22] The
distribution of water vapor in our atmosphere can be attributed
to two factors: One, the planetary winds; and, two, the topography of the sea.

Looking at the North American continent and the United
States in particular, we must include the physical aspects of
the earth and its behavior as a planet. The earth is situated
approximately ninety-three million miles from the sun and
has a weight of two hundred thousand billion tons, which constitutes its gravity and allows such gases as water vapor and
oxygen to be held in its atmosphere. [23]

The rotation of the earth and the tilting or inclination
of its axis from the perpendicular contribute to our planetary
wind pattern. The United States is primarily situated in the
prevailing westerly wind belt, which indicates that our general winds will be moving in a northeasterly direction across
the continent.

[22]Samuel N. Namowitz and Donald B. Stone, Earth Science: The World We Live In
(New York: D. Van Nostrand Company, Inc., 1953), p. 321.

[23]Richard Brinckerhoff, Burnett Cross, Fletcher Watson, and Paul F. Brandwein,
The Physical World (New York: Harcourt, Brace and World, Inc., 1958), p. 5.

The huge amount of water vapor collected over the Pacific Ocean travels eastward and runs into no great obstacles until it encounters the Sierra Nevada mountain range. Here physical properties of *adiabatic* cooling take place as the heavily laden air cools with increased elevation. The word adiabatic is used to describe a temperature change within the substance itself caused by its own expansion or compression. [24] As the air rises, molecular motion decreases causing an increase in density to the point where the air is unable to hold the water vapor and precipitation occurs. This results in a mass of air nearly void of water vapor and allows little chance of precipitation as it moves eastward over the great Nevada basin. The basin has an annual rainfall of less than ten inches and results in near desert conditions.

We could trace the same pocket of air as it continues across the continent keeping in mind the cycle of evaporation, condensation, and precipitation time and time again as it moves through such a traversed path. Our problem concerns all phases of the hydrologic cycle, but mainly the distribution of the precipitation that has reached the earth.

Oceans are the ultimate source of all water. However, we do not obtain most of our water directly from precipitation, but rather from wells and springs called *ground water*, (See Figure 9) or from lakes and streams called *surface water*. Water used by growing plants also is obtained from moisture that soaks into the soil and is absorbed by root systems of plants.

Although the total quantity of water has changed little throughout eons of geological time, the pattern of distribution over the face of our planet has varied radically from age to age, century to century, and year to year. Climates may change over thousands of years as indicated by the ice ages and increasing aridity of some deserts, and every year some area may suffer from drought while others are plagued by floods. [25]

As indicated previously, the greatest reservoir of water for the earth is the ocean. The energy necessary for lifting this great quantity of water from the ocean in the form of water vapor comes from the sun. This evaporated water, in vapor form, is carried inland in great masses of maritime air.

[24]Samuel N. Namowitz, op. cit., p. 286.

[25]Iowa Conservation Education Council, Conservation Source Book (Ames: Iowa State University Press, 1962), p. 21.

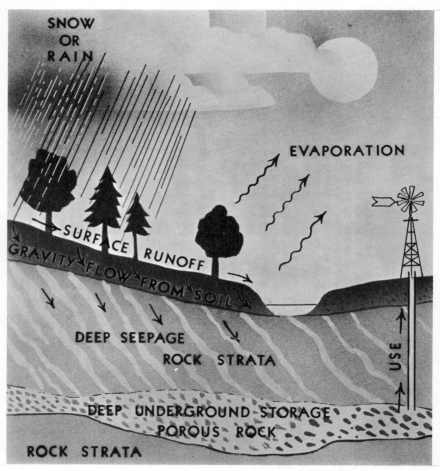

United States Forest Service

Figure 9. Groundwater

When cooled, water is released onto the land in the form of
rain or snow.

When rain or snow reaches the surface of the land, several things may happen to it. If the ground is dry, large quantities will soak into the soil and become soil moisture or
ground water. If the rain falls faster than the ground can
soak it up, it runs downgrade over the surface and is called
runoff. Runoff may replenish lakes and streams directly, but
it also may create problems of erosion and flood when it occurs in quantities too large for drainage systems to handle.

Tremendous quantities of water lie exposed on the earth's
surface in rivers, lakes, oceans and, in the solid state, in
glaciers. But, beneath the surface, hidden from sight, is
another great store of water. Underground reservoirs in the
United States (See Figure 10) contain far more usable water
than all our surface reservoirs and lakes combined. And, we
depend on this underground supply for about one-fifth of our
total water needs. [26]

Underground water, subsurface water, and subterranean
water are all general terms used to refer to water in the pore
spaces, cracks, tubes, and crevices of the consolidated and
unconsolidated material beneath our feet.

Underground water is divided into two major zones: the
zones of aeration and the zone of saturation. The water table
marks the upper surface of the zone of saturation. Within the
zone of aeration is a belt of soil moisture from which many
plants draw their moisture and from which some moisture is
also evaporated back to the atmosphere. In many cases this
belt lies in an area where water is held by molecular attraction (adhesion) and where little movement occurs except during periods of rainfall which is followed by infiltration.

Underground water supplies are more difficult to survey
than surface water. The porosity or the ability of a material
to absorb water varies from material to material. Porosity
is measured in per cent of total volume that is occupied by
voids or interstices. Size and the pore space between particles are the most important factors concerning porosity. In
general, a porosity of less than five per cent is considered
low; from five to fifteen per cent represents medium porosity,
and over fifteen per cent is considered high. Unconsolidated

[26]L. Don Leet, Sheldon Judson, Physical Geology (Englewood Cliffs: Prentice-Hall,
Inc., 1958), p. 198.

Ground-water Areas in the United States

Patterns show areas underlain by aquifers generally capable of
yielding to individual wells 50 g. p. m. or more of water containing
not more than 2,000 p. p. m. of dissolved solids (includes some areas
where more highly mineralized water is actually used)

Watercourses in which ground water can be replenished
by perennial streams

Buried valleys not now occupied by perennial streams

Unconsolidated and semiconsolidated aquifers   Both unconsolidated and consolidated-rock aquifers

Consolidated-rock aquifers   Not known to be underlain by aquifers that will
                                                                generally yield as much as 50 g. p. m. to wells

Figure 10.   Yearbook of Agriculture 1955

deposits of clay, silt, sand, and gravel have porosities ranging from about twenty to as much as fifty per cent. [27]
         The permeability of the aquifer carrying the water is
another important factor. Permeability may be defined as
the ability of a substance to transmit water. Materials which
will not carry water are said to be impermeable. Two impermeable layers separated by a permeable layer which has a
high porosity is considered to be a good aquifer and accounts
for much of our underground water supply. Such aquifers can
be found in a number of areas throughout the United States,
but they vary in discharge because of the material or the area
of outcrop which furnishes the water. A typical formation
can furnish huge amounts of water which is used in industry
and provide community water for many cities and surrounding
suburbs.
         As water moves over the earth's surface and through
the underlying rocks, it dissolves substances from the materials with which it comes in contact. Generally, the farther
the water moves and the longer it is in contact with the materials, the more of the substances it dissolves. Ground water
commonly has more dissolved solids than surface water be-

[27]Ibid., p. 202.

cause its rate of movement is much slower; therefore, it remains in contact with the rocks for longer periods of time. However, ground water, especially from deep sources, is usually free of pathogenic organisms, whereas most surface water today is contaminated to some extent.

The chemical quality of ground water is often a factor limiting the use of the water. Revised standards by the U. S. Public Health Service (1961) for chemical constituents in drinking water used aboard common carriers include the following recommended maximums:

TABLE I

MAXIMUM CHEMICAL CONSTITUENTS IN DRINKING WATER AS RECOMMENDED BY THE UNITED STATES PUBLIC HEALTH SERVICE IN 1961

Element or Radical	Parts per Million (ppm)
Arsenic	0.5*
Copper	1.0
Lead	0.05*
Iron	0.3
Manganese	0.05
Nitrate	45.0
Selenium	.01*
Zinc	5.0
Chloride	250.0
Fluoride	0.6 - 1.7**
Sulfate	250.0
Hexavalent chromium	0.5*
Phenols	0.001
Total dissolved solids	500.0

* Presence in excess of stated figure constitutes grounds for rejection of supply.

** General range. Actual limits depend on air temperature and fluoridation practices as outlined by United States Public Health Service.

In addition to the constituents listed in the preceding table, the degree of hardness is of much importance to domestic users and industrial users such as laundries or steam-generating plants. The following table has been adapted by the United States Geological Survey for use in hardness classification throughout the United States.

TABLE II

CLASSIFICATION OF WATER HARDNESS
BY UNITED STATES GEOLOGICAL
SURVEY

Hardness Range (ppm)	Rating
0-60	Soft
61-120	Moderately hard
121-180	Hard
181-	Very hard

Water to be used in industrial processes often must meet certain standards, which vary with the type of industry. If the water is used for condensing or cooling or in some cleansing operations, the quality may not be of primary importance, although the temperature may be. On the other hand, the standards for water used in food processing and in the manufacture of some commodities such as paper and plastic are rigid. Some types of modern high pressure boilers require water which approaches distilled water in quality.

The quality of ground water in Minnesota and North Dakota varies greatly, both in total dissolved solids in the relative proportions of the various constituents. Most glacial-drift aquifers yield water that is moderately hard to very hard. Shallow-drift aquifers composed of sand and gravel, such as those in alluvial or outwash deposits, generally yield water of the best quality. [28]

28O. F. Paulson, Ground Water, Geological Survey, U. S. Department of Interior, Information Bulletin 1 (Grand Forks, North Dakota: 1962), p. 17.

The paramount problem facing mankind today is to provide ample food and water for our growing world population.
United States population alone increases at a rate of 8,000 people per day with a projected population of 350 million by the
turn of the century. [29] Such huge populations place gigantic demands on a nation for better crop production and a larger water
supply to nourish such crops. To sustain such food production
and to provide water for personal use in an ever increasing industrial economy requires a scientific approach and sound conservation methods.

Increased land fertility may be achieved through fertilizer
application and wise land management practices. The United
States Soil Conservation Service makes available, through its
district offices, professional advice and assistance to land owners and farmers who wish to improve their land. Such a service not only improves soil fertility, but also takes into consideration watershed development, drainage, and a balanced wildlife habitat.

Studies have been made concerning transpiration rates
of various species of flora in regard to watershed management.
John P. Decker states that altering natural succession may become a major way of modifying plant cover, thereby increasing
water yield. [30] Plants need huge amounts of moisture and
through transpiration release tons of water vapor to the surrounding air. Scientists believe certain plant species, which
have a low transpiration rate, may be able to adapt to a new
locality foreign to their environment. New plant adaptation
will increase soil cover, water infiltration, and reduce evaporation through transpiration.

Methods of replenishing surface and ground water are
extremely important, but wise use of the available water is
also a must if we are to live as our society demands. Use and
reuse of water can be obtained through adequate filtration and
sewage disposal plants. Runoff must be kept to a minimum
through an adequate watershed management program.

A running stream can purify itself (natural purification)
if it is not carrying too great a load of pollution. The time
needed for this process of self-purification depends on the

[29]Stanley E. Williamson in his speech "The Place of Science in Our Schools and
Society Today," given at the Upper-Midwest National Science Teachers' Conference, 1963.
[30]John P. Decker, "Water Relations of Plant Communities as a Management Factor
for Western Watersheds," Science, Vol. 138, October 26, 1962, p. 352.

amount of waste material in the water and on the character of
the stream.

In clean flowing streams, the water is usually saturated
with oxygen that has been absorbed from the air and from green
plants living in the water. This oxygen is used by bacteria in
the water and in the wastes dumped into the stream. These
bacteria clean the water by breaking down the unstable wastes
carried by the current. The large solids of filth emptied into
the stream settle to the bottom.

The amount of oxygen in the water controls the rate at
which the bacteria can purify the stream. The used-up oxygen
is replaced by a continuing supply of oxygen from aquatic
plants and from the air. If the oxygen supply is lessened
drastically, the bacteria will be unable to continue purifying
the water. When large amounts of sewage are dumped into a
stream, the water becomes murky; sunlight can no longer
reach the aquatic vegetation and it dies. Purifying bacteria,
deprived of oxygen from these plants, use up oxygen faster
than it can be replaced from the air. The oxygen supply becomes so low that the bacteria are unable to continue their job
of purification. Then the murky water becomes foul smelling
and greasy. Fish and other water life die out. The water becomes so polluted that it is unfit, possibly even dangerous,
for use in homes, for irrigation, and for many industrial processes. (See Figure 11)

Examples of man's waste and the ever present problem
of water pollution can easily be seen. If river disposal of
waste were suddenly denied the city of St. Louis, the city
fathers would have to decide what to do with the daily discharge
of 200,000 gallons of urine and 400 tons of solid body wastes,
to say nothing of all the industrial waste.[31] River disposal of
human waste, though cheap, involves a double loss of resources.
On the one hand there is the polluted river; on the other, the
depleted soil. So long as the losses are deemed less important than the production of commodities which they support,
we will have to accept our befouled streams and depleted soils
as part of the cost of our standard of living.

The American standard of living is not a wholly unmixed
blessing. In achieving such luxuries as the flush toilet, synthetic detergents, cheap newspapers, and atomic power, we

---

[31]Charles C. Bradely, "Human Water Needs and Water Use In America," Science,
Vol. 138, October 26, 1962, p. 490.

Minnesota Department of Public Health

Figure 11. Municipal sewage treatment plant

find ourselves also achieving polluted streams, sudsy well
water, radioactive milk, and poisoned oysters.

The proverb, "Cleanliness is next to godliness, " can
boomerang as a dilemma if one thinks how man tries to rid himself of mother earth.   The automatic washing machine certainly gets a workout, to say nothing of the dishwasher.

At the moment, pollution by modern detergents is drawing the most attention.   Cause of the trouble is a chemical
known as A. B. S. -- alkyl benzine sulfonate.   It comes from
petroleum and is basic in most detergents.   A. B. S. does not
decompose as soap does, through the action of bacteria in
sewage treatment facilities.   In a river, A. B. S. can travel
downstream more than one hundred miles and still be less
than one-third decomposed.   When water is reused by a downstream city, another batch of A. B. S. is added and the double
dose passes downstream to another city. [32]

The threat of detergents to human life has not been determined, but these wastes are actually toxic to fish and wildlife
when present in large quantities.

Tests in Wisconsin have shown that some of the underground water in sixty-four of the state's seventy-one counties
is polluted by A. B. S. [33]

At Oregon, Illinois, during the winter, a pile of suds
forty feet high accumulated in front of ice that had jammed up
in the Rock River just below the dam.

Operators of sand and gravel pits at Phoenix, Arizona,
complain that detergent has found its way into the pits, and as
a result, the aggregate they sell makes poor concrete.

In West Germany, some waterways are so saturated with
detergent residue that billowing suds interfere with navigation.
Foam frequently is picked up by the wind and splattered on
windshields of nearby autos.

United States manufacturers are racing to get a "soft"
detergent which is organic in structure and which will decompose in sewage treatment plants.   The manufacturers state that
they expect the new detergent will be available very soon.

Experts on water pollution are looking beyond the detergent dilemma to other problems that will have to be solved as
the nation turns increasingly to reusing water.   The government is spending around $750, 000 a year on "advanced waste
treatment" research in cooperation with industry.   The aim is

[32]"Just How Safe Is Your Drinking Water?" U. S. News and World Report, July 15,
1963, p. 74.
[33]Ibid.

to find improved ways of treating sewage so that it will be possible to re-use water again and again with safety.

The problem is such: Four billion pounds of detergents
are poured into the nation's water each year.   Use of detergents
is increasing at a rate of five per cent a year.   Forty per cent
of the U. S. population uses water that has been used at least
once before. [34]   In some cities, water reaching consumers has
been used five times.   Seventy-five million people -- forty per
cent of the population -- now depend on septic tanks to handle
sewage.

Secretary of Health, Education and Welfare, Anthony J.
Celebrezze, estimates there is a backlog of two billion dollars
of construction needed for communities with inadequate sewage
treatment facilities or no such facilities at all.

States are also interested in pollution and available water
supplies.   Connecticut, Pennsylvania, California, Wisconsin,
Nebraska, Minnesota and many other states are considering
bills to regulate water pollution.

Summing up, Mr. Celebrezze says: "America's waters
are not clean; nor will they ever be unless we increase our effort, our expenditures, and our dedication.   As our population
expands and our national product grows, the problems of water
supply and pollution control, which must be considered against
the reality of a fixed amount of water, will become ever greater. "[35]

Using his God-given talents, man has the ability to seek
out new sources of water.   As stated before, the total amount
of water on our planet is relatively stable, so man must go to
sources other than surface and ground water.   The mighty
oceans and seas are untapped, but their salinity presents a
problem.

Southwestern United States is already plagued with too
many people and not enough water.   Recently a Supreme Court
ruling did this: Threatened the already arid southwest with an
actual cutback in water supplies for fast-growing southern
California from its biggest source, the Colorado River. [36]

There are de-salting plants already established at San
Diego, California, and Freeport, Texas.   These are two of
five ambitious experimental plants planned by the United States

[34]Ibid. , p. 75.
[35]Ibid.
[36]"Too Many People Not Enough Water," U. S. News and World Report, June 17,
1963, p. 62.

Department of Interior in a twenty million dollar de-saltation program. De-salting is already successfully used on a small scale, but the cost is still too high to be practical economically. A large scale break-through would make huge supplies of sea water and brackish inland waters available. [37]

With the advent of the space age, the problems of food, body wastes, and water present enormous obstacles to the space scientists.

With the development of synthetic vitamins, the problems of supplying the body with proper nourishment has been solved. But it remains for man, conditioned by custom and habit, to accept the solution. The thought of replacing the appetizing smell of beef steak with a pill could hardly be called a morale builder.

Tests under simulated space flight conditions show that man has been able to get along, quite nicely, without solid food and that such conditions do not seem to affect his appetite to any serious degree. Tests also show that men subjected to space flight conditions do not desire food as their earthling brothers would.

Experiments have also shown that the muscular system of the body is capable of producing the regular swallowing effect even under the unnatural state of weightlessness. Squeeze tubes similar to our toothpaste tubes have been developed to insert in the head gear of the astronaut, whenever food intake is necessary. Such tubes could easily provide the 3, 500 calories a day, which is the estimated daily requirement needed.[38]

Scientists have been experimenting with one variety of algae, *Chlorella,* which is almost all food: It contains little inedible tissue. [39] Dr. Russell O. Bowman, as astrobiologist, with Vought Astronautics, a division of Chance Vought Aircraft, has been working with algae. Dr. Bowman points out that algae can be treated to taste like steak, roast beef, coffee, and even caviar, but getting rid of the green color is so difficult that it seems to be impracticable. Independent studies indicate that an algal system large enough to supply the total food and oxygen requirements in a space ship would weigh at least five

[37]"Water," Life, December 22, 1961, p. 79.

[38]William A. Kinney, Medical Science and Space Travel (New York: Franklin Watts, Inc. , 1959), p. 93.

[39]James S. Hanrahan and David Bushnell, Space Biology (New York: Basic Books, Inc. , 1960), p. 54.

hundred pounds per man. [40] If such an ecological system can
be developed and carried in a space craft, algae will prove
highly desirable. Dean Burk of the National Institute of Health
feels it would be worthwhile to quadruple the funds spent on
algal research, in order to have such a system ready in time
for manned space travel.

If a system of recycling human wastes could be developed,
the problems of concentrated foods, cultivating algae and others
would be lessened. The American Machine and Foundry Company, under the direction of the Air Force has a contract to
develop a waste collection system. It is estimated that such
a system would save weight on food and water requirements
amounting to 3, 000 pounds per crew member per year. [41] The
problems of miniaturization of such a system is still ahead.

The problem of supplying an adequate water supply is
not great in a closed ecological system, if urine and the moisture of the feces is converted. Conversion of water from
urine can be done by absorption, filtration, ion exchange,
refrigeration, electrodialysis, freeze-drying, and distillation.
Eugene B. Konecci, heading a human-factors team for Douglas
Aircraft Company confirms that water purified in this way
would not only be palatable, but would contain no pathogens
and also would have a lower bacterial count than most tap water
consumed in our homes. The Aeronautical Division of the
Minneapolis Honeywell Regulator Company has actually constructed for the Air Force a seven-ton space simulator in
which waste water and urine are purified by chemical treatment, filtering, super-heating, freezing, and final filtering
through activated carbon. [42]

Other problems arise in maintaining a relative humidity
within the cabin, which will allow a suitable metabolism for
maximum comfort and mental alertness.

In summary, water conservation is not the duty of any
one individual or group, but is the responsibility of every citizen -- man, woman, and child.

We are surrounded by limits set by nature in respect to
the quantity of water available. Such limits present problems
in distribution and use of the available supplies.

We know our population will not decrease, nor will our

[40]Air Force Times, November 25, 1959.
[41]Astronautics, May, 1948, p. 8.
[42]Aviation Week, August 17, 1959, p. 59.

industries require less water, but rather greater demands
will be placed on our present reservoirs.

We are plagued by pollution from industries and community sewage wastes. Science has brought forth inorganic detergents to cleanse us, but which leave us with a dilemma of
bubbling streams and sudsy drinking water.

Man, through his quest for personal monetary gains,
has destroyed our watersheds and cultivated land which should
have been used for grazing. He has used underground water
for irrigation, thus depleting reservoirs for human use and
has caused untold damage to our wildlife by draining wetlands
for real estate gains.

Man, ignorant as he may seem, also has the ability to
see his mistakes and with foresight can plan corrective measures to insure an ample supply of clean water for all.

The space age presents enormous problems to scientists
in developing systems that will provide adequate food, water,
and elimination of waste products in manned space vehicles.
Out of this scientific endeavor may come new methods of obtaining usable water for mankind.

ACTIVITIES

1. Prepare a report or general map of the local water
    sources. The municipal water department is an excellent
    source. *S–C*
2. Check the hardness of the local water supply. Use several
    samples from various wells and the city water supply. A
    local commercial water softening firm will have kits avail-
    able and will usually come in and give such a demonstra-
    tion. *S–C*
3. Demonstrate natural filtration, using muddy water and
    filtering through a column of assorted sand and gravel.
    Use a milk carton cut off at both ends with a fine screen
    to hold the gravel in the carton. *E–S*
4. Make a general survey of possible water pollution in your
    locality and the means being used to curb such pollution.
    S–C
5. Demonstrate the transpiration of plants by placing a plastic
    bag over a house plant. Leave some holes in the plastic to
    allow gases to escape. Moisture should condense on the
    inside of the bag. *E–S–C*

6. Make a list of the local and state laws enacted to pressure water conservation and curb pollution. *S—C*

7. Make a large diagram or bulletin board display explaining the hydrologic cycle. *S*

8. Make a bulletin board display of recent articles on water conservation and pollution. *S—C*

9. Demonstrate the principle of capillary action by placing a lump of sugar in a shallow dish with some ink on the bottom. The ink will rise in the sugar at once. In the same manner, water moves through the soil to furnish plants with some of the moisture they need. *E—S*

10. The principle of osmosis may be demonstrated by placing a small plant (its soil washed from the roots) into a solution of colored water. Observe how it is colored by the water as it is taken up by the plant. *E—S*

11. Take photographs of water eroded areas or polluted streams. *S—C*

12. Take a field trip to the local sewage disposal plant. Find out prior to the trip if the plant is partial or a full treat-ment plant. *E—S—C*

13. Take a field trip to the municipal water treatment plant. Find out prior to the trip if the plant obtains its water from underground or surface reservoirs. *E- S—C*

14. The effect of the gradient on water erosion can be demon-strated by placing three shallow pans filled with fine sand or soil at different angles of elevation. *E—S*

15. Prepare a list of local personnel that could be used by your school as resource people in teaching about water conservation. *C*

16. Make posters pointing to water conservation or pollu-tion. *E*

17. Map the major water sources in the local community -- include ponds, lakes, rivers and streams. You may wish to indicate depth or width. *S—C*

18. Using the biology texts used throughout the country, desig-nate by specific pages on a chart those having to do with conservation, or specifically with water conservation. *C*

19. Compile a list of free and inexpensive materials for teaching conservation, or specifically water conservation, especially at the state level. See *Conservation Handbook*. *C*

20. Using a film such as *Nature's Plan,* use the class as guinea pigs: that is, if they were junior high youngsters, in showing how to introduce and follow-up a film in conservation. *C*
21. Explain to the class the artesian well and its implications for water conservation. You may wish to prepare a diagram. *E–S*
22. Research questions: Why can or can not the waters of the ocean be used for irrigation? Would irrigating desert regions be profitable? *E–S*
23. Write a research paper on creating artificial rain. *S–C*
24. Give an oral book report on a work of fiction such as *The Rainmaker* or *The Rains Came. S–C*
25. Water supply is crucial to entire countries. Use current news stories about Israel or Jordan or the ancient history of China or Egypt to tell the story. See *Conquest of the Land Through 7,000 Years. S–C*

BIBLIOGRAPHY

A Desert In Your Own Backyard. Washington, D. C.: National Wildlife Federation. *E*

Bradely, Charles C. "Human Water Needs and Water Use in America," *Science,* Vol. 138 (October 26, 1962), p. 490. *S–C*

Brinckerhoff, Richard, Burnett Cross, Fletcher Watson and Paul F. Brandwein. *The Physical World.* New York: Harcourt Brace and World, Inc., 1958. *S–C*

Carhard, Arthur H. *Water -- Or Your Life.* Philadelphia: J. B. Lippincott, 1959. *S–C*

Clean Water: A Challenge to the Nation. Public Health Service Publication No. 816, U. S. Department of Health, Education and Welfare. Washington: U. S. Government Printing Office. *S–C*

Conservation: Soil and Water. Bismarck, North Dakota: Department of Public Instruction, 1948.

Decker, John P. "Water Relations of Plant Communities as a Management Factor for Western Watersheds," *Science,* Vol. 138, (October 26, 1962), p. 352. *S–C*

Gallant, Roy A. *Man's Reach Into Space.* Garden City, N. Y.: Garden City Books, 1959. p. 132. *E*

Hanrahan, James S. and David Bushnell. *Space Biology.* New York: Basic Books, Inc., 1960. pp. 49-60. *S–C*

Heffernan, Helen and George Shaftel. *The Water Story.*
    Chicago: L. W. Singer Company, 1963. *E*
Iowa Conservation Education Council. *Conservation Source
    Book.* Ames: Iowa State University Press, 1962. *E-S-C*
"Just How Safe Is Your Drinking Water?" *U. S. News and
    World Report* (July 15, 1963). p. 74. *S-C*
Kinney, William A. *Medical Science and Space Travel.* New
    York: Franklin Watts, Inc., 1959. *E-S*
Leet, Donald L. and Sheldon Judson. *Physical Geology.*
    Englewood Cliffs: Prentice Hall, Inc., 1958. *S-C*
Namowitz, Samuel N. and Donald B. Stone. *Earth Science.*
    New York: D. Van Nostrand Company, Inc., 1952. *S-C*
Parker, Bertha Morris. *Water* (Basic Science Education
    Series). Evanston: Row Peterson and Company, 1944. *E*
Paulson, O. F. *Ground Water,* Geological Survey Information
    Bulletin. Grand Forks: U. S. Department of Interior,
    1962. *S-C*
Soil, Water and You, General Leaflet No. 6. Washington:
    National Wildlife Federation, 1954. *E*
"Too Many People Not Enough Water," *U. S. News and World
    Report* (June 17, 1963), p. 62. *S-C*
United States Department of Agriculture. *Water: The Year-
    book of Agriculture.* Washington: U. S. Government
    Printing Office, 1955. *S-C*
Walsh, Mary. *Water, Water Everywhere.* New York:
    Abingdon, Cokesbury Press, 1953. *E-S*
Wells, Robert. *Alive in Space.* Boston: Little, Brown, and
    Company, 1961. pp. 80-84. *S*
Williams, Albert N. *The Water and the Power.* New York:
    Duell, Sloan and Pearce, 1951. *C*
Williamson, Stanley E. "The Place of Science in Our Schools
    and Society Today"(Speech). Upper-Midwest National
    Science Teachers Conference, 1963. *S-C*
Zumberge, James H. *Elements of Geology.* New York: John
    Wiley and Sons, Inc., 1958. *S-C*

AUDIO-VISUAL MATERIALS

16 mm. FILMS

Arteries of Life - (EBF)

> This film points out the importance of water in providing topsoil with necessary moisture, and of forests in storing and regulating the flow of water over large areas. Clearly explains the water cycle and the water table. *S-C*

City Water Supply - (EBF)

> Animated drawings describe the relationship between rainfall and life; the sources of city water supply -- wells, rivers, lakes, and watersheds; waterborne diseases, and methods of distribution. Other photography depicts water tunnels and aqueducts; the dependence of cities upon an adequate water supply; and the necessity of safeguarding water sources and distribution. *S-C*

Clean Waters - (Gen. Elec.)

> Role of water in daily life, effects of pollution, and the operation of a sewage plant. *S-C*

From the Ridge of the River - (Soil Conservation Service)

> Shows local organization for watershed management. *S-C*

George Washington's River - (USDA)

> With an introduction of the water problems faced by Egyptians of Biblical times, this film presents a dramatic touchback to early American history. *S-C*

Lifeblood of the Land - (Forest Service)

> Shows the water cycle, destructive force of uncontrolled water. *S-C*

Man's Problem - (EBF)

> Points to conservation measures through storage dams. Illustrates erosion and pollution. *S-C*

Marsh Waters -- Waste or Wealth - (U. of M.)

Presents the surface water problem through the eyes of those acquainted with various phases of the problem -- the flood relief worker, geologists, fire wardens, trappers, waterfowl hunters, landowners, and nature hobbyists. *S-C*

Natures Plan - (EBF)

Shows importance of water and watershed. *S-C*

Pipeline to the Clouds - (Gen. Elec.)

Demonstrates the structure and operation of water purification plants -- and how water is safeguarded. *S-C*

The River - (UW)

Documentary musical film giving a graphic portrayal of the story of the Mississippi River, what it has meant to us and what it has cost us. Dramatized in ten principal sequences. Music composed by Virgil Thomason, composer and authority on modern music. *S-C*

Rivers - (GPI)

How a river is formed from tiny mountain streams and its journey to the sea. *E*

Valley of Still Waters - (Nebraska)

Pilot project to lessen damage and improve farmland. *S-C*

Water - (Soil Conservation Service)

Water is essential, but destructive when not controlled. *E*

The Water Cycle - (EBF)

Traces movement of water through its cycle of eternal change from ocean to sky and back to coean. Relates evaporation, saturation, condensation, and precipitation and in simple terms clearly explains principles underlying the phenomena. *S-C*

The Water Famine - (CFI)

The problems of water supply and its relation to world growth, world health, and industry are examined. It shows the modern miracle of de-salinization by the "flash freezing" process used in Israel and the electro-dialysis process used in the United States. *S-C*

Waters for the Prairies - (NFB of C)

A study of conservation along the watershed of the Rockies. The film illustrates the steady recession of the underground water table, careless exploitation of timber stands and gradual melting of glaciers have made conservation a major concern. It presents positive measures undertaken by the government. *E-S*

Water, Water Everywhere - (Cor)

The passage of water from the earth into the air by evaporation, how clouds are formed, and why rain falls. *E*

Working Water - (PDP)

How water is stored and brought to dry lands and how used. Stresses necessary balance of soil, sunshine and water to produce food crops. *E-S*

FILMSTRIPS

Conserving Water and Soil - (Dowling)

Tells of causes of excessive runoff. Pictures flood damage to top soil, cities and people. *S-C*

Irrigation - (ACE)

Reasons and effects of irrigation. *S-C*

Nothing Can Live Without Water - (Popular Science)

Hits on methods of conservation, water cycle, sources, uses and importance of water. *S-C*

Water Conservation - (Visual Sciences)

Problems and solutions of water conservation. *S-C*

The Water Cycle - (Dowling)

Indicates what happens to water when it reaches the earth, as well as the sources of water. *S*

Water Resources - (Curriculum)

Series ranges from pollution and flood control to water for personal use. *S*

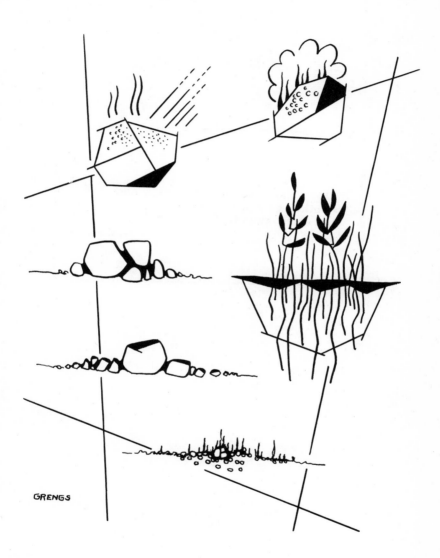

GRENGS

One generation passeth away, and another generation cometh, but the earth abideth forever.

Ecclesiastes

Chapter IV

SOIL CONSERVATION

OBJECTIVES

   I. To indicate the nature of soil -- its characteristics and classifications.

  II. To highlight the main ramifications of soil destruction and soil saving.

 III. To emphasize the destructive force of wind and soil erosion.

 IV. To appraise the interrelationships that exist between water and soil conservation.

      The soil formation process was begun centuries and centuries ago by the heating and the cooling of solid rock that was the original land surface of the earth. Then other forces, like wind and water, began to act upon the rock. The rock was split into smaller and smaller pieces by freezing water, by glacial action, and by carbonic acid -- carbonic acid being formed when carbon dioxide in the air combined with water during rainfalls. Then, lichens (plant associations of algae and fungi) grew on the rocks; and when these plants died, they supplied food for the tiny organisms, like bacteria, which furnished other materials for the soil. After thousands of centuries, with the process expanded and accelerated, soil -- or pulverized rock capable of supporting higher forms of life -- was formed. Scientists figure it takes from four hundred to one thousand years to create one inch of topsoil.[43]

      Depth is a basic consideration in the classification of soils. Depth refers to the thickness of topsoil and subsoil down to the unaltered parent material, or the layer on which the soil was built. A soil is called *deep* if it is more than twenty inches through topsoil and subsoil to the parent material. A soil is called *shallow* if the range is from ten to twenty

---

[43] Helen Heffernan and George Shaftel, The Soil Story (Syracuse: L. W. Singer Company, 1963), p. 25.

inches, and *very shallow* if it is less than ten inches deep. [44]
A vertical section through a well-developed soil shows three
distinct layers -- the soil profile. The fairly porous, usually
dark layer (layers are often called horizons) is the topsoil.
Below this layer is a lighter more compact layer called the
subsoil. Below this subsoil is the parent material from which
the subsoil and topsoil come, and under the parent material is
the original bedrock.

There are many hundreds of soils, a wide variation of
soil types, and many reasons for variation in soils. Soils come
from a variety of parent materials -- lava, limestone, muck,
sand, for example. Soils may be residual, or they may have
been transported and deposited by water (alluvial), by moving
ice (glacial), or by wind (eolian). Some soils are young, geo-
logically speaking; some soils have been developing over a long
period of time. The kind of vegetation, or the lack of it, growing on the soil causes variety in soil. Temperature, rainfall,
minerals -- even the slope of the land -- and each affects soil.
Steep slopes lose much soil as it forms, and it becomes an alluvial deposit. Temperature and rainfall not only affect the
rate of decomposition of the parent material, but also the vegetation and rate of erosion.

It is to be noted that there is a constant movement of
material back and forth between the upper, organic layers of
the soil and the lower, inorganic layers. [45] When rain comes,
some of the water enters the soil and passes through the porous
space, carrying materials downward, both in solution and sus-
pension. During drought, however, the movement is reversed,
and the moisture rises either as vapor or through capillary action (the action by which fuels travel upward in a lamp wick).

The movement of water and vapor also causes the soil to
breathe. As the water and vapor enter the pores of the soil,
they expel the air. As they leave, fresh air is drawn in. Fresh
air is necessary to the growth of vegetation. If the pores are
clogged, diminishing the supply of oxygen, the productive activities of the soil are retarded. [46]

[44]Sellers G. Archer, Soil Conservation (Norman, Oklahoma: University of Oklahoma
Press, 1956), p. 25
[45]Charles E. Kellogg, The Soil That Supports Us (New York: The Macmillan
Company, 1956), p. 65.
[46]Karl B. Mickey, Man and the Soil (out of print).

Texture and permeability are basic considerations in soil classification. Texture relates to surface soil, permeability relates to subsoil. Texture and permeability both relate to the density of the soils or the fineness of the individual soil particles. The percentage or proportionate amounts of sand, silt, and clay give soil its texture. A soil of coarse texture may be called sandy soil. A clay soil will be one of fine texture. A soil of medium texture, having a fairly even distribution of sand, silt, and clay is called a loam soil. Texture is associated with and is responsible for certain physical characteristics of soil. For example, water tends to run through coarse soils quickly; such soils also warm more quickly in spring than those largely composed of clay. Coarse soils also "work more easily" in farming. Silty soils are easily eroded by wind and moving water and offer poor moisture control.

The primary functions of subsoil, agriculturally speaking, are to receive and store moisture and to permit roots to penetrate in search of minerals and moisture. Clay subsoils are "slowly" or "very slowly" permeable to the invasion of air, water, or roots. Coarse, sandy subsoils are indicated as "freely" or "very freely" permeable.

In many clays and silty soils, particles of soil are arranged in groups. This grouping is called *soil structure.* (Structure of soil is sometimes referred to as the degree of friability or crumbliness.) This grouping creates larger pore spaces which more easily permit the penetration of air and the roots of growing plants. Also, the cultivating qualities of the soil are greatly improved. Good soil structure is promoted by the presence of lime and by the growth and decay of plants or the addition of organic fertilizer.

Soil is where the mineral, vegetable, and animal kingdoms of the earth meet and mingle, and react one upon another. Seemingly so solid, from forty to sixty per cent of soil is porous space filled with air and water.[47] The remainder of the soil consists of solid inorganic matter (minerals), inorganic matter in solution, living organic matter (roots of living plants, small animals, bacteria, fungi), and dead organic matter. The bulk of most soils is made up of earth minerals. These minerals supply many of the chemical elements (about fifteen) required for the proper growth of plants. The more abundant elements in most soils are oxygen, silicon, aluminum, and iron. Some elements are obtained by plants directly from the

[47]Ibid., p. 18.

atmosphere.   The larger number, however, are secured in
solution through the root systems. [48]

A soil that is deficient in soluble, or easily dissolved,
mineral matter is a poor soil.   Some elements are abundant
in most soils; some elements are less likely to be plentiful --
especially potassium, phosphorus, nitrogen, and calcium.
These four elements are very necessary to the growth of plants.

Russian scientists were responsible for the development
of the first systematic scheme for grouping soils on the basis
of climatic and vegetative factors. [49] Soils may be said to be-
long to four major soil groups:

Latosolic soils[50] (from the Latin meaning "brick") dominate equatorial belts of Africa and South America, southeastern
parts of Asia and North America, as well as northeastern
Australia and the larger islands of the western Pacific Ocean.
Latosolic soils have been formed under forest and savanna
vegetation in tropical and sub-tropical and humid to fairly dry
climates.   As a whole, the humid forest soils are leached
(frequent rains dissolve and remove soluble mineral matter);
prevailingly light in color (red and yellow are common because
of the large amounts of iron oxides formed through intense
weathering); and comparatively low in organic matter and mineral plant food.   The laterites, for example, are tropical red
soils that have been leached to the degree that they are porous
and extremely infertile.   Productivity is normally low when
latosolic soils are used without benefit of modern science and
industry.   Most latosolic soils are easily penetrated by water
and plant roots, but are resistent to erosion.

Podzolic soils (from the Russian meaning "ash beneath")
dominate a broad belt in the higher latitudes of the northern
hemisphere and some smaller areas in the southern half of the
world.   Podzolic soils were formed under forest vegetation in
humid, temperate climates.   (The soils developed under deciduous forests are superior to those developed under coniferous
forests, as is indicated by the amount of deciduous forests that
have been cleared of trees to make the soil available for agri-

[48]Vernon C. Finch, Glenn T. Trewartha, M. H. Shearer, The Earth and Its
Resources (New York: McGraw-Hill Company), p. 425.

[49]Firman E. Bear, Earth: The Stuff of Life (Norman, Oklahoma: University of
Oklahoma Press, 1962), p. 11.

[50]U. S. Department of Agriculture, Soil: The Yearbook of Agriculture (Washington:
Government Printing Office, 1957), pp. 28-31.

cultural purposes.)[51] The true podzols, formed under coniferous forests, are commonly acid -- therefore making conditions
unfavorable to the existence of earthworms which mingle decayed vegetation with other soil parts. The podzols, as a
whole, are poor agricultural soils, but they are responsive
to scientific management.

Chernozemic soils (from the Russian meaning "black
earth") have been formed under prairie or grass vegetation
in humid to semiarid and temperate to tropical climates.
Chernozemic soils of temperate zones are among the most
fertile soils in the world. These soils produce about ninety
per cent of the grain in commercial trade channels. In the
United States, the chernozemic soils form the heart of the
Corn Belt and the Wheat Belt. The surface material of the
chernozem is black or dark brown in color. When cultivated,
this soil, because of its excellent structure, crumbles into a
fine seedbed having a large capacity for holding water. The
reserves of organic and mineral plant foods are so abundant
that the soils will stand much cropping without fertilization.

Desertic soils have been formed under mixed shrub and
grass vegetation or under shrubs in arid climates. These
soils are found in the great range of climates -- from hot to
cold. Desertic soils have been very slightly weathered and
leached. The shortage of moisture which restricts weathering
and leaching also limits plant growth, leaving the soils low in
organic matter and nitrogen. Some of the desert soils, however, when irrigated and given proper care, may be made
highly productive. Because of the low rainfall the soluble
substances, called salts, may never have been carried off by
water; in that event, these salts may be a problem when irrigation water is supplied.

In his book, *Rich Land, Poor Land,* Stuart Chase makes
a strong statement: "American soil vitality suffers from three
plagues: erosion, depletion through cropping, and leaching --
all man made. "[52] Although there are those who would take
exceptions to this statement, citing catastrophic events and
indicating that man is not the only cause of erosion, none-the-
less, man ought to be concerned with those things he can do
something about. Some leaching is desirable and beneficial.

---

[51] Vernon C. Finch, Glenn T. Trewartha, M. H. Shearer, The Earth and Its
Resources (New York: McGraw-Hill Company, 1959), pp. 432-435.

[52] Stuart Chase, Rich Land, Poor Land (New York: Whittlesey House, McGraw-Hill
Company, 1936), p. 84.

Minnesota Department of Conservation

Figure 12. Advanced stage of soil erosion

It removes certain soluble salts that otherwise would become
so concentrated in the soil solution that crops would not grow.
Natural erosion has been going on for countless centuries. It,
too, is beneficial, having formed fertile and productive soils.
Trouble comes when man, through ignorance, recklessness,
or neglect removes natural processes and forces. Man should
not rationalize away his responsibility in saving the soil.

In erosion, both plant food in the form of mineral matter
and the earth itself slide downhill. (See Figure 12) In depletion, only the minerals are taken away, largely incorporated
in the crop and shipped away to market. In leaching, minerals

are dissolved in rain water and the plant food is carried underground out of the topsoil.

But, by far the greatest danger to the soil is erosion.
There is water erosion and wind erosion. In the spring of
1934, the greatest series of dust storms in the history of the
United States began on the Great Plains. The storms were
caused by extreme drought and the removal of natural grasses.
Nature was responsible for the drought, but man was responsible for the removal of the grasses. [53]

The years following World War I saw a tremendous demand for wheat and beef all over the world. American cattle
raisers allowed the great herds to over-graze the grasslands
until the bare soils were exposed. American farmers, seeking
more wheatlands, moved westward beyond the 100th meridian.
They plowed under the soil-binding grasses of these grazing
lands and raised wheat in a climate of uncertain rainfall. [54]
Thus, by overgrazing and out-of-place agriculture, the protective natural vegetation was stripped from the soil and laid
the foundation for the disastrous dust storms of the 1930's.
(See Figure 13)

Things went well enough until 1934, although many fields
had already been abandoned as the demand for wheat declined.
In that year, a severe drought occurred. The cultivated crops,
unable to survive the lack of moisture, withered away. But,
now there were no grass roots to hold the soil together. The
prevailing westerly winds, blowing over the plain states found
loose crumbling topsoil and whisked it into the air. Blowing
vast clouds of precious topsoil off the face of millions of acres
of once productive farm land, the winds raised the dust high
into the atmosphere and eastward across the country in a succession of "storms" that continued through the summer and
into the fall. Wherever they went, the storms darkened the
skies, reaching even to eastern seaboard cities of New York
and Washington.

It was in this series of dust storms that the Dust Bowl
was born. The Dust Bowl, so-named in 1934, included parts
of Texas, New Mexico, Colorado, Kansas, Nebraska, Wyo-
ming, Montana, South Dakota, North Dakota, and even Saskatchewan in Canada. The drought continued for several years,
and more than 150,000 people were forced to abandon their

[53]S. N. Namowitz and D. B. Stone, Earth Science, The World We Live In (New
York: D. Van Nostrand Company, Inc., 1953), p. 198.
[54]Ibid., p. 181.

Minnesota Department of Conservation

Figure 13. Results of wind erosion

farms and their homes -- truly a tragedy in man's quest for more land and more wealth without proper foresight.

Water erosion can, for convenience in discussion (there is no line of demarcation between the stages), be divided into three stages: Sheet erosion, rill erosion, and gully erosion.[55] In *Conserving Soil Resources,* however, Chapman, Fitch, and Veatch refer to *splash* erosion.[56] When a tiny raindrop hits

[55]Mickey, Op. cit., p. 28.

[56]Paul W. Chapman, Frank W. Fitch, Jr., and C. L. Veatch, Conserving Soil Resources (Atlanta: Turner E. Smith and Company, 1950), p. 73.

Figure 14. Rill and sheet erosion

Figure 15. Rill erosion and deposition

United States Soil Conservation Department

bare soil, it kicks up a splash of dirt and makes a tiny crater.
Raindrops break down clods and soil granules into smaller
particles. When raindrops strike sloping land surfaces, the
major portion of the splashed material is thrown downhill. As
the patter of raindrops continues, there may be a gradual flow
of the soil toward the bottom of the slope.

Sheet erosion is an insidious wasting away of the soil
which may take place for years without giving visible warning.
(See Figure 14) The chief clues to sheet erosion are constantly
decreasing yields of crops even with fertilizer or the sudden
appearance of a patch of subsoil on a slight rise of ground.
Sheet erosion can be prevented by providing a cushion of vegetation to absorb the shock of rain pellets.

Rill erosion is visible. (See Figure 15) The run-off digs
out little furrows or channels in the soil. In rill erosion (sometimes called finger erosion) a network is formed, like tributaries to a river -- smaller rills flowing into larger rills. In
rill erosion, one heavy rain can be a grave danger. Farmers
sometimes try to hide the rills by plowing and harrowing, but
this simply accelerates the process.

When one furrow becomes a main channel, gully erosion
has set in. (See Figure 16) The longer the gullying process
continues, the harder it is to cure, because most subsoils do
not possess the fertility required by most cover crops. Gullied
land can soon become a wasteland. Badly gullied land ought to
be put back into woods or other vegetative growth which can
survive on exhausted soils. (See Figure 17)

Reference is also made to riverbank and seashore erosion in conservation literature. As river currents swirl and
grind against the bank, they make an undercut, which eventually caves into the water. Riverbank erosion cuts back the
edges of streams and washes the caved-in soil downstream.
The actions of tides and waves are in constant motion, building and tearing down the seashore. Silt and sand can fill in
accesses to port cities; and if retaining walls are not built,
violent waves can eat away the very foundations of seaside
buildings -- or during a storm, flood the city.

Although there is natural erosion, man accelerates the
erosive process. [Often he burns over land which destroys not
only the ground cover which holds the rainfall and allows most
of it to penetrate the soil, but also destroys the organisms of
the soil. The farmer plows up and down the slope, or plows
ground that is too steep and which should never be plowed. He

Figure 16. Beginning stages of erosion

Figure 17. Advanced stages of gully erosion

United States Soil Conservation Department

may, year after year, plant crops like cotton or corn which
burn out the organic matter and by clean tilling he makes erosion easier. Farmers sometimes fail to plant cover crops to
protect the croplands during the winter months. Sometimes
ranchers overgraze the land, or cut off too much of the woods
and vegetative cover. These are but a few of the misdeeds of
man.

Not only is the eroded soil made useless, but further
problems are also created downstream. Material washed out
of gullies is swept down into river valleys to shore streams,
filling reservoirs, and destroying water storage for irrigation.[57]
Many reservoirs are being rapidly filled with soil, the average
rate of loss of storage capacity being from two to three per
cent a year. Lake Mead, for example, is being filled with silt,
its life being estimated at less than one hundred and fifty
years.[58]

The immediate and specific effects of erosion are of
major concern: Erosion reduces crop yields, lowers farm
income, decreases the profits of business and industry, im-
pairs health, and increases the damage done by destructive
floods.[59] Records of the continuous flow of streams from
eight small watersheds in North Carolina indicate that bare,
eroded lands contribute more potential flood waters than do
watersheds which are well protected with vegetation. These
records show the average maximum flood flow from forested
watersheds was six cubic feet per second per square mile.
From eroded agriculture lands the flow was four hundred and
three cubic feet per second per square mile, and from badly
gullied land, seven hundred and eighty-five cubic feet per second per square mile. In no instance was the storm run-off
from forested watersheds sufficient to cause floods, whereas
on the eroded farm acres the maximum flow reached flood
proportions many times during the two-year period while
records were being kept.[60]

That erosion reduces crop yields can be dramatically
illustrated: At Temple, Texas, a field having only slight erosion produced seven hundred and seventy-one pounds of seed
cotton per acre, while a field with seventy-five per cent of

[57]W. C. Lowdermilk, Conquest of the Land Through 7,000 Years, Agriculture
Information Bulletin No. 99, U. S. Department of Agriculture (Washington: Government
Printing Office, 1953), p. 29.

[58]Bear, Op. cit., p. 187.

[59]Chapman, Fitch, and Veatch, Op. cit., p. 80.

[60]Ibid., pp. 93-94.

the topsoil washed off yielded twenty-five pounds. [61]

That erosion lowers farm income (and capital worth of holdings) can be exemplified by a reverse situation. In Jacksonville, New York, Delmar Hammond reclaimed a one hundred and twenty-five acre dairy and cash crop farm. Corn production increased to one hundred bushels per acre from a pre-conservation production of forty to fifty bushels. Hay production jumped from three-fourths of a ton to three tons per acre, bean production from fifteen to twenty-six bushels, and his pastures now feed three animals per acre where they could formerly support less than half that number. [62]

Even when man has failed to prevent erosion, he is not helpless. There are many techniques he can apply in controlling erosion. First, steep slopes can be taken out of cultivation and returned to natural cover. Less steep slopes may be planted in grass and be used as pasture. Second, adequate ground cover can be provided all year around, but especially in summer when heavy rains occur. Third, crop rotation can balance soil-depleting crops with soil-conserving crops. Fourth, mechanical practices such as terracing, stubble mulch protection, and contour cultivation have proved to be valuable vehicles for soil saving. Fifth, wind-strip cropping and tree planting (or wind breaks) are effective against wind erosion. Tree planting is an important step in fighting wind erosion on level ground. Not only do the young trees serve as "soil binders" with their roots, but also as most valuable wind breaks against the gales which start the surface of the topsoil blowing away during the dry seasons. [63] Sixth, check dams and gully planting (as kudza) are curative treatments in gully erosion. Seventh, organic matter and animal life can be maintained in the soil by use of fertilizer and by avoiding burn-off. Eighth, building ponds and taking care of roadways can be of tremendous benefit in erosion control. Ninth, soil can be conserved by draining waterlogged fields and by flooding fields where toxic salts have accumulated, to leach out the salts. Finally, feed crops can be increased in safe grazing areas to eliminate overgrazing when grass is short and thin.

And these ten techniques only begin to scratch the surface, for there are many, many ways man may control erosion.

[61]Ibid., p. 82.

[62]Archer, Op. cit., p. 5.

[63]C. B. Colby, Soil Savers (New York: Coward-McCann, Inc., 1957), p. 28.

Man will never be able to control all kinds of erosion. The job of the soil conservationist is to protect the land from erosion and exhaustion according to its needs, and to see that it is used according to its capability to grow things.

It is to be noted that water conservation and soil conservation are inseparable, and no where is this more graphically illustrated than in watershed control. The entire land surface consists of watershed units; each watershed has a sloping surface which causes all moisture which falls upon it to flow in one direction. The goal in watershed conservation is to hold water to insure an adequate supply of water for both farms and factories. Holding the water will eliminate or reduce serious flooding. But, to obtain good holding power, all lands -- farms, forests, pastures, even roadsides -- must be well covered with grass, trees, or shrubs. There cannot be gullies or streams running muddy.

Even the water cycle shows the intimate relation between soil and water conservation: precipitation falls upon the earth. The water becomes surface run-off, is temporarily stored, or infiltrates into the earth. The ground water returns to the surface through plants, soil, or streams. Moisture evaporates from ponds, soil, or plants, and the cycle is repeated.

In summary, the soil beneath our feet is a renewable natural resource, in contrast to iron ore, coal, or gas, but it remains for man to provide adequate measures to keep the soil in place and to renew the supplies of mineral nutrients that are carried off in crops or by carelessness. Even when man fails to take preventive measures to save the soil, there are conservation methods that can be applied in a curative way. Soil conservation is one of the several links in the conservation chain -- related to water, forests, etc. -- and day by day, man with his ever increasing need and demand of this great earth resource, should think not only of today, but also of tomorrow. For, today's man was yesterday's child, and today's child is tomorrow's man.

ACTIVITIES

1. Fill one flower pot with topsoil, another with shallow subsoil taken directly below where the topsoil was obtained, and the third with deeper subsoil obtained at the same place. From the same packet, plant a few seeds in each of the flower pots, being sure each pot gets the same

attention as to sunlight and rain. Observe the rate of growth and general appearance. What conclusions can be drawn? *E-S*

2. Make a survey or check of the local community to discover erosion hazards. *E-S*

3. Make models (of clay, paper mache, etc.) to illustrate contour plowing, strip cropping, or other soil conservation techniques. *E-S*

4. Find clippings or photographs for your notebook, scrapbook, or file on soil conservation. *C*

5. Hold a round table discussion on "Why city people should be interested in soil conservation." *E*

6. Experiment: Show how friction of rocks helps form soil. Rub pieces of limestone, sandstone, etc., together to illustrate how long it takes nature to form soil. *E-S*

7. Have a panel discussion. Possible topic: "What have political parties, farm organizations, government done about soil conservation?" *S-C*

8. Divide the class into committees to discover what other countries or regions have done in conservation. (Preplanning with the library is essential, if this activity is to succeed.) *S-C*

9. Experiment: Have two separate mounds of topsoil and a small fan. Cover one mound with sod, grass and leaves, and leave the other mound bare. (1) Sprinkle water lightly on each slope and notice where the greatest loss of soil and water occur. (2) When the two mounds of topsoil have dried off, turn an electric fan on them. Watch to see from which one the most soil blows. *E-S*

10. Develop your own experimental design in determining what kind of soil has the greatest moisture holding power. *S-C*

11. Plan a dramatization in which an employee of the Soil Conservation Service explains to one or more farmers how they can use their land more wisely. *E*

12. Experiment: Fill a large glass container half full with a variety of ingredients -- sand, gravel, clay, etc. Then add enough water to make the entire mixture fluid. Shake the container several minutes. What happens when the container sets over night? *E-S*

13. Prepare simple graphs showing the loss of soil in the United States (or in a specific state) during a year, decade, or score of years. *S-C*

14. Ask the county agent or a representative from the Soil Conservation Service to speak to your class or show slides demonstrating erosion and ways of combating it. *E-S-C*
15. Make a "movie" of drawings by class members, showing the principles of soil conservation. The individual pictures can be pasted together and unrolled like the old-time scroll. *E*
16. Make up a story or tale using soil conservation as a theme. *E-S*
17. Make a bulletin board display of various kinds of erosion. Check your farm magazines and the local newspaper. *E-S*
18. Prepare written reports about any one of the following:
    a. The major soil regions of the world *C*
    b. The structure and development of soil *S*
    c. The early settlers misused the land *E*
19. Have the class write a letter requesting pamphlets from the United States Department of Agriculture on soil conservation. *E*
20. Interview several farmers as if you were preparing a radio broadcast on "The Dangers of Soil Erosion." You may wish to tape record the interviews and edit for class presentation. *S-C*
21. Smokey the Bear has become the symbol of fire prevention. Who or what do you think would make a good symbol for "Save the Soil?" You may wish to make some drawings. *E*
22. Send a questionnaire to the farmers in a community to discover if they believe soil erosion is a serious problem, what methods can be used in combating it, etc.? *C*
23. The class may wish to conduct their own poll to discover the attitude in the school and community regarding soil conservation. *S*
24. Research these questions:
    a. Why was the Soil Conservation Service organized when it was? *S-C*
    b. What is the organizational structure of the Soil Conservation Service? *S-C*
25. Experiment: Plant five beans in five different pots of soil. Water the pots and place them in sunlight. Keep a record of plant growth and development. What conclusions can be drawn? *E-S*

BIBLIOGRAPHY

Archer, Sellers G. *Soil Conservation.* Norman, Oklahoma: University of Oklahoma Press, 1956 **C**

Bear, Firman E. *Earth: The Stuff of Life.* Norman, Oklahoma: University of Oklahoma Press, 1962. **S-C**

Bennett, Hugh Howard. *Elements of Soil Conservation.* New York: McGraw-Hill Book Company, 1955. **S**

Blanck, Fred C. *Handbook of Food and Agriculture.* New York: Reinhold Publishing Corporation, 1955. pp. 1-20. **C**

Chapman, Paul W., Frank W. Fitch, Jr., and Curry L. Veatch. *Conserving Soil Resources.* Atlanta: Turner E. Smith and Company, 1950. **S**

Colby, C. B. *Soil Savers.* New York: Coward-McCann, Inc., 1957. **E**

Department of Public Instruction. *Conservation, Soil and Water, for the Public Schools.* Bismarck: State of North Dakota, 1948. **C**

Finch, Vernon C., Glenn T. Trewartha and M. H. Shearer. *The Earth and Its Resources.* New York: McGraw-Hill Company, 1959. **S-C**

Gee, C. W. *The Soil That Went to Town,* United States Department of Agriculture, Information Bulletin 95. Washington: Government Printing Office, 1952. **E-S-C**

Goetz, Delia. *Deserts.* New York: William Morrow and Company, 1956. **E**

Gustafson, A. F. *Conservation of the Soil.* New York: McGraw-Hill Book Company, 1937. **S-C**

Hart, Henry C. *The Dark Missouri.* Madison: The University of Wisconsin Press, 1957. **C**

Heffernan, Helen and George Shaftel. *The Soil Story.* Syracuse: L. W. Singer Company, 1963. **S**

Kellogg, Charles E. *The Soil That Supports Us.* New York: The Macmillan Company, 1956. **S-C**

Lathrop, William H. *From the Dust of the Earth,* United States Department of Agriculture, Information Bulletin No. 78. Washington: Government Printing Office, 1952. **E-S**

Lauber, Patricia. *Dust Bowl.* New York: Coward-McCann, Inc., 1958. **E-S**

Lindsay, Leon. "Farmer's Foe: Erosion," *The Christian Science Monitor,* December 13, 1961. **S-C**

Namowitz, S. N. and D. B. Stone. *Earth Science: The World
   We Live In.* New York: D. Van Nostrand Company, Inc.
   1953. *S*

Philips, Alfred W. *The Value of Soil Conservation, Problems
   of Conserving Soil, Water, and Wildlife.* Lincoln:
   Nebraska University Publishing Company. *S*

Sanderson, Ivan T. *The Continent We Live On.* New York:
   Random House, 1961. *E−S−C*

Schickele, Rainer. *Agricultural Policy.* New York: McGraw-
   Hill Book Company, 1954. pp. 95-117. *S−C*

Sears, Paul B. *Deserts on the March.* Norman, Oklahoma:
   University of Oklahoma Press, 1947. *S−C*

Shepard, Ward. *Food or Famine, the Challenge of Erosion.*
   New York: The Macmillan Company, 1945. *S−C*

United States Department of Agriculture. *Soil: The Yearbook
   of Agriculture.* Washington: Government Printing Office,
   1958. *C*

Van Dersel, William R. and Edward H. Graham. *The Land
   Renewed: The Story of Conservation.* New York: Oxford
   University Press, 1946. *E−S*

AUDIO-VISUAL MATERIALS

16 mm. FILMS

Birth of the Soil - (EBF)

> This film contrasts the productive capacity of topsoil
> with that of subsoil -- and shows the slow process of
> making soil. *S−C*

Deeper Acres - (Midland Corporation)

> A farm family improves its livelihood by sound conser-
> vation practices -- shows Midland's productive facili-
> ties. *S−C*

Earth - (GPI)

> Rangers get interested in the resources beneath the
> earth's surface -- the importance of the thin layer of
> topsoil which sustains plant and animal life. *E*

Erosion - (GPI)

A trip to the mountains reveals the common causes of erosion -- water, wind, ice, and roots. *E*

Face of the Earth - (EBF)

The "wearing down" forces of the earth such as the action of landslides, running water, and glaciers, are shown in this film. *E-S*

From the Ground Up - (Soil Conservation Service)

Planned conservation, world food supply, and the soil surveys as they relate to soil conservation highlight this film. *S-C*

The Golden Secret - (Soil Conservation Service)

This film has a cartoon fairy story of how the golden topsoil was prevented from washing away. *E*

Irrigation Farming - (EBF)

This film illustrates irrigation by furrow and flooding methods, canvas dams, flooding, and sprinkling. It shows the necessity of mutual, cooperative planning in irrigation. *S*

Keep Your Eye on the Soil - (Deere)

Soil management is the essence of this film. *C*

Land and Waters of the Earth - (Cor)

On a picnic a young boy becomes aware of the various kinds of land and water forms -- mountains, valleys, rivers etc. *E*

Our Soil Resources - (EBF)

Photography and animation are used to show the formation of soil, different soil zones, and the conservation aspects of soil control. *S*

Raindrops and Soil Erosion - (Soil Conservation Service)

This film is a technical discussion of different kinds of soils as affected by rain. *C*

Soil Test

Soil sampling, testing, and advisory services are explained in animation and live demonstrations by Iowa State College Soils Laboratory. *S-C*

This Is Our Land - (Ethyl)

Overview of soil, soil nutrients, and soil conservation is the concern of this film. *S-C*

Understanding Our Earth: Soil - (Cor)

The soil profile, soil elements, soil types, the process of making soil, and the importance of soil conservation are demonstrated in this film. *E-S*

The Wearing Away of the Land - (EBF)

The various processes of wearing away by chemical decomposition of rocks, glaciers, wind, and waves are presented. *S-C*

The Work of Rivers - (EBF)

The erosion cycle of water on the earth's surface is presented. Special features explained are ox bow lakes, sand bars, water gaps, and lakes. *S-C*

The Work of Running Water - (EBF)

The film shows formation of deltas and flood plains. Special attention is given to Mississippi bottom lands. *S-C*

The World At Your Feet - (NFBC)

Soil structure and chemistry, life in the soil, and the significance of soil to mankind highlight this film. *S-C*

FILMSTRIPS

Conserving Soil and Water - (Popular Science Pub. Co.)

The effects of floods, poor forestation, and good agricultural conservation practices are shown. Filmstrip of the Month, Art, Inc. *E–S*

Saving the Soil - (Popular Science Pub. Co.)

The relationship of soil to human survival and how to conserve the soil are shown. *S*

Soil and Its Conservation - (Eyegate)

This explains the nature of soil and the process of conservation. *E–S*

Soil Conservation Series - (EBF)

This series of eight filmstrips explains what soil is, how it is used and misused, and how it can be made productive. *S–C*

"Animal Life and the Soil"
"How Long Will It Last?"
"How Man Conserves Soil"
"How Soil Is Formed"
"Minerals in the Soil"
"Plant Life and the Soil"
"Use of Soil"
"Water and the Soil"

Testing Soil - (Popular Science Pub. Co.)

It explains the necessity for testing soil and shows how it is done. *S–C*

What Is Soil - (Popular Science Pub. Co.)

The structure and composition of soil are explained. *E–S*

GRENGS

Take a straw and throw it up
into the air, you may see by
that which way the wind is.
                    John Seldon

Chapter V   **AIR POLLUTION**

OBJECTIVES

I.   To develop an awareness of the ever present problem of air pollution.
II. To investigate probable causes of contamination that pollutes the atmosphere.
III. To focus attention toward the detrimental effects directly related to air pollution.
IV. To point out progress being made internationally, nationally, and locally to curb contamination of the atmosphere.

All men, regardless of color or creed deserve the inalienable right to breathe pure wholesome air. It is so necessary that all terrestrial creatures have their biological structures patterned with set limits as to the quantity and quality of the air they breathe.

At sea level, our atmosphere consists of the following invisible gases by volume: 78 per cent nitrogen, 21 per cent oxygen, and the remaining one per cent chiefly argon (0.94%), a little carbon dioxide (0.03%), and mere traces of neon, krypton, xenon, helium, and hydrogen. Add another trace of ozone, which has an odor. Such a mixture, practically odorless and invisible in all its parts, is the material we call air. [64]

Man is limited in breathing by the amount of oxygen present and as one reaches 12,000 feet or more, depending on an individual's adaptation, breathing may become difficult. Lack of oxygen causes shortness of breath, while too much oxygen, as in the case of over-administration to babies in incubators, can cause blindness. Man is certainly limited to the quantity of oxygen present in the air he breathes, but other limits exist as well, such as: suspended particles,

[64] Samuel N. Namowitz and Donald B. Stone, Earth Science (New York: D. Van Nostrand Company, Inc., 1953), p. 270

which include pollen, smoke, dust, chemicals, and fall-out or
radioactive isotopes which can be directly related to nuclear
explosions.

Air pollution has been with us since time began, if we
think of a pollutant as any suspended particle or foreign matter which is not considered native to the mixture of gases
which constitute our atmosphere. In England in 1306, a law
was passed against air pollution. No one was permitted to
burn coal while Parliament was in session.[65] In the Middle
East, the air has been polluted for thousands of years by farmers burning brush and grass. Forest fires, started naturally
by lightning or by man's carelessness contaminate the atmosphere with carbon dioxide and unburned hydrocarbons. (Hydrocarbons are compounds consisting of the elements of hydrogen
and carbon. All petroleum products are hydrocarbons.) Dust
storms, at times, make breathing nearly impossible and visi-
bility almost zero. Chemical gases and unburned particles released by industry along with the exhaust fumes from the millions of transportation vehicles literally saturate the air with
pollutants. Radioactive fall-out resulting from atmospheric
nuclear testing has drawn attention because of its detrimental
effect on man and beast.

Many people are plagued by what is called "hay fever"
-- as the pollen count rises at various times of the year.
Others suffer from asthma, bronchitis, and emphysema.

Cities in all parts of the world, because of their geographical location, are engulfed by smog. Smog is a term
used to describe a mixture of smoke and fog. One has to enter
such an atmosphere only once to realize that the tightening of
his throat and the burning sensation in his eyes is due to smog.
In 1962, over 400 people lost their lives in the London smog.[66]
Many people in all parts of the world contract infections which
can be directly or indirectly traced to polluted air.

It is estimated that the cost of air pollution is twelve
million dollars per year in the United States alone.[67] This is
more than sixty dollars per person annually. However, this
cost includes the damage done to property, such as crops,
buildings, and cattle. Every day the average person inhales
6,000 gallons of air.[68] Some of it inevitably is polluted air.
(See Figure 18)

[65]Thomas G. Aylesworth, "Smoke, Smog, and Smell," Current Science,
Vol. XLIX, No. 2, September 16-20, 1963, p. 10.
[66]Ibid.
[67]"Air Pollution," Senior Scholastic, Vol. 81, January 16, 1963, p. 17.
[68]Ibid.

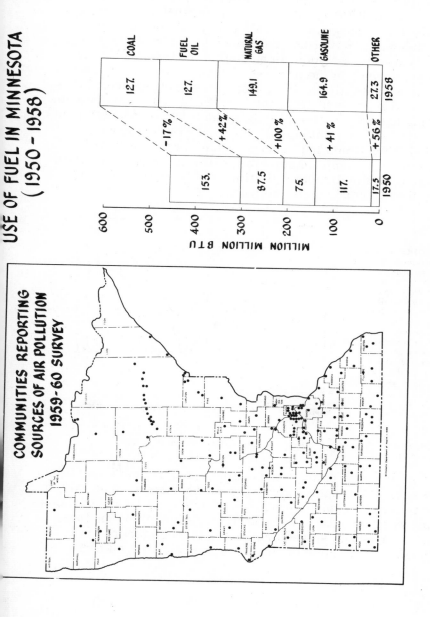

Figure 18.   Minnesota Department of Health

The causes of air pollution are manyfold, but it stems largely from combustion involving a conglomerate of materials. Air pollution itself is confined neither to large industrial cities nor to places that topography makes smog-prone. In fact, warns the U. S. Surgeon General, every city of more than 50,000 has an air pollution problem. [69]

City dwellers seldom light their own fires, yet their daily lives depend on the process of combustion. The medallion home with its all electric, flameless conveniences, ultimately derives its heat from the burning of coal or petroleum. Something has to be burned to make the television function or warm your feet on a cold night. In most cities, the garbage is burned; sometimes it is burned twice, in the backyard and again in the city dump. Automobiles are highly mobile "burners" throughout their active lifetime and when they are outmoded, they too end up on the pyre. [70] (See Figure 19)

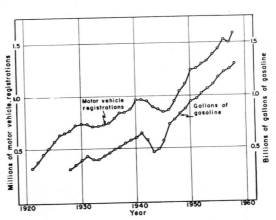

AUTOMOBILE exhaust is an important source of air pollution especially in large metropolitan areas and in smaller communities where terrain and weather limit dispersion of air pollutants. Motor vehicles emit significant quantities of carbon monoxide, hydrocarbons, nitrogen oxides, and other organic gases.

Figure 19. School Health News, Minnesota Department of Health, 1961.

The internal combustion engine, modern and powerful as it may seem, is roughly twenty per cent efficient. The United States consumer expects his automobile engine to start instantly in all weather, and to accelerate rapidly with no engine knock. To meet these requirements, manufacturers build large high compression engines that operate best on high-

[69]Ibid.
[70]Walsh McDermott, "Air Pollution and Public Health," Scientific American, Vol. 205, October, 1961, p. 51.

octane gasoline, a fuel that burns with low efficiency, except
under optimum operating conditions. Hydrocarbons escape
both through the exhaust and as vapors from the fuel tank and
carburetor vents. Exhaust fumes from the tail pipe vary considerably, depending somewhat on engine size and the condition of the engine, which is a result of the faithfulness of the
upkeep. The fumes are concentrated the most during low-
speed driving, such as occurs twice a day during rush hours
on the freeways. On a hot day, in traffic, the emission from
the carburetor and fuel tank approximates that of the tail pipe.
(See Figure 20)

According to Leslie A. Chambers, research director of
the Los Angeles Air Pollution Control District, the daily output of every 1,000 operating automobiles in an urban community burdens the air with 3.2 tons of carbon monoxide, 400 to
800 pounds of organic vapors (hydrocarbons), and 100 to 300
pounds of nitrous oxides, plus smaller amounts of sulfur and

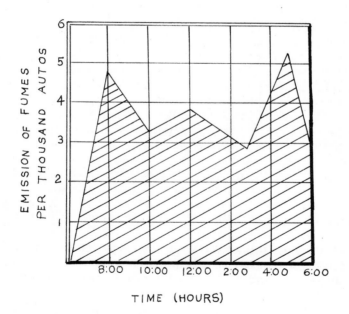

TIME (HOURS)

MAXIMUM CONCENTRATION OF FUMES
IN RELATION TO PEAK TRAFFIC HOURS

Figure 20

other chemicals.[71] The hydrocarbons and nitrous oxides are
highly important.

When an olefin and nitric oxide (NO) in concentrations of
parts per million are exposed to ultraviolet radiation in the
presence of oxygen, a rapid oxidation of nitric oxide occurs.[72]
Like the paraffins, of which gasoline is a member, the olefins
are combustible; also, they form explosive mixtures with air
or oxygen.[73] A number of aromatic hydrocarbons, which are
rich in carbon and burn with a smoky flame, participate as
effectively as the olefins in atmospheric photooxidation reactions in the presence of nitrogen oxides and ultraviolet light.
Judged both on the basis of reactivity and concentrations in the
atmosphere, the aromatic hydrocarbons cannot be ignored as
contributors to the photo-chemical type of air pollution.[74]

The automobile makes a further contribution to air pollution in the form of highly pulverized rubber and asphalt,
generated by abrasion of tires upon streets. This aspect of
air pollution has not been studied in much detail, but there is
reason to believe that contamination from rubber and asphalt
is appreciable.

In metropolitan areas, atmospheric contamination can
be traced to various sources. Listing them in descending
order of importance, they are: automobiles, industrial plants,
household and municipal installations. All the above-listed
sources give off approximately the same combination and relative volume of chemicals to the air. Whether the contamination becomes a community problem at any one time depends
on population density and the weather. Topographic breezes
that transport the great air masses over the continent regularly bring fresh air into most U. S. cities, and in the absence
of breezes, the air may be cleaned by updrafts and convection
currents that dilute and carry away both the smoke and the
vaporized chemicals. Very frequently these natural ventilation processes fail, and there may be no air movement over
a particular area for a matter of hours and sometimes days.
This stalemate can be attributed to geographic location and
local topography and results in what is known as a "thermal

[71]Ibid.

[72]A. P. Altshuller, I. R. Cohen, S. F. Selva, and S. L. Kopczynski, "Air Pollution: Photooxidation of Aromatic Hydrocarbons," Science, October 19, 1962, p. 442.

[73]E. Werthein and Harold Jeskey, Organic Chemistry, (New York: McGraw-Hill
Book Company, 1956), p. 49.

[74]Altshuller, Cohen, Selva and Kopczynski, loc. cit.

inversion. "[75] Normally, the air is warmer at the ground and colder above. The convection currents so needed to move the air result from a temperature gradient. In a thermal inversion, a layer of warm air forms at a higher altitude and traps the heavily laden cold air at the ground. When an inversion occurs, the cold air nearly saturates itself with pollutants producing a smog condition well known in Los Angeles. This can occur in any season of the year in most of the cities of the world. (See Figure 21)

Los Angeles is a prime example of smog concentration, not only because of its geographic location, but also because of its enormous population density. Situated on a narrow strip of sunny seacoast and backed up by the coastal mountain range, the local area and the city itself is an ideal target for an inversion. There are more than six million people with three million cars that burn 5.5 million gallons of gasoline per day, plus the industrial plants that together pollute the air and set up the conditions for inversion.

Los Angeles is plagued with nearly one hundred days of smog per year, but other cities as well have many days of concentrated smog. Practically any city has its days of heavy fog and contaminated air.

Another aspect of air pollution is fall-out directly related to atmospheric testing of nuclear weapons. Studies are continually being made as to the effect of fall-out on both plants and animals. A relatively new area in science known as "health physics" concerns itself with the prevention and control of hazards from ionizing radiation and radioactive materials.

Strontium 90, cesium 137, and iodine 131 are radioactive isotopes directly related to fall-out and form the nucleus for many investigations.

Strontium 90, which follows the metabolic pathways of calcium, is deposited in bones and teeth. Absorption is greatest during the period of growth. Thus, children, who presumably have a higher biological radiosensitivity than adults, accumulate the radioisotope more readily. The amount of radiation delivered to bone marrow, with the possible effects of leukemogenesis is important. [76]

It has been known for some time that rainfall is the

[75]McDermott, op. cit., pp. 51-52.

[76]Louise Zibold Reiss, "Strontium 90 Absorption by Deciduous Teeth," Science, Vol. 134, November 24, 1961, p. 169.

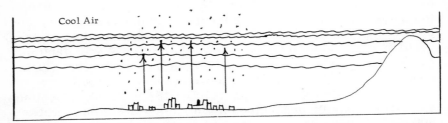

THERMAL INVERSION, common in Los Angeles, is the main meteorological factor in smog formation. Diagram indicates normal dissipation of pollutants with the warm air rising carrying contamination away.

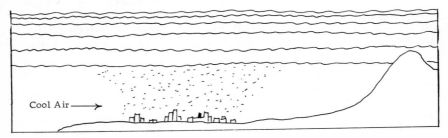

INVERSION SETS IN when cool sea air moves in under warm air and traps pollutants.

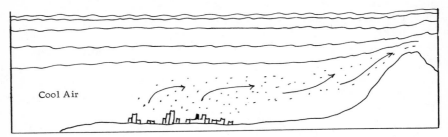

INVERSION PERSISTS until the weather changes and the warm air eventually rises allowing the cool air to escape carrying the concentration of pollutants with it.

Figure 21. INVERSION PROCESS

Warm Air

primary process by which fission products in the atmosphere are deposited on the earth's surface. From an extensive monthly rain collection network in the United States in 1956, linear relationships between strontium 90 deposition and amount of rainfall were observed within a limited geographical area.[77] Other studies conducted in the United States and the United Kingdom with open vessel collectors and soil analysis have borne out the linear relationship. (See Figure 22)

The presence of cesium 137 and 134 in Alaskan Eskimos varies extensively depending on their diets. Eskimos whose diets consist mainly of caribou and reindeer have average Cs-137 counts of 421 nancuries (nc); whereas the maximum human burden is 790 nancuries.[78] The reindeer and caribou obtain their high level of Cs-137 from lichens and pass it on to man when the meat is consumed.

High Cs-137 counts were first noticed in Norwegians and Swedish Lapps.[79] It is felt that Cs-134 originates from

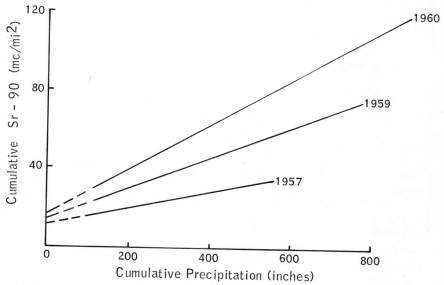

Figure 22. Linear relationship between strontium 90 deposition and rainfall in Clallam County, Washington. Taken from Science, Vol. 134, 1962.

[77]Edward Hardy, Lyle T. Alexander, "Rainfall and Deposition of Strontium 90 in Clallam County, Washington," Science, Vol. 136, June 8, 1962.

[78]Harvey E. Palmer, Wayne C. Hanson, Bobby I. Griffin, and William C. Roesch, "Cesium 137 in Alaskan Eskimos," Science, Vol. 142, October 4, 1963, p. 64.

[79]Harvey E. Palmer and Richard W. Perkins, "Cesium 134 in Alaskan Eskimos and in Fallout," Science, Vol. 142, October 4, 1961, pp. 66-67.

the fission of uranium 235 and not cesium 133 found in soil. Cesium 134 seems to be world-wide and continuing.

It is difficult to awaken the slumbering populace from the apathy and serenity they show, but if one only opens his eyes and looks at the increased cases of bronchitis-emphysema! It was once considered a dull disease by medical students and young physicians, and research on the subject has been correspondingly neglected in university circles. The chronic cough and progressive loss of breathing may be completely incapacitating and eventually lead to heart failure.

The tiny lung sacs where the transfer of oxygen to the blood takes place merge to form a large sac, thus allowing less surface area for exchange, and reducing the millions of tiny lung sacs to a much smaller number. As the disease progresses, it affects both lungs and eventually puts a tremendous strain on the heart.

At one time, emphysema was considered an occupational disease of trombone players and the like, but this is hardly the case today. The disease is considerably more common among city dwellers than country people. There is some indication, however, that the advantage of country living can be canceled by cigarette smoking, which is in effect, a portable form of air pollution. There are, however, arguments for and against cigarette smoking and emphysema. People who have never smoked and live in the so-called clean fresh air of the country have emphysema. A hereditary susceptibility may be involved and it may be that the disease represents a fundamental aging process. Men are three to five times more frequently affected than women; both the illness and the death rate go up sharply after the age of 45, death being caused by heart failure or pneumonia.

It is not difficult to conceive of the role of air pollution in the disease process. Both the hydrocarbon and the sulfuric compounds are highly irritating, and the bronchi are continuously exposed to them during periods of high pollution. Natural exposure to either type of smog in low concentrations of pollutants have produced tissue damage in plants and in cultures of animal cells and scarring of the lungs of laboratory animals.

In London in 1952, there was an "excess" mortality of 4,000 to 5,000 persons during one week of intense fog.[80] The deaths in London occurred almost exclusively among those

---

[80]McDermott, op. cit., p. 54.

with previous bronchopulmonary disease. It seems almost in-
credible, but the veteran bronchitis patients served as warning systems because they could detect approaching smog by
noting discomfort six to twelve hours before it was evident to
others that an episode of smog was at hand.

Fall-out, though less impressive, presents many long
range hazards. Initiated in 1963, there is an atmospheric
test ban agreement among nations. It is hoped that with this
agreement the radioactive fall-out will decrease and the threat
of world contamination will be curtailed. Strontium 90 seems
to be of extreme importance, because of its relationships to
calcium uptake and deposition in the bones and teeth. The
threat is not acute to adults, but presents alarm for children
because they absorb Sr-90 at a greater rate than adults. The
possibility of high Sr-90 uptake and increased cases of leuke-
mia among children causes great concern among all peoples.

Atmospheric contamination both chemical and from
nuclear explosions are of high concern to all. Currently,
methods to curb such contamination are being taken by local,
state, national, and international groups.

California has enacted restrictions on debris burning or
excessive exhaust fumes from automobiles. State-wide air
pollution patrols enforce such laws as to keep contamination
at a minimum. Industry has cooperated by installation of a
series of filters, mechanical and electrical, to lessen exhaust
fumes from factory smoke stacks.

The auto industry has installed on all new cars a by-pass
valve which recirculates crankcase fumes back through the intake manifold to be reburned. Such a device will not only increase the efficiency of the automobile engine, but will also
greatly reduce the unburned hydrocarbons. The new breather-
type system is a step in the right direction, but individual
maintenance by auto owners in keeping their automobile engines in excellent mechanical condition would lessen the
mobile smoke screens which migrate down our asphalt jungle
each day. (See Figure 23)

Increased cases of respiratory ailments are beginning
to draw attention. According to a recent study prepared for
the United States Senate, several fatal diseases -- pulmonary
emphysema, lung cancer, chronic bronchitis and colds -- have
been linked to air pollution. In fact, more people suffering
from emphysema are today receiving Social Security disability
benefits than the victims of any illness other than arterio-

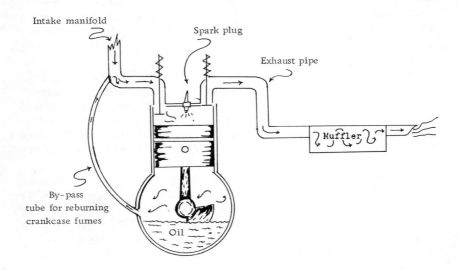

Figure 23.   In the normal crankcase ventilation system a crankcase breather pipe leads
from the crankcase to the outside atmosphere. In the new type breather
system a by-pass tube leads from the crankcase to the intake manifold
there to be mixed with incoming gas-air mixture and reburned in the
cylinders.

sclerotic heart disease. As communities increase in size and
the air becomes filled with carcinogenic contaminants, death
rates from respiratory system cancers begin to rise. [81]
    For some years, the United States Public Health Service
has conducted a modest program of high quality, covering the
sources and control of pollution at its Robert A. Taft Sanitary
Engineering Center in Cincinnati, Ohio, to seek epidemi-
ological data through community surveys such as are now being conducted in New Orleans, Louisiana, and Nashville,
Tennessee. This work has drawn new impetus from the
establishment of the Division of Environmental Health as
one of the main operating units of the Public Health Service.
From the quickened interest, we can expect medical science
to contribute the much needed research in the areas of
bronchitis-emphysema and pulmonary heart disease.
    The National Conference on Air Pollution held in Wash-
ington, D. C. in 1963 had an official theme titled "Let's Clear

[81] St. Paul Pioneer Press, January 5, 1964, p. 8.

the Air". One panel dealt with Agriculture, Natural Resource, and Economic Considerations. A resume concerning this topic appeared in "Heating, Piping and Air Conditioning, March 1963. " The resume stated: The chemical composition of a mass of air varies as it moves from place to place and as chemical reactions within the mass proceed. New contaminants pumped into the air mass from motor vehicles and stationary sources replenish the supply of contaminants and keep the reaction going. Although some of the source pollutants are in themselves responsible for injury to plants and animals, a number of the products of these chemical reactions occurring in the air also have injurious effects. [82]

One of the products, ozone, is damaging to many sensitive plant species; another, peroxyacetyl nitrate, also damages many kinds of crop plants. These photochemical pollutants decrease the photosynthesis of plants, injure leaves, increase respiration, slow growth, and cause lower yields. Fluorides damage food, fiber forage, and forest crops. [83]

The irony of air pollution and its effect on plant life can be seen as we motor down our concrete jungle in one of Detroit's fuming monsters. As we gaze across beautiful fields of corn swaying gently in the breeze, think not of its aesthetic value and bountiful production, but the tons of tetra-ethyl lead being absorbed by those graceful leaves.

In summary - air pollution is with us and will not decrease unless conservation methods are heeded by all. The population is steadily increasing throughout the world triggering increased industrial production both at home and abroad. With the continued growth of the nation's gross products, more and more automobiles will sputter and fume to blanket our atmosphere with hydrocarbons.

Steadily, more and more pollutants are being poured into the air. In certain cases many human ailments can be directly or indirectly linked with atmospheric contamination. Such illnesses as emphysema and lung cancer show a linear relationship to exposure and air pollution.

The test ban agreement on nuclear weapons testing shows progress in the right direction to lessen atmospheric contamination. However, continued research and investigation are needed to establish maximums concerning nuclear

---

[82]A reprint from Heating, Piping and Air Conditioning, March 1963.
[83]Ibid.

fusion and fission products and their long term effects on plant and animal life.

Alert scientists are realizing the need for research concerning the effect of air pollution on plant life. The world depends upon vegetation to furnish the bulk of its food supply. Slowly the environmental atmosphere finds its way through chlorophyll studded leaves into the mouths of the human inhabitants but the extent of contamination is yet to be discovered.

With the aid of local, state, and national governments progress is being made toward control of air pollution. Industries are also cooperating at great expense to themselves. But we must all realize that the need is great and the time is short.

ACTIVITIES

1. Construct a resource unit which would compare your state and local air pollution controls with that of other states and communities. *C-S*
2. Prepare a list of local personnel that could be used by your school as resource people in teaching about air pollution. *E-S-C*
3. Keep a news bulletin board with up-to-date articles about air pollution. *E-S-C*
4. Construct a bulletin board which would indicate sources of air pollution. *E-S*
5. Prepare a bibliography of materials about air pollution available in your school or community library. *S-C*
6. List obligations and duties as citizens that each student should do to lessen atmospheric contamination. *E-S*
7. Contact the local Civil Defense director and ask him to give a talk on the dangers of fall-out and civil defense. *E-S-C*
8. Discussion or debate: What are the possible results if our urban populations continue to grow with increased numbers of automobiles and industries needed to service such a society? What controls can be instituted to lessen wholesale air pollution? *S-C*
9. Make a scrapbook of clippings, drawings, and pictures concerning air pollution. *E-S*
10. Make a chart showing increased cases of respiratory ailments contributed to air pollution. *S-C*

11. Make posters showing sources of air pollution. *E‑S*
12. Make posters illustrating controls that can be instituted by industry and citizens. *E‑S*
13. Set out clean microscope slides or pieces of tag board and inspect them a few hours later to show dust and smoke particles in the air. A thin coating of gelatin to aid in collecting is helpful. *E‑S*
14. Bring in a dirty furnace filter to illustrate the dust and foreign particles found in household air. *E‑S‑C*
15. Contact the local Health Department to check on the strontium 90 count found in the local milk supply. *E‑S‑C*
16. Write an essay about the need for controls of air pollution. *E‑S*
17. A lesson in observation: Count a specific number of automobiles and note the number with excessive exhaust fumes. A graph can be made showing the relationship. *E‑S*
18. Make a survey in your block or classroom of those who have incinerators in their homes to point out local contamination. *E*
19. Find out from the local health department or city hall what is done with the local garbage. *E‑S*
20. Discussion: Is air pollution a problem in your community? *E‑S‑C*
21. Research question: How does geography or topography influence air pollution? *S‑C*
22. City dwellers often say they are driving out to the clean country air. Is this necessarily an accurate comment? List the causes of "dirty" city air. *E‑S*
23. Debate the question of whether air pollution would have become a problem with or without the atomic bomb. *S*
24. Questions to discuss: Is there any relationship that can be established between soil protection and air protection? Is there any relationship between air pollution and food pollution -- as in milk and vegetable products? *E‑S‑C*
25. Relate air pollution to the *possible causes* of diseases such as lung cancer, heart trouble, allergies. (See film listed in audio‑visual materials.) *S‑C*

BIBLIOGRAPHY

"Air Pollution, " *Senior Scholastic,* Vol. 81 (January 16, 1963),
p. 17. **S–C**

Air Pollution: The Facts. New York: National Tuberculosis
Association, 1963. **S**

Altshuller, A. P., I. R. Cohen, S. F. Selva and S. L.
Kopezynski. "Air Pollution: Photooxidation of Aromatic
Hydrocarbons, "*Science,* October 19, 1962, p. 442. **C**

"Automotive Air Pollution, " *A Report of the Panel of Technical
Advisors on Automotive Air Pollution to the Joint State
Government Commission.* Harrisburg: General Assembly
of the Commonwealth of Pennsylvania, 1963. **C**

Aylesworth, Thomas G. "Smoke, Smog, and Smell, " *Current
Science,* XLIX (September 16, 1963), p. 10. **S–C**

Chambers, Leslie. *Air Pollution.* New York: Academic
Press, 1962. **S**

Cook, James G. *Our Astonishing Atmosphere.* New York:
Dial Press, 1957. **S–C**

Fisher, James. *Wonderful World of Air.* Garden City:
Garden City Books, 1958. **S–C**

Frisky, Margaret. *The True Book of Air Around Us.* Chicago:
Children's Press, 1953. **E**

Gross, Paul M. (chairman) *Report of the Committee on En-
vironmental Health Problems to the Surgeon General,*
Public Health Service Publication No. 908. Washington:
U. S. Government Printing Office, 1962. **C**

Hardy, Edward and Lyle T. Alexander. "Rainfall and Deposition of Strontium-90 in Clallam County, Washington, "
Science, CXXXVI (June 8, 1962), p. 881. **C**

Holly, Hazel. *What's In The Air?* Public Affairs Pamphlet
No. 275. New York: Public Affairs Committee, Inc.,
1958. **S**

Mallette, F. C. *Air Pollution.* New York: Reinhold Publishing Corporation, 1955. **C**

McDermott, Walsh. "Air Pollution and Public Health, "
Scientific American, CCV (October, 1961), p. 49-57. **S–C**

McLean, D. D. (revised by D. A. Williams) *Dust Control In
Industry.* Technical Information Service Report No. 8.
Ottawa: National Research Council, March, 1963. **C**

Namowitz, Samuel N. and Donald B. Stone. *Earth Science.*
New York: D. Van Nostrand Company, Inc., 1953. **S–C**

Palmer, Harvey E., Wayne C. Hanson, Bobby I. Griffen and William C. Roesch. "Cesium-137 in Alaskan Eskimos, " *Science*, CXXXXII (October 4, 1963), p. 64. **C**

Perkins, Richard W. and Harvey E. Palmer. "Cesium-134 In Alaskan Eskimos and in Fallout, " *Science*, October 4, 1961, pp. 66-67. **C**

Pilkington, Roger, *The Ways of the Air*. New York: Criterion Books, 1962. **S−C**

Reiss, Louise Z. "Strontium-90 Absorption by Deciduous Teeth," *Science*, CXXXIV (November 24, 1961). **C**

St. Paul Pioneer Press, January 5, 1964. **E−S− C**

Sanford Research Institute. *Smog Problem in Los Angeles County*. Los Angeles: Western Oil and Gas Association, 1954. **S−C**

Thomas, Moyer D. "Air Pollution Review 1954-1955, " *Industrial and Engineering Chemistry*, Vol. 48 (September, 1956), pp. 1522-1527. **C**

U. S. Department of Health, Education and Welfare. *The Health Effects of Air Pollution*, Public Health Service Publication No. 640. Washington: Government Printing Office, 1961. **S**

Wertheim, E. and Harold Jeskey. *Organic Chemistry*. New York: McGraw-Hill Book Company, 1956. **S−C**

AUDIO-VISUAL MATERIALS

16 mm. FILMS

Air - (Gateway)

This film explains the importance of the properties of air to plant and animal life. **E**

Allergies - (EBF)

Describes allergy as a pronounced sensitiveness of a given part of the body to pollen, dusts, etc. **S- C**

Atmosphere and Its Circulation - (EBF)

Animated drawings are used throughout to explain the structure and the dynamics of the atmosphere. The first part of the film gives a detailed presentation of the structure; the chemical composition; the gaseous nature; the distribution of the air and its circulation. **E- S**

Atom and Biological Science - (EBF)

Deals principally with the biological effects of high
energy radiations. Explains how we are learning to
utilize the good effects of these radiations on organisms
as well as to guard against their harmful effects.
Points out the different types of high energy radiation.
S-C

Atom and the Weather, The - (AEC)

This film explains why tests of atomic weapons have
no effect on the weather, how radioactive fallout is
carefully traced to protect the public and how radioactivity from atomic tests is used as a research tool
by the weatherman. **S-C**

Breathe at Your Own Risk - (USDHEW)

Showing scenes of air pollution at its worst, from Los
Angeles to New York, this documentary highlights vir-
tually all aspects of air pollution as a national problem. **S-C**

Cancer - (EBF)

Describes the wide spread research into the causes
and control of cancer. **S-C**

Channel 4 Reports - (USDHEW)

This is a technical description of a study of air pollution and asthma.   The potential health ramifications
and their relationship to meteorological factors are
explained. **S-C**

Chemistry of Air - (McGraw Hill)

Shows why oxygen is necessary for burning, why
materials rust and corrode, and tests for carbon
dioxide. **S**

City's Future, The - (USDHEW)

This film portrays the impact of air pollution on a
contemporary urban area. The health, economic,
control, and public education aspects of the problem
are discussed. **S-C**

Fallout and Agriculture - (USDA)

Discusses the means for protecting against radiation and minimizing the contamination of soil, crops, and other foods. **S-C**

Fallout Atom, The - (CaFI)

An examination into the scientific facts of human radiation. Attempts are made to find out how much radioactive material the human body possesses naturally, how much we have been exposed to as a result of nuclear bomb tests, and the effects on health and life. **C**

Fallout -- When and How To Protect Yourself Against It. - (CDM)

Using techniques which will interest audiences at all levels, this animated filmography illustrates in simple terms the cause and effects of radioactive fallout. It describes preparations which should be made now to safeguard lives and to protect food and water supplies. **E-S-C**

No Smoking - (Sid Davis Productions)

Shows the effects of smoking on the human body. **C**

Nothing But Air - (EBF)

Small boy discovers many facts about air. **E**

Nuclear Radiation Fallout - (CSC)

With every new nuclear explosion, additional radioactive debris is spread throughout our atmosphere. We have always lived with some background radiation from cosmic rays; however, with continual addition of man-made radioactive contamination, the cumulative effect could, in time, cause serious effects. It goes into the three types of fallout and deals with radioactive isotopes of Strontium-90, Cesium-137, and Carbon-14 showing the sensitive balance in a cell when it is upset by the powerful ray. **S-C**

Our Poisoned Air - (USDHEW)

A panel discussion penetrates beneath the surface aspects of the problem and the participants discuss varying points of view important to all segments of the public. Two five-minute film sequences graphically portray many of the common sources of air pollution. *S-C*

Ocean of Air, The - (United World)

Provides a basic understanding of the characteristics, composition, and importance of air. *E*

Radiological Defense - (CDM)

This film illustrates the menace of radioactive fallout; it also describes the nature and effects of fallout, and shows how the nation's radiological defense operates at all levels of activity. *S-C*

Respiration - (United World)

Covers internal and external respiration. *E-S*

Sources of Air Pollution, Effects of Air Pollution, Control of Air Pollution - (USDHEW)

Each of these films are designed to acquaint the viewer with the relationship between our modern, technological way of life and air pollution. They stress the need for expanded research and for increased control effort. *S-C*

FILMSTRIPS

Air and Life - (Eyegate)

One of a series of science in everyday life. *E*

Air Around Us, The - (Eyegate)

One of a series of filmstrips on fundamentals of science at the junior high level. *S*

How Animals Live in the Air - (Curriculum)

Adaptation of animals -- how they breathe. **E—S**

Importance of Air in Nature, The - (Jim Hardy)

One of a series of six filmstrips having to do with understanding the atmosphere and the importance of air to
man. **S**

Ocean of Air We Live In, The - (McGraw-Hill)

One of the "Learning About Nature Series" filmstrips,
set #5. **E**

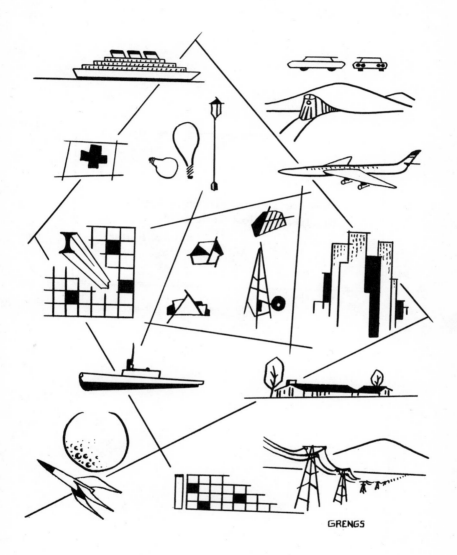

GRENGS

Riches are gotten with pain, kept with care, and lost with grief.

Thomas Fuller

MINERAL CONSERVATION

Chapter VI

OBJECTIVES

I. To note the economic importance of minerals -- especially coal, petroleum, iron, and uranium.
II. To indicate the relationship of minerals to soil development and plant growth.
III. To point to the classification and diversity of mineral resources.
IV. To highlight the major conservative techniques and methods in mineral conservation.

Mineral conservation is one of the most crucial areas in the whole field of conservation for two significant reasons: First, the consumption of minerals is rising at an ominous rate in response to increasing demands of the economy and an increasing population. Secondly, minerals are not renewable. Unlike trees or field crops, minerals cannot be planted and grown when needed.

The United States has a mineral-based economy. Minerals are used to build automobiles, airplanes, bridges, buildings, and homes. Energy producing minerals such as coal and oil are needed to run machines and equipment. In fact, the American way of life depends upon the wide and diversified use of minerals in this technological age.

Minerals may be classified in a variety of ways. Although the principal classification of minerals is based on their chemistry, in the study of conservation minerals are generally classified in terms of chemical, physical, and use characteristics. An abbreviated and basic classification of minerals is as follows: (See Figure 24)

Metals		Non-Metals	
Ferrous	Non-Ferrous	Mineral Fuels	Other Non-metals
Iron	Tin	Petroleum	Stone
Manganese	Copper	Natural Gas	Salt
Molybdenum	Aluminum	Coal	Sulfur
	Gold		Mica
	Magnesium		Asbestos
	Platinum		Clay
	Uranium		
	Radium		

Figure 24. Classification of minerals

In terms of industrial economy mineral resources may be said to be *basic* or *contributory;* when mineral resources apply to national defense, they may be said to be *strategic* or *non-strategic;* in world trade, minerals may be said to be *primary* as products of first capture from nature, or *secondary* as products of recovered scrap or by-products. [84]

The fundamental relationship of mineral conservation to the larger ramifications of conservation relate to the influence of minerals on soil formation and vegetation development. The soil supports all forms of life on land -- vegetation directly and animals indirectly. Soil consists of broken and decomposed minerals and rocks, with added products of decaying organic matter from previous generations of plants. Minerals enable plants to grow. Even marine life feeds upon the mineral salts dissolved from the land in the long history of the earth. [85] Obviously, the animal, vegetable, and mineral kingdoms are interdependent.

[84]Shirley W. Allen, Conserving Natural Resources: Principles and Practices in a Democracy (New York: McGraw-Hill, 1955), p. 265.
[85]Richard M. Pearl, Rocks and Minerals (New York: Barnes and Noble, Inc., 1956), p. 1.

Mineral is the parent material of soil. Through disintegration (physical process) and decomposition (chemical process) soil material is produced. Decomposition may be through
hydration (water enters into chemical combinations with minerals, changing old and producing new compounds), oxidation
(some minerals in rock take on oxygen when exposed to air
and moisture to increase volume), carbonation (increases
solubility of minerals), and dissolution. However, without
microorganisms and organic matter, unconsolidated minerals
alone do not make soil.

Plants require a variety of minerals to grow. Plants
require considerable quantities of nitrogen, potassium, phosphorus, carbon, calcium, oxygen, hydrogen, and sulfur.
Lesser amounts of iron and magnesium are necessary for
plant growth. In certain instances, cobalt, zinc, copper,
and boron are essential to maintain vegetation.

Lime is a good example of mineral influence on
vegetation development. Lime supplies the calcium necessary as an actual nutrient material in plant growth, as well
as a "sweetener"of acid soil. A sour soil condition is unfavorable to the growth of clover, alfalfa, and beans; lime
can amend the sour soil condition to make it possible to grow
such crops. The high calcium content of lime is especially
important in growing legumes.

There are perhaps 1000 or 1500 different kinds of minerals (depending upon the classification used); and although
the conservation practices and economic importance of each
of the minerals vary greatly, the following conservative techniques may be applicable in most instances:

1. Use a plentiful mineral for a less plentiful mineral.
2. Use a synthetic mineral.
3. Discover and develop new deposits of minerals.
4. Salvage waste and scrap materials.
5. Improve mining and milling methods.
6. Mine submarginal and low-grade mineral deposits.
7. Improve preparation and utilization practices.
8. Economize in the use of minerals.
9. Spread the resource base of industry by using a wider
    variety of minerals.
10. Discover techniques for using basic materials which were
    previously considered unusable. [86]

[86]J. Frederic Dewhurst and Associates, America's Needs and Resources (New York:
The Twentieth Century Fund, 1955), pp. 781-782.

There are some minerals that are of such economic
importance -- and the need for their conservation is so essential -- that specific attention must be given to them.   Among
them are coal, petroleum, iron, and uranium.

COAL

Coal is actually a form of sedimentary rock.   It consists
of materials derived essentially from carbon of plant tissues.
Coal beds developed through the accumulation of plant remains
buried beneath swamp waters, beneath layers of mud, sand,
and lime.   Pressure and the passage of time resulted in coal.
There are several varieties of coal which actually represent stages in the evolution of swamp deposits into high-grade
coal.   *Peat* is blackened organic remains -- the beginning of
coal. *Lignite,* older and more compact, is crumbly brown
coal.   *Bituminous coal,* soft coal, provides high-grade coal
to be used in making coke for iron smelting furnaces or in
providing fuel for power.   *Anthracite,* or hard coal, is a
smokeless, high quality fuel which is low in gas and high in
carbon.

Coal is probably the most valuable resource of the United
States.   No other single product gives the American public so
many things they use every day: Transportation requires
coal.   Warmth and shelter, through the construction and heating of buildings, depend in large measure on coal.   Basic
chemicals, coal tar medicines, and anesthetics are coal derivatives.   In fact, the value of coal produced in the United
States every year is said to be five times as great in value
as that of gold produced here in the same length of time. [87]
And incidentally, no great nation has grown great that did not
have access to ample supplies of coal.   It is significant that
the acknowledged industrial world powers -- the United States,
Great Britain, Germany, France, and the Soviet Union -- lead
the world in coal resources and production.

Since high quality coal is easily accessible, it is being
mined rapidly, and the conservation of coal becomes an immediate problem.   This would leave only poorer grades of
coal -- as lignite -- for future generations.   Also, for every
ton of coal mined, more than one-half ton is lost through
leaving coal pillars to support mine roofs, through prepara-

[87]Raymond E. Janssen, Buried Sunlight (Evanston, Illinois: Row Peterson and
Company, 1941), p. 9.

tion, and through handling.

Several effective devices have been introduced to help in coal conservation. A wide variety of non-coking coals are being blended with coking coals to extend the life of the exist- ing coking-coal reserves. The introduction of automatic stokers, which use a greater part of the heat value, has done away with careless firing methods. There has been a shift away from coke ovens, which waste by-products, to by-product coke ovens, which save them. Improved mining methods are reducing loss. In addition to reducing waste caused by im- proper mining methods, and in addition to improving the qual- ity of poorer grades of coal by chemical treatment, an impor- tant way to conserve coal is through improving the efficiency of steam engines and steam turbines. [88]

PETROLEUM

Petroleum is derived from microscopic marine organ- isms whose remains were originally intermingled with marine deposits, and this may be the reason why petroleum is found in quantity in sedimentary rocks only.

The United States could not get along without petroleum under present conditions and continue the same standards of living. Although the chief uses of petroleum are fuel, power, lubrication, and light, there are some five hundred or more ways in which petroleum products are used in everyday life.

That motor vehicles alone burn more than 46,500,000,000 gallons of gasoline (chief product of petroleum) every year in the United States points to the conservation problem. [89] Petro- leum is a non-renewable resource; there is a limited amount available for use. Even though petroleum explorers continu- ally find new oil fields in the jungles of South America, the deserts of Africa, or offshore United States, the demand is rising. The world uses about 6,400,000,000 barrels of oil a year. [90]

As a result, government and industry have adopted con- servation measures to insure oil resources for the future through conservation laws, oil-field conservation, and re-

[88]Vernon C. Finch, Glenn T. Trewartha, and M. H. Shearer, The Earth and Its Resources (McGraw-Hill Book Company, Inc., 1959), p. 450.

[89]William B. Harper, "Petroleum," The World Book Encyclopedia (Chicago: Field Enterprises Educational Corp., 1960), XIV, p. 296.

[90]Ibid., p. 297.

Minnesota Department of Business Development

Figure 25. Great Northern Oil Refinery
Pine Bend, Minnesota

finery conservation. (See Figure 25) The major national conservation law is the Connally Act of 1935 which prohibits oil
not produced in accordance with state conservation laws from
being sold in interstate commerce. Oil-field conservation involves methods of obtaining crude oil (which cannot be mined
by the usual methods) through forcing oil into nearby wells
where it is recovered, by forcing the oil to the surface by
pressure, or by plugging back to shallower deposits. In refinery conservation, check joints, pumps, and pipes are
checked for leaks. Water that is run through coolers and
condensers at the refineries is run through settling basins

to recover any oil. Also, loss is reduced by painting storage tanks a light color to reflect heat and reduce evaporation.

IRON

The United States is the leading iron-ore mining country, mining about 110, 000, 000 tons of iron ore each year, and each year the steel companies in the United States produce over 1400 pounds of steel for every individual. Nearly forty per cent of all jobs in manufacturing industries in the United States depend on the manufacture and use of steel. [91]

Iron is by volume the most important metal, and it is one of the most useful. Without it, the industrial economy of the United States could not function.

Although a survey by the United Nations after World War II showed that there are enough known iron-bearing deposits to supply the world's iron needs for at least eight hundred more years, the *richer* iron ores which can be mined economically are being used quickly. Already, steel companies are working to develop economical methods of using low-grade iron ores and taconite. (Taconite, after processing, is commercially feasible because it complies with the requirements of the steel companies for high-grade ore and can be transported to the mills at reasonable cost. Taconite is a flint-hard, iron ore-bearing rock found in great quantities near the surface of the ground in the Lake Superior region.)

It is to be noted that the taconite industry of northeastern Minnesota stands on the threshold of its second great round of growth. (See Figure 26) (The first occurred between 1953-57 when a half billion dollars were spent in developing taconite plants and related mining and shipping facilities.) At least four companies are planning or seriously considering taconite projects in Minnesota to go into production within four or five years. The new round of growth was brought about by the elimination last year of taconite taxation as a controversial political issue, and the prospect that the state's voters in 1964 will approve a constitutional amendment guaranteeing tax stability for taconite. [92] (See Figures 27 and 28)

Chief among the conservation methods in iron processing and steel production is the collection and use of scrap iron

[91]Max D. Howell, "Iron and Steel, " The World Book Encyclopedia (Chicago: Field Enterprises Educational Corp. , 1960), IX, p. 347.

[92]Leonard Inskip, "New Boom in Taconite Shaping Up, " Minneapolis Morning Tribune, February 4, 1964, p. 4.

Erie Mining Co. , Hoyt Lakes; Pickands Mather & Co. , Agents

Figure 26.   Erie Mining Company's $300,000,000 Hoyt Lakes Taconite Plant
processes over 22.5 million tons of Taconite rock in 7.5 million
tons of iron ore pellets

and steel -- old cars, old farm machinery may be reincarnated
as a Volvo or Volkswagon. Also, in the production of iron and
steel, scrap from waste is swept up and preserved for later
use.

The usefulness of iron can be increased by making
stronger and more durable steel with alloy metals. The quality of lower-grade ores can be improved, developed, or invented, which is called beneficiation. Iron and steel products
also can be built to last, and in some instances other materials

Erie Mining Co. , Hoyt Lakes, Minnesota; Pickands Mather & Co. , Agents

Figure 27.   Taconite Harbor, north shore of Lake Superior

such as stone can be used as substitutes for iron.[93]

URANIUM

The new king of the metals may be uranium; prospecting for uranium recalls in a small way the gold rush.   The fissionable fractions of uranium, U-235 and U-238, produce an atomic explosion when allowed to disintegrate uncontrolled.   Tremendous heat is produced in a reaction with controlled disintegra-

[93]Henry F. Becker, Resources for Tomorrow (New York: Holt, Rinehard and Winston, Inc. , 1964), p. 56.

Erie Mining Co., Hoyt Lakes; Pickands Mather & Co., Agents

Figure 28.   In the quarter mile run concentrator building of the Erie Mining
Company, taconite is ground to flour fineness in huge mills containing
heavy steel rods and steel balls. Magnetic separators remove the
waste from the ground taconite and the iron concentrate is pumped
to the pelletizing plant.

tion and this heat is transmitted by liquid or gas into a pressure that creates power.

Many, many uses have been found for this controlled
power. The heat may be transmitted into electrical power.
Submarines now operate under atomic power. Advances in
food preservation, and medicine -- especially in cancer research -- have resulted in the peace time uses of atomic
energy.

"At the present time, the future demand for uranium
appears to be unlimited."[94] Uranium has been found in more

[94] E. G. Warman, Strike It Rich With Uranium (Uniontown, Pennsylvania:
E. G. Warman Publishing Company, 1955).

than thirty of the United States to date. However, the majority of uranium ore now produced in the United States comes from the Colorado Plateau of Colorado, Utah, New Mexico, and Arizona.

To some, uranium is a great hope: Atomic energy can provide a substitute for resources such as coal and petroleum. However, experts seem to agree that atomic power is unlikely to replace gasoline in automobiles or diesel fuel in locomotives. [95] It is to be noted that uranium is never found in a free metallic state in nature -- therefore, processing must be done with great skill and care. Also, it is to be noted that U-235, the small fissionable fraction which is the heat or power source, is only 0.7% of the whole. Even uranium is a limited resource! The key words of conservation, *wise use,* also apply to uranium.

In fact, our sources of energy in 1985 will not be much different from what they are today. [96] The greatest difference will be the use of nuclear energy to replace part of the coal. This change will occur even though there is a much greater reserve of coal than either petroleum or natural gas; the labor cost of extracting coal will be much greater compared to other fuels.

The lack of space prevents discussion of many other valuable resources such as copper, lead, zinc, aluminum, etc. At pre-war consumption rates, known economic copper supplies of the United States would last about thirty years. While lead and zinc production have declined since the 1920's, the demand for each of the metals increased by more than a third. Reserves of high-grade bauxite in Arkansas, formerly the nation's main source of aluminum, are approaching an end. [97] This kind of situation also exists regarding several other minerals.

Man truly works in mysterious ways. Once gold was the king of minerals. Man risked his life to find it -- and having found it, one way or another, he ostentatiously displayed it in utensils or in ornament. But, today petroleum is the black gold, and it is a rich man who finds it in his own back yard. In 1975, aluminum may be the light gold which carries

[95] Ernest Behrendt, Petroleum (Garden City, N. Y.: Nelson Doubleday, Inc., 1963) p. 61.

[96] John J. McKetta and Clayton A. Umback, Jr., "Energy: A Look Into The Future," The New York Times, May 31, 1959, p. M13.

[97] J. Frederic Dewhurst and Associates, America's Needs and Resources (New York: The Twentieth Century Fund, 1955), pp. 770-771, 756.

man to new worlds. Through the ages -- stone, bronze, copper -- man has made a variety of minerals king for a day,
because with his brain and his thumb, he has learned and ad-
justed. What new mineral will man use for tomorrow?

Of great significance is the economic impact on an area
when mineral deposits are discovered. To mine a mineral
men and machines are brought in. Men must be housed and
clothed. Machines must be maintained and repaired. The
raw mineral captured from the earth must be transported by
waterway, roadway, or railway. As the demand for the mineral increases and as the mining operation becomes more
productive, more personnel and more services are required.
Men bring their wives and children to a nearby community or
develop a new community as the mining operation becomes
established. Schools, churches, drug stores, and clothing
stores become necessary. Even dairy farms and truck gardens spring up to help feed the expanding population.

The boom towns that grew up around the gold finds and
the silver strikes in the last century illustrate the expanding
economy of a community blessed with mineral riches. And
the ghost towns in the west also emphasize (in reverse) what
happens when a valuable mineral "runs out. "

In summary, mineral conservation is as basic as soil
production and plant growth; it is as modern as atomic energy
and space exploration; and it is as comprehensive as the over
1000 mineral species which provide the content for study.
Today's technological age exists only because of the finesse
in processing and using mineral resources. The future depends on the implementation of know-how in conservation.

ACTIVITIES

1. Bring examples of coal and/or petroleum products to
    class. *E*
2. Make a series of charts showing the locations of major
    mineral resources in the world. (The class may use an
    outline map to "color in" the various mineral locations.
    Educational Section, National Coal Association, Washing-
    ton, D. C. , publishes a map on the coal areas in the
    United States.) *E–S*

3. Make a line graph or table showing the position of the United States relative to other nations in various mineral resources. *E–S*

4. Using a large wall map, have a location contest. Using the spell down technique, have students locate places famous for specific mineral deposits. Examples: Atacama, Bingham, Mesabi, Ruhr, and Saar. *E–S*

5. Experiment: In six different flower pots, plant beans or corn, keeping the conditions as consistent as possible. When the plants are three inches tall, add a tablespoon of lime to one pot, salt to another, potash to another, petroleum (gasoline or fuel oil) to another, and sulfur to another. Be sure to leave one plant as a control. What happens to the plants? Can you explain why? *S*

6. Establish a pen pal club to write to various parts of the country to obtain samples of various minerals. (United States Steel will send free a kit with samples of iron ore, coke, limestone, steel rod, pig iron, along with a film-strip.) Inter-school correspondence to various part of the same state would be very desirable. *E–S*

7. Prepare a report on the various kinds of coal or iron ore. Give locations, uses, reserves, value, etc. *S–C*

8. Write a skit or short story of what life will be like 1000 years from now when many of the mineral resources will be exhausted. *S*

9. Prepare a display or exhibit of the rocks and minerals found in the immediate locale or state. *E–S–C*

10. On a bulletin board, using yarn and thumbtacks, show where American industry is exploring and mining for petroleum. *S–C*

11. If an oil refinery or taconite plant is nearby, plan a field trip. (It is absolutely essential that the teacher or tour guide make a prior visit to plan in detail.) In some instances a bus tour can be made to open pit coal mines, limestone quarries, oil fields, etc. *S–C*

12. Research: What are the following minerals? What are their values? Kyanite, mica, fluorspar, vanadium, tungsten, manganese, molybdenum, veryllium, titanium, cobalt, platinum. *S–C*

13. Just for fun, give the class a series of multi-choice exercises like the following: **E-S**

1.	gravel	a.	fertilizer material
2.	potash	b.	insulating material
3.	clay	c.	ceramic material
4.	asbestos	d.	chemical material
5.	sulfur	e.	building material

    *   *   *

1.	base	a.	radium
2.	light	b.	tin
3.	precious	c.	gold
4.	rare	d.	aluminum

14. Arrange an assembly program around the theme of "mineral conservation. " **S**

15. Have a committee or committees search out how coal, iron ore, and petroleum developed in prehistoric times. Cartoons or charts can make the presentation more graphic and interesting. **E-S**

16. Have an informal class poll to discover how a father's or mother's job relates to minerals. Note: the secretary's pencil and typewriter; the businessman's car burns gas and is constructed of metals. **E**

17. Study one mineral (or industry) in depth. Coca Cola, Standard Oil, etc. often furnish free or inexpensive materials for each individual child in a class. **E**

18. Read poems, short stories, or sing songs that relate to mining or industry. Examples: "John Henry, " "I've Been Working on the Railroad, " "Luck of the Roaring Camp. " **E-S**

19. Make a model of an oil derrick, a diorama of a coal mine or iron ore pit to illustrate the ming process. **E**

20. Write a research paper on one of the outstanding leaders in the mining industry: Henry Clay Frick, John L. Lewis, William Kelly, Sir Henry Bessemer, Ichabod Washburn, E. W. Davis, E. L. Drake. **S-C**

21. Divide the class into several four-member groups. Have one member be responsible for each of the following teaching elements: Introduction, body, summary, and evaluation in the teaching of a specific unit of mineral conservation. **C**

22. Make a card file of resource people and/or community resources to correlate with conservation units of study. **C**

23. Test various minerals such as gypsum, talc, kaolin, halite, etc., as to hardness, heft, feel, order, color, streak, fracture, luster, cleavage, etc. Mimeographed or printed cards can be made for this purpose. (See *My Hobby Is Collecting Rocks and Minerals* by David E. Jensen.) **S-C**

24. On a visit to an oil refinery, an open pit mine, or a steel mill, take a series of slides to bring back to class to illustrate the step by step procedure involved. **S-C**

25. Show a series of films on methods of conservation not discussed in this chapter (such as copper conservation, nickel conservation, etc.) in order to show likenesses and differences that would be involved in conservation methods. (See attached film bibliography.) **E-S**

BIBLIOGRAPHY

Allen, Shirley W. *Conserving Natural Resources. Principles and Practices in a Democracy.* New York: McGraw-Hill Book Company, 1955. **S**

Becker, Henry F. *Resources for Tomorrow.* New York: Holt, Rinehart and Winston, Inc., 1964. **S**

Behrendt, Ernest. *Petroleum.* Garden City: Nelson Doubleday, Inc., 1963. **E-S**

Cormack, M. B. *The First Book of Stones.* New York: Franklin Watts, Company, 1950. **E**

Dewhurst, J. Frederic and Associates. *America's Needs and Resources.* New York: The Twentieth Century Fund, 1955. **S-C**

Drake, H. C. *The Uranium and Fluorescent Minerals.* Portland: Minerologist Publishing Company, 1953. **S-C**

Fenton, Carroll Lane and Mildred Adams Fenton. *Riches From The Earth.* New York: The John Day Company, 1953. **E-S**

Finch, Vernon C., Glenn T. Trewartha, and M. H. Shearer. *The Earth and Its Resources.* New York: McGraw-Hill Book Company, Inc., 1959. **S-C**

Harper, William B. "Petroleum," *The World Book Encyclopedia.* XIV, 296-297. Chicago. Field Enterprises Educational Corporation, 1960. **S-C**

Heffernan, Helen and George Shaftel. *The Mineral's Story.* Syracuse: The L. W. Singer Company, 1963. **S**

Howell, Max D. "Iron and Steel, " *The World Book Encyclopedia*. IX, 347. Chicago: Field Enterprises Educational Corporation, 1960. *S-C*

Hurlbut, Cornelius S. *Minerology*. New York: John Wiley and Sons, Inc., 1959. *C*

Inskip, Leonard. "New Boom In Taconite Shaping Up, " *Minneapolis Morning Tribune*, February 4, 1964, p. 4. *S*

Janssen, Raymond E. *Buried Sunlight*. Evanston, Illinois: Row Peterson and Company, 1941. *E*

Jensen, David E. *Getting Acquainted With Minerals*. New York: McGraw-Hill Book Company, 1958. *C*

_____. *My Hobby Is Collecting Rocks and Minerals*. New York: Hart Book Company, Inc., 1955. *E-S-C*

Lindsay, Leon. "Beneath The Earth's Crust, " *The Christian Science Monitor*, January 2, 1962. *S-C*

Loomis, Frederic B. *Field Book of Common Rocks and Minerals*. New York: G. P. Putnam Sons, 1948. *S-C*

McKetta, John J. and Clayton A. Umback, Jr. "Energy: A Look Into The Future, " *The New York Times*, May 31, 1959, M13. *S-C*

Pearl, Richard M. *How To Know The Minerals and Rocks*. New York: Signet Key Books, 1958. *S-C*

_____. *Rocks and Minerals*. New York: Barnes and Noble, Inc., 1956. *S-C*

Reinfeld, Fred. *Treasures of the Earth*. New York: Sterling Publishing Company, 1955. *S-C*

Sherman, Allan and Allen B. Macmurphy. *Facts About Coal*, Bureau of Mines, U. S. Department of the Interior. Washington: Government Printing Office, 1950. *S-C*

Verrill, A. Hyatt, *Minerals, Metals, and Gems*. Boston: L. C. Page and Company, 1951. *S-C*

Warman, E. G. *Strike It Rich With Uranium*. Uniontown, Pennsylvania: E. G. Warman Publishing Company, 1955. *S-C*

AUDIO-VISUAL MATERIALS

16 mm. FILMS

Alaska: Reservoir of Resources - (EBF)

The tremendous reservoir of resources of Alaska -- agriculture and fishing, as well as mining and lumbering -- are shown. Note is also taken of Alaska's transportation problems. **E- S**

America's Iron Frontier - (P. M. and Co.)

This film shows the construction of a taconite plant, harbor development, and iron ore research. **S-C**

How Metals Behave - (MC-ASM)

The film discusses what metals are and the important role they play in everyday life. Microscopic views are shown revealing the composition of various metals. **S-C**

Iron Country - (LSIB)

The iron ore mining process in northern Minnesota is shown. The story of taconite is also presented. **E- S-C**

Lead From Mine to Metal - (Bureau of Mines)

Modern mechanical equipment is shown mining the ore. Milling and smelting are also illustrated; major uses of lead are also given. **E-S- C**

Metals and Non-Metals - (Cor)

The film shows the relationship of laboratory work to a general understanding of metals and non-metals. **S-C**

Minerals and Rocks - (EBF)

The film defines a mineral and differentiates between minerals and rocks. The formation of the three types of rocks -- igneous, sedimentary, and metamorphic -- are discussed. **E-S**

Natural Resources of the Pacific Coast - (Cor)

Conservation is emphasized in this film, showing the magnitude of mining, farming, lumbering, etc. , on the Pacific Coast. ***E-S***

Oil From The Earth - (SOC)

This film explains the origin of petroleum, the methods of locating new oil fields, the process of drilling oil wells, the transportation and refining of crude oil -- and the value of petroleum products. ***S-C***

Our Productive Industry - (PDP)

Inter-dependence of industries is explained. The film shows water-powered mills and modern power sources. ***E-S***

Pioneer of Progress - (AI & SI)

The film shows how steel is made and the vital role it plays in everyday life. ***E-S-C***

Riches of the Earth - (NFB of C)

This film shows how Canada's underground resources developed and how they have become the raw materials for man's work. ***S-C***

Rocks and Minerals - (Children's Press)

This is essentially a listing of several kinds of rocks and minerals. ***E***

Story of Bituminous Coal - (B of M)

The many uses and by-products of coal are outlined. The use of modern power machines in minig is shown. ***E-S-C***

Story of Copper - (Bureau of Mines)

Various mining operations in Arizona are illustrated. The history and development of copper uses are illustrated showing mining, concentrating, smelting, and refining of copper. ***S-C***

Story of Nickel - (Bureau of Mines)

Various aspects of nickel processing are presented in Canada and the United States. **S**

Sulfur and Its Compounds - (Cor)

History, uses, and mining of this indispensable element are highlighted. **S-C**

Texas and Its Natural Resources - (Bureau of Mines)

This film depicts the mineral wealth of Texas, as well as agriculture, cattle raising, transportation, etc. **E-S**

This Is Aluminum - (Bureau of Mines)

Mining of bauxite ore, and processing and manufacturing of aluminum are detailed. **S-C**

Tin From Bolivia - (Bureau of Mines)

This film covers nearly every phase of mining, milling, smelting and refining of tin, one of the few important, metals not mined in the United States. **S-C**

FILMSTRIPS

Coal - (SVE)

This film moves from nerve center to various coal workers -- a step-by-step procedure in coal mining. **E-S**

Coal Mining - (Eye Gate)

The four ways of mining coal are shown. **E**

Iron and Steel - (Eye Gate)

This filmstrip shows how steel is made and some of its uses. **E**

Iron Ore - (NFB of C)

The exploration, development, production, transportation and stockpiling of ore is illustrated. **E-S**

Petroleum in Today's Living - (American Petroleum
Institute)

This filmstrip emphasizes the great variety and use of
petroleum. *E*

In a moment the ashes are made, but
a forest is a long time growing.

Seneca

Chapter VII   **FOREST CONSERVATION**

OBJECTIVES

    I.   To point to the ecological ramifications of forest conservation.

    II.   To indicate the goals and guidelines of forest conservation and management.

    III.   To note the major forest areas of the United States and to point briefly to the economic aspects of forest conservation.

    IV.   To specify the enemies of the forest and the measures that can be taken to guard against them.

      To many people, forest conservation is synonymous with preventing forest fires. There is some justification for this: "More than a twentieth of our woodland is burned and damaged every year."[98] (See Figure 29)

      The actual destruction of forests by fire is dramatic, but the side effects -- directly and indirectly -- are just as dramatic. Fires can cause floods, a specific example of which will be cited later. Fires can destroy grazing lands. Fires kill wildlife. Fires ruin recreational areas and destroy beauty. And in many instances, human life perishes -- as in the Peshtigo Fire in Wisconsin in 1871, where 1,500 people were killed.

      But, forest fires are only one of the enemies of the woodland. Disease takes its toll. The chestnut blight is a case in point. It was brought to this country on little trees from China. It spread through the forests quickly. From 1904, when it was first reported in New York City, it has completely destroyed the American chestnut from Canada to the Gulf of Mexico. This disease reduced the value of millions of forest land acres because less valuable trees have replaced the chestnuts. In fifty

---

[98]You and Forest Fires, Advertising Council, State Foresters and the U. S. Department of Agriculture, Forest Service, December, 1952, p. 8.

Minnesota Conservation Department

Figure 29. Fire can be destructive

years, the disease completely wiped out one of America's most valuable trees. [99]

Certain species of insects also do much damage to trees. These insects not only help spread disease, such as the little beetle that carries the Dutch elm disease, but some insects dig into the bark of trees or destroy the leaves. If the leaves of a tree are destroyed, the manufacture of food is stopped and the tree starves.

[99]Alma Moore, The Friendly Forests (New York: The Viking Press, 1954), pp. 63-67.

Animals such as squirrels, gophers, and porcupines, when they become numerous, may do considerable damage to trees. Some foresters, in fact, say that the economic loss caused by the porcupine is second only to that caused by fire. The porcupine kills the tree by feeding on the bark of the tree, destroying the growing layer. The United States Forest Service has estimated that porcupines have done $1,500,000 worth of damage in the forests of the Pacific Northwest. [100]

The ecological ramifications of forest conservation are as specific as the destructive force of the porcupine or as general as the old Chinese proverb: To rule the mountain is to rule the river.

To illustrate the proverb: The forest land on the hill and mountainside is essential. Forest land in addition to producing forage, timber, and wildlife, has enormous value as a regulator of water flow. Not only do forest soils retain moisture and store water; they also have much to do with controlling water movement both on and beneath the surface. Even snow accumulation and melt is influenced by the forest cover. [101]

The disastrous effects of not ruling the mountain can be demonstrated by what happened in Los Angeles County, California, in 1934. A flood surged out of Pickens Canyon destroying four hundred homes, taking thirty-four lives in the town of Montrose. Why? About a month earlier a forest and brush fire had burned over the watershed area above the canyon destroying the cover which helps absorb falling water. Heavy rains occurred over the whole mountain area, but it was from the burned-over watershed above Pickens Canyon that the damaging flood waters came.

As Joseph Hazard has said: "Forests are great equalizers. They retard both temperature and humidity changes. They absorb downpours and distribute runoff. They reduce erosion to the irreducible minimum. Forest rills, rivulets, creeks, streams, and rivers run clear water, and keep running. [102]

Ecological alteration affects animal life. Forest removal takes food and shelter from tree-using species, just

[100]George Shaftel and Helen Heffernan, The Forestry Story (Syracuse: L. W. Singer Company, 1963), p. 99.

[101]Bernard Frank and Clifford A. Betts, Water And Our Forests, Agriculture Information Bulletin No. 71 (Washington: U. S. Government Printing Office, 1951), pp. 7-10.

[102]Joseph T. Hazard, Our Living Forests (Seattle: Superior Publishing Company, 1948), p. 284.

as planting shrubs and trees in parks and lawns provides habitats for animals that previously could not occupy the sites.

The kind of forest determines the kind of animal life
found within the forest. The moose, for example, is so closely
associated with coniferous forests that ecologists have called
it the *spruce-moose* biome. The moose eats the bark of the
trees in winter and in summer thrives on the ground cover and
the aquatic plants of ponds and lakes generally found in coniferous forests. The white-tailed deer is typical of the eastern
deciduous forests -- browsing at the margin of the forest in
summer, scrounging the deep woods in winter to find tender
twigs. The crossbills, a variety of bird, is confined to coniferous forests because their beaks are adapted to extract seeds
from pine cones. The bob-white needs the open grasslands
near deciduous forests in which to grow and multiply.

Forestry, agriculture, aid to game and fur species, are
all direct or indirect ecological manipulations. Man has greatly improved his ability to alter his surroundings: He has power
saws which can quickly strip the forests. (See Figure 30) He
has heavy bulldozers that can level a thicket in minutes. And,
he has airplanes from which he can drop chemical poisons to
control the enemies of the forest.

In the larger sense, forests are the skeleton and waterways, the bloodstream in the whole system of life on the skin
of the earth.

To imagine a world without trees would be to imagine a
wasteland. In the United States there are many wooden houses
with wooden roofs, doors, and window frames -- houses fur-
nished with wooden furniture. For breakfast, an American
might have maple syrup (a forest product) over his hotcakes,
while he reads the morning newspaper (a forest product). At
lunch, he might cook hamburgers over charcoal (a forest
product) while wearing a rayon apron (a forest product).
Everything from toothpicks to battleship decks is made of
wood. Paper and pencil, plastic telephone and telephone pole
-- the list is almost limitless. More than a million men,
trained to work in wood, are dependent upon our forests. [103]

A world without forests and wood would also be an
aesthetic tragedy as well as an economic disaster. With the
destruction of the forest, the voice of birds would no longer
be heard in the land. The bright gashes of green in the landscape would be replaced by dull browns and greys.

[103]Moore, op. cit., p. 79.

Minnesota Historical Society

Figure 30. Cut over timber land

Very early individuals, government, and the private
sectors of our economy recognized the major significance of
forest conservation. In fact, it may be said that the whole conservation movement developed out of the concern over preserving the forest lands of America. As early as 1799, the young
republic recognized the need for husbanding timber supplies
as in the Federal Timber Purchase Act which appropriated
$200, 000 to buy timber for naval purposes. State govern-
ments very early also recognized the significance of forest
conservation. In 1837, the Massachusetts legislature authorized a survey of forest conditions, with a view to encouraging

landowners to consider the importance of "continuing, improving, and enlarging the forests of the state." Around the turn of the century, the forest conservation movement boomed under the forceful leadership of Gifford Pinchot, who brought the word *conservation* into popular usage, as it applies to natural resources. During the next two decades, the forestry profession was established. The United States Forest Service was born, and the national forest system was developed and expanded. Then, following the First World War, cooperation between private forest landowners, the several states, and the national government accelerated. More recently, under the Kennedy administration, under Stewart Udall's leadership, the conservation movement has again attained headline significance. But, even in light of many accomplishments over a long period of time, conservation of forest resources has a long way to go.[104] Fires still burn millions of acres of forest land each year. Wasteful timber cutting methods still continue to be used. And, as mentioned before, considerable damage is done by insects, disease, and mammals each year.

How can the forest resources be conserved? Below are a few goals and guidelines:

1. More attention must be given to preventing and controlling forest fires. Not all forest fires can be prevented, but through an educational program more fires can be prevented. In teaching man care in the disposal of burned matches and cigarette butts, some forest fires will be prevented. In teaching man care in the use of camp fires, open fireplaces, and other open fires, there would be a considerable lessening of the fire hazard. And, be it admitted, some forest fires are incendiary in nature. Incidentally, since a considerable number of fires are caused by lightning, experiments are under way in the western states to eliminate this hazard by eliminating lightning. This can be done by preventing the upward movement of super-cooled clouds. By seeding super-cooled clouds with iodide, the moisture is changed into ice and drops as rain.

2. There will always be the fires caused by sparks from a passing train, or other causes difficult to prevent. But,

---

[104]Forest Service, Highlights in the History of Forest Conservation, Agriculture Information Bulletin No. 83, U. S. Department of Agriculture (Washington: Government Printing Office, 1952).

quick reporting of the fire and then the quick containment and elimination of the fire is essential. This requires a variety of highly trained personnel -- whether it be the operator of a helicopter or airplane delivering chemical bombs, a smoke-jumper parachuting into remote areas, or a bulldozer operator making a fire break. There must be personnel to man the look-out towers. (See Figure 31) Laboratory research for new chemicals and apparatus affecting technique in operation of fire control is being given more and more consideration.

3. Considerable time must be devoted to containing harmful insect destruction and preventing the spread of disease.

Minnesota Conservation Department

Figure 31. Forest ranger at work

Minnesota Historical Society

Figure 32. Tree planting by machine

This may be as simple as pruning and burning diseased trees, or as complex as introducing a new insect species to re-establish an ecological balance. Care must be taken in importing new trees and seeds, since new diseases and tree enemies may stow away surreptitiously. Efforts are under way, however, to produce hybrids or new kinds of trees that will be resistant to disease and insects. Aluminum sheets or metal wiring can protect trees from the teeth of mammals. More patience and less impulsiveness is needed in the critical area of controlling the tree enemies.

4. When windstorm, logging, fire, or disease has leveled a forest, then it is mandatory to reforest the area. The drudgery of hand planting of seedlings seems to be one of the most effective devices. (See Figure 32) In logging,

Minnesota Department of Business Development

Figure 33. Pulpwood for Mando Mills from Mando Mills Tree Farm
near International Falls, Minnesota, American Forest
Product Industries

a few seed trees should be left -- reseeding by nature has
not been supplanted by a better way.
5. When trees are harvested, great care must be taken to
make use of all parts of the tree. For example, sawmill
leftovers are being converted into new uses. This has
been called "the finest story of conservation in the
world. "[105] Plywood, newsprint, insulating boards,

[105]Willialm D. Hagenstein, "Forest Engineers," Citizens Conference on Pacific
Northwest Forest Resources (Portland: Reed College, 1957), p. 59.

masonite are but a few of the products made from what was
once waste products. (See Figure 33) New and improved
machinery has resulted in less production waste. The de-
barking machine and gang saws are examples. Strange as
it may seem, valuable logs (maybe worth a hundred dollars
apiece) may be lost in the forest or under water (as they
are floated down stream for milling, for example). Now,
recovering these logs -- salvage logging -- has become a
worthwhile effort in such states as Idaho and California.
Men with aqualungs and skindiving suits have been diving
in lakes and rivers in the west discovering hidden treasures of logs.

6. Another important way of conserving forests is by improving the wood product itself. The Forest Productions Laboratory (U. S. Department of Agriculture) at Madison,
Wisconsin, has done considerable experimentation in this
area. By chemical soakings, the lifetime of wood can be
extended. Even wood that is fireproof has been developed.
The Forest Products Laboratory has developed wood materials that will not warp, shrink, or swell. The longer life
of wood -- whether window sill or fence post -- gives
longer life to forests that otherwise would be cut to meet
the demands of a wood-using public.

7. By returning otherwise unproductive land back to forest
land, and by improving forest care methods (such as thinning), the base from which forest resources can be obtained is extended. Also, by devoting more land to state
and national forest reserves, improvement would be made
in watershed protection, wildlife conservation, flood control -- a multiplicity of benefits.

8. Research work (as at the Institute of Forest Genetics at
Placerville, California) to develop new breeds of trees
which will be superior in rate of growth, in quality of
wood, and in resistance to disease and drought will further help conservation efforts. The research procedure
is to cross-pollinate trees to get hybrids that have the
good qualities, but not the bad qualities of both parent
trees. A hybrid tree, for example, could be benficial
in erosion control in an area where before it was too cold
for such a tree to grow -- or too dry for such a tree to
grow. In the future, burnt over areas could again have
forests in a few brief years.

9. Finally, increased efforts must be made through education

to protect forest lands. Conservation can be integrated into the curriculum of elementary and secondary schools. Well trained, competent personnel must be obtained for the Forest Service. The forest industry must see that their goose may be the one that laid the golden egg, unless great care is taken.

In the United States there are 180,000,000 acres of national forests -- administratively organized into about one hundred and fifty units. These national forests are of major significance in forest conservation in this country. It is to be noted that these national forests were "set aside basically to accomplish two quite different objectives: The production of timber that is to be harvested and processed to serve the public, and the protection of vital watersheds."[106]

The national forests are managed to satisfy the more material wants of people. They are operated under a policy of "multiple use." This policy, in addition to encouraging the sale of timber to private enterprises, permitting sheep and cattle grazing by farmers and ranchers, also encourages favorable fish and wildlife conditions and promotes the development of picnic, camping, and winter sports.

The national forests yield large and important water flows. Without assurance of adequate supplies of usable water, the people and economy of the western states face an uncertain future. How efficiently national forests are managed is, therefore, of paramount concern to the water users in over half the area of the United States.[107]

National forests are a keystone of forest conservation in this country. Even though the national forests contain only one-sixth of the country's commercial timberland, since the historic act of 1891, which authorized the President of the United States to select and proclaim forest reserves from the public domain, national forests have stood as a bulwark against the exploitation and wrecking of the great forests of this country. And today, these forests remain as shining examples of what can be done to use, yet preserve, the superb beauty of the green gold of America.

In addition to national forests, there are many state forests. Minnesota, for example, has five million acres of

[106]Arthur H. Carhart, The National Forests (New York: Alfred A. Knopf, 1959), p. 4.

[107]Bernard Frank, Our National Forests (Norman: University of Oklahoma Press, 1955), p. xiv.

state forests, more than any other state. State forests serve the public in many ways: They provide recreational and economic dividends.

There are also 10,000,000 acres in the United States owned and operated by counties and cities. As with federal and state forests, these forests can provide income and job opportunities, as well as recreational benefits.

Millions of acres of forests are owned and operated by industries such as lumber, pulp, paper, mining, land, and railroad industries. The objective of these industries is different from that of the government, for their aim is a successful financial operation. Therefore, the regard for the wildlife, watershed, and future growth of the forest sometimes becomes relatively unimportant. Laws have never forced these industries to maintain any standards of conservation. These industries have, and often still do, operate on a wasteful basis, burning and cutting without regard to conservation practices. However, some industries are beginning to see the error of their ways and are beginning to show some signs of forest management. The pulp and lumber industries, for example, practice intensive forest management. A great deal of progress in forest conservation practice is needed in the bulk of privately owned forests.

Tree farms are a new idea in forest management. Private land is stocked with trees and then protected and managed carefully for future commercial value. The owner must assure his willingness to carefully manage and protect his forest. This development is an important factor in bringing privately owned forests under management.

Significantly sixty per cent of the commercial forest land in the United States is in small private holdings, and about one-half of this is in farm woodlands averaging slightly over forty acres each. The problem is that as a rule farmers who have a substantial amount of merchantable timber have sold their timber "lump sum" without provision for proper cutting. After such liquidation of the growing stock, there is a long waiting period before another sale can be made.

Only in recent decades has the idea of continuously productive forests been given much consideration. Before the 1930's timber owners and operators thought mainly in terms of the immediate returns. Through judicious cutting, the growing stock can be improved, and at the same time a considerable harvest of wood products can be obtained. Obviously, selective cutting can be applied to one acre, to one stand, or to an entire forest property.

In selective cutting the merchantable timber stand is never cut all at once. Instead small groups of trees or single trees are removed. By this method, timber can be harvested from the stand continuously, without the long waiting periods that are required after stands have been clear-cut.

In the Pacific Northwest clear-cutting in strips or patches is used, with provision for natural seeding-in from uncut stands bordering clear-cut areas. (In this area a major problem is the transition from a timber economy based on virgin Douglas fir to one based on second growth.) Clear-cutting in strips is also used when pulpwood is the major product, since mature, high-quality trees for saw logs are not an objective of management.

In any discussion of forest conservation in this country there must be some indication of the forest regions of the United States and a succinct reference to the kinds of trees to be found in each of the regions.

Trees fall into two chief family groups -- conifers and broadleafs. A conifer is more commonly called a needle tree (because of its needle-like leaves), or a soft wood (because the wood of most conifers is soft). Most soft woods are evergreen, i. e., their leaves, or needles, stay on the entire year. Broadleaf trees, so named because of broader leaves than conifers, are also called hardwoods, because their wood is usually hard, and deciduous, because their leaves do not stay on all year.

In the United States there are six major forest regions: *The Northern Forest* consists chiefly of softwoods such as white pines, spruce, firs, and a few hardwoods such as maple and birch. This region was especially hard hit by lumbermen. Although red pine and white pine are making a comeback, the "weed trees" such as fir and aspen cover much of the land. (Weed trees are not of much value commercially; however, they do fulfill valuable functions in holding down the soil, providing cover and food for wildlife, making the landscape green. New uses are being found for the so-called weed trees.)

The Hardwood Forest is the largest region of hardwood trees in the country, and still maple, beech, hickory, elm and oak are to be found in some quantity in these woods. Walnut trees and tulip trees are less common; their beautiful wood, almost opposite in texture and workability, was much

in demand: walnut for furniture, and tulip trees for flooring
and building.   A few pines are found in this region also.   Considerable strides have been made in replanting and proper cutting in this region.

The Southern Forest is the land of the softwood -- the
white pine and the yellow pine.   Today, these pines are the
only source of large timber in the eastern part of the United
States.   The pines have made a tremendous comeback after
awful cutting and burning.   A few hardwoods such as the magnolia, sweet gum and ash are found in this region.   Resin and
turpentine are important forest products of this region.

The Rocky Mountain Forest is scattered -- there are
large areas where no trees grow.   This also is essentially an
area of softwoods: western white pine, ponderosa pine, and
the Douglas fir.   A few sycamore and cottonwood represent
the hardwoods in this region.   This area also suffered from
the lumberman's axe, after the forests eastward were depleted.   But again, strides have been made in reforestation.

The Pacific Coast Forest is a forest of the hardwoods
and softwoods, and it is the domain of the Douglas fir and the
redwood.   Although this forest covers only one-seventh of the
whole forest area of the United States, the Pacific Coast Forest contains more than one-half of this country's saw timber.
Fortunately, forest conservation efforts were being felt in
time to save this forest from the savages of undisciplined
lumbermen.   Even virgin forests still remain in this area.

The Tropical Forest is found only on the tip of Florida
and the tip of Texas.   Trees here only grow in the tropics:
palm, mahogany, and mangrove.   The cypress and live oak
are found here as well as farther north.

In summary, the enemies of forests are many -- fires,
insects, and man -- but rational man is not helpless; in fact,
he can see the ecological ramifications of forest conservation:
To rule the mountain is to rule the river.

National forests, virgin forests, still stand as symbols
of what man can do if he will.   There are a multitude of conservation practices and techniques that man can implement
in order to make wise use of America's forests.   Forest conservation, in many ways the key to the whole conservation
movement, offers mankind a great opportunity.   Now the question is: Will he meet the challenge?

ACTIVITIES

1. Compile a list of forestry terms (such as seedling and pulpwood) with definitions attached. Compile a list of forestry products (such as lacquers and cellophane) with uses attached. *E-S-C*

2. Discover how youth organizations such as Boy Scouts, Girl Scouts, Camp Fire Girls, and 4-H Clubs carry on projects in forest conservation. Representatives, adults or children, can appear before the class. *E-S-C*

3. On an outline map of the United States, or the world, designate the forest regions. *E-S*

4. Make a bar graph showing the states or countries leading in production of forestry products. *S*

5. Use mathematics involving forestry -- especially as an introductory or closing activity. See *Ranger Rithmetic For Sixth and Seventh Grade Teachers,* Washington, D. C., Government Printing Office, 1954. *E-S*

6. As a class project, make bookmarks (such as a burning tree or Smokey Bear) to distribute to other classrooms to call attention to forest conservation. (See Figure 34) *E*

7. Call attention to forest conservation on special days: Plant a tree on Arbor Day; stress safety in the care of Christmas trees; serve maple syrup candy as a special pre-Thanksgiving treat. *E*

8. Draw an editorial cartoon or a comic strip having to do with forest conservation. *S-C*

9. Have a round table discussion on career opportunities in forestry or forest conservation. See especially Walter Greenleaf's *Occupations and Careers* and Anthony Humphrey's *Choosing Your Career,* as listed in the following bibliography. *S*

10. Report on the major forest fires in this country indicating causes and destructive effects. *S*

11. Make a time line showing the major steps in forestry legislation. *S-C*

12. Make an exhibit for the school showing the major species of trees in the locality. The trees may be distinguished by differences in bark, wood, texture, leaves, silhouette, etc. *E-S*

13. Write and present a skit showing a conflict situtation between a lumberman and a conservationist. *E-S*

Minnesota State Department of Conservation

Figure 34. Little Smokey's imploring plea speaks more eloquently than his
namesake's poster in urging man to be careful.

14. Make a bibliography of "Related Literature" having to do
    with trees and forestry conservation -- use poetry, short
    stories, novels, essays. Selections from these lists can
    later be used in teaching elementary and secondary stu-
    dents about forest conservation. *C*
15. Form a penpal club on forestry. Write to other schools,
    far and near, about forest conservation in their school
    community. *E-S*

16. Make a conservation trail. Identify by placards the major trees, flowers, and vines. **S-C**
17. Make a community resource guide on forest conservation, that is, a list of speakers from newspapers and college staffs; a list of local places to visit, as lumber yards, saw mills, tree farms. **S-C**
18. Demonstrate to the class how a forest fire can be attacked or contained using a map, a model, or the blackboard. **S-C**
19. Take a walk in the immediate vicinity of the school to see how many trees can be identified. Many handbooks on tree identification are available -- several in local drugstores for a dollar or less. **E-S-C**
20. Have a contest to see how many items made from wood each student can identify in a five or ten minute period. **E-S**
21. Make a miniature watershed showing the ecological relationships. **E-S-C**
22. Make a mural picturing the great men in forest conservation. **S**
23. Interview and tape responses of important community leaders regarding what can be done in the area of forest conservation. **S-C**
24. Plan a concert or lyceum around the theme of forest conservation. **S**
25. Visit the local conservation department, furniture factory, tree farm, national forest, saw mill, etc. **E-S-C**

BIBLIOGRAPHY

Allen, S. W. *An Introduction to American Forestry*. New York: McGraw-Hill Book Company, 1950. **S-C**

Andrews, Ralph W. *This Was Logging*. Seattle: Superior Publishing Company, 1954. **E-S-C**

Blough, Glenn O. *Lookout For The Forest*. New York: Whittlesey House, McGraw-Hill Book Company, 1955. **E**

Carhart, Arthur H. *The National Forests*. New York: Alfred A. Knopf, 1959. **S-C**

_____. *Timber In Your Life*. Philadelphia: J. B. Lippincott, 1955. **S-C**

Combs, Charles I. *High Timber: The Story of American Forestry*. Cleveland: The World Publishing Company, 1960. **S**

Cormack, Maribelle. *The First Book of Trees*. New York: Franklin Watts, Inc., 1951. **E**

Dudley, Ruth H. *Our American Trees*. New York: Thomas Y. Crowell Company, 1956. **E−S**

Floherty, John J. *Forest Ranger*. Philadelphia: J. B. Lippincott, 1956. **S**

Forest Adventures of Mark Edwards. Washington, D.C.: American Forest Products Industries, Inc., 1960. **E**

Forest Service. *Highlights In The History of Forest Conservation*, Agriculture Information Bulletin No. 83, U. S. Department of Agriculture. Washington: Government Printing Office, 1952. **S−C**

Frank, Bernard. *Our National Forests*. Norman: University of Oklahoma Press, 1955. **S−C**

Frank, Bernard and Clifford A. Betts. *Water and Our Forests*, Agriculture Information Bulletin No. 71. Washington: Government Printing Office, 1951. **S−C**

Greeley, William B. *Forests and Men*. Garden City: Doubleday and Company, 1951. **S− C**

Greenleaf, Walter. *Occupations and Careers*. New York: McGraw-Hill Book Company, 1955. **S**

Haden-Guest, Stephen, John K. Wright, and Eileen M. Teclaff. *A World Geography of Forest Resources*. Ronald Press, 1956. **C**

Hagenstein, William D. "Forest Engineers, "*Citizens Conference On Pacific Northwest Forest Resource*. Portland: Reed College, 1957. **S−C**

Hazard, Joseph T. *Our Living Forests*. Seattle: Superior Publishing Company, 1948. **S−C**

Holbrook, Stewart H. *Tall Timber*. New York: The Macmillan Company, 1955. **S**

Humphrey Anthony. *Choosing Your Career*, Guidance Series Booklets. Chicago: Science Research Associates, 1961. **S**

Moore, Alma C. *The Friendly Forests*. New York: The Viking Press, 1954. **E− S**

National Forest Vacations. Washington: U. S. Government Printing Office, 1960. **E− S−C**

Shaftel, George and Helen Heffernan. *The Forestry Story*. Syracuse: The L. W. Singer Company, 1963. **S**

Trees: The Yearbook of Agriculture, U. S. Department of
Agriculture. Washington: Government Printing Office,
1949. *C*

You and Forest Fires. Advertising Council, State Foresters
and the U. S. Department of Agriculture, Forest Service,
December, 1952. *E-S*

AUDIO-VISUAL MATERIALS

16 mm. FILMS

Everyone's Empire - (Forest Service)

Refers to the multiple uses of the national forests.
S-C

Forest Conservation - (EBF)

Indicates how man has depleted forests. Points to dire
results if exploitation continues. Suggests what can be
done and what is being done to save the forests. *S-C*

Forest Grows - (EBF)

Explains forest zones as affected by temperature and
rainfall. Also illustrates "the climax forest. " Shows
the contribution of elements in making a mature forest.
S-C

Forest Produces - (EBF)

Explains watershed's underground reservoir. Shows
the recreational facilities of forests for man. Hints at
how forest resources are threatened by man. *S-C*

Forest Ranger - (EBF)

The duties of the forest ranger are illustrated -- especially in fire prevention and control. Tells the story of
the rangers' work in water conservation, lumbering,
and fire fighting. *E-S*

NOTE: Free 16 mm. color and sound movies on forest conservation, tree farming and the lumber industry are available to organized groups from Modern Talking Picture
Service, 45 Rockefeller Plaza, New York 20, New York.

Forestry and Forest Industries - (MAhVG)

Shows how government has acted to protect forests. Shows the number of jobs allied to wood. Lays the background of what has happened to forests in the past. **S**

Forests and Conservation - (Cor)

The growth sequence of trees is presented. Shows fire fighting scenes -- and indicates ways of preventing foreest fires. **S–C**

Green Gold - (UN-Ass. F)

The link between forest and consumer is illustrated. Experts of the Food and Agriculture Organization seek a lasting solution to the problem of timber shortage. **S– C**

It's A Tree Country - (Association Films, Inc. (free)

This film demonstrates up-to-date techniques of forest conservation. **E**

Life In The Forest- (EBF)

The forest is compared to the city. The forest is shown as a community -- a combination of plants and animals, soil and climate, all woven together in a unique life pattern. **E-S**

Life of a Tree, The - (Indiana University)

Uses the cross section of a tree stump to explain the events in the life of a tree. Tells how insects, weather, hurricanes and urbanization affect the life of a tree. Describes the functions of the parts of a tree trunk. **S**

Little Smokey - (Forest Service)

Hopalong Cassidy joins forces in telling how to prevent forest fires. **E–S–C**

Piece of Wood, A - (Forest Service)

Shows the work of the Forest Products Laboratory at Madison, Wisconsin. **S–C**

Rainbow Valley - (Forest Service)

Illustrates the benefits of the forest and shows the work of the forest ranger. *S-C*

Redwood Saga - (BaF)

Shows the various aspects of the lumbering industry of northern California -- cutting, transportation, loading, and finishing. *E-S-C*

Science and Wood Utilization - (Cor)

Shows how research discovers new means of utilizing all the products of wood. Shows the role that the Forest Products Laboratory in Madison, Wisconsin, plays in conservation. *S*

FILMSTRIPS

Forest and Its Importance, The - (Colonial)

Indicates how forests are important to recreation and for wood products. Shows the great damage caused by improper management. *S-C*

Forests of the United States - (A.C.E.)

Shows the history of the United States forests and indicates problems. *S*

Growing Trees for Tomorrow - (Dowling)

Stresses the importance of keeping the forest as a continuing resource. Shows how to aid natural reforestation and the best methods of harvesting. *S*

Lumber Mill - (Curriculum Films)

Elementary presentation from cutting the tree down to following it through the lumber mill. *E*

Lumber States - (United World Films)

Presentation of lumbering in Washington and Oregon. Discussion of protection of forests and also forest products. *E*

Story of Forests - (Am. Forest Products Industries)

Brief scenes of kinds of forests, shows uses of forests, and process of lumbering. *E*

Susan and the Forest Fire - (S. V. E.)

Series of six filmstrips ranging from rules to follow when visiting a forest to how a fire damages the forest. Work of fire fighters is also shown. *E*

Timber From Forest To House - (Bowman)

Shows lumbering methods and important wood products. *E*

Using Our Forests Wisely - (Popular Science Pub. Co.)

Shows value of trees, uses, danger to forests. Also shows duties of forest rangers, ways of saving forests. *E-S*

GRENGS

And I will send grass in thy fields
for thy cattle that thou mayest
eat and be full.

Deuteronomy

Chapter VIII   GRASSLAND CONSERVATION

OBJECTIVES

I. To point out the significant position grasslands hold in our civilization.

II. To bring into focus the settling of the prairies, the management and mismanagement of grassland.

III. To achieve a broader understanding of the role grass plays in preserving our land.

IV. To point out some of the common species of grasses, their environmental adaptations and the migration of climaxes.

Of all the plants, the grasses are the most important to man. All our cereals -- corn, barley, oats, wheat, rye, rice, and sugarcane are grasses. Bamboos and mesquite are also grasses.

The grass family (Poaceae) includes about 525 genera and 5,000 species, with world-wide distribution. It has been subdivided into two subfamilies, and as many as 27 tribes. [108] Fourteen tribes, including about 1,500 species, occur in the United States. Of these species, about 140 are important native forage plants, and about 60 are cultivated in the United States. [109]

Some species are raised primarily for their seeds, others are used for making fiber products, but the ecological association with other vegetation and organisms places grasses as one of the most important botanical families on earth. Animals either depend primarily on grass for food or feed on other grass eating animals. Even microscopic organisms living in the soil feed on grass roots. Because these organisms, together with the grass roots, decay and thus improve

---

[108] C. L. Porter, Taxonomy of Flowering Plants (San Francisco: W. H. Freeman and Company, 1959), p. 186.

[109] Ibid.

the soil, most grasses are more effective than any other type
of plant in conditioning the soil for continued high production.
When all these uses and the distribution of grass are considered,
the truth of John J. Ingall's grass tribute is evident; "Should its
harvest fail for a single season, famine would depopulate the
earth. "[110]

Grass is the world's biggest crop. Not only does it cover
more than a fifth of the land surface of the globe, but it is also
the most widely distributed of all plants. In the United States,
over half the land -- nearly a billion acres -- produces grass
that is used for grazing livestock. In the west, the percentage
is even higher.

Grasslands have been prevalent throughout the world, on
all the continents. In the United States vast prairies, such as
the migrating pioneers encountered, created an awesome sight
because the pioneers were used to the smaller stretches of New
England grasslands. The pioneers hesitated on the edge of the
large prairies with their seemingly endless expanse of thick
grass: The land of the big and little bluestem. There was a
sense of vastness about them that seemed overpowering, an
impression of a greatness that could not be subdued. Some
contended that they would not be brought under cultivation for
centuries.

There were many reasons for their hesitation on the edge
of the prairies. Mounted on horses, the Plains Indians were a
much more effective barrier to the advance of the white men
than the native population to the eastward had been. For two
and a half centuries the Plains Indians maintained themselves
against the Spaniards, English, French, Mexicans, Texans,
and Americans, despite missionaries, whiskey, diseases,
gunpowder, and lead. [111]

Besides, it was generally believed that this region was
unfit for white settlement. The geographers of the day pictured large portions of it as the Great American Desert. In
addition, the rush to the gold fields in 1849 and the years immediately following, made California the great objective of
those moving west. The Great Plains and the Rocky Mountain
region became merely a long, tedious, and hazardous roadway
to the Pacific coast. The basic reason, however, for the halt

[110]J. S. McCorkle, Grass: The Rancher's Crop, Conservation Service Leaflet No.
346, U. S. Department of Agriculture (Washington: Government Printing Office, 1954).
[111]Everett E. Edwards, "The Settlement of the Grassland," U. S. Department of
Agriculture Yearbook (Washington: Government Printing Office, 1948), p. 21.

of the frontier at approximately the eastern edge of the Great Plains was that it, by virtue of its climate, challenged the accepted methods of agricultural conquest.

There was also the lore of woodland farming that associated certain types of soil with specific stands of timber. Besides, forests were of great importance to the pioneer economy. They sheltered the game that constituted a chief source of food and clothing. They provided logs for cabins, stock shelters, fuel, fences, furniture, and tools. They offered protection from winds and storms that open prairies did not give.

In addition to the lack of timber, the prairies did not provide a proper water supply until wells could be dug. Another reason for avoiding the prairies was the desire to be near the water courses that provided avenues of transportation. Trails into the prairies were practically impassable in the spring because of the mud.

Largely because of its natural vegetation, the Great Plains became the scene of a range cattle industry that far exceeded in scale and results any of its predecessors in American history. The building of the railroad brought hunters who supplied the construction crews with buffalo meat, and with its completion in 1869, let in additional throngs who literally massacred the buffalo and left the grasses of the plains unused.

With the completion of the railroad, the huge herds bred in Texas were driven northward to Abilene and other shipping points in Kansas. Later, herds were pushed into Nebraska, the Dakotas, and Montana, first to provide meat for the Indian reservations and military posts, and later to raise cattle for eastern markets. From these cattle drives come the color and folklore of American history through western stories. The grass supply of the vast range of the Great Plains seemed unlimited, and the region was regarded as a permanent paradise for cattlemen.

About 1880 the boom element began to enter the cattle industry. The number of cattle increased rapidly, and soon the range was fully stocked. The land was still largely unclaimed public domain, unfenced except for some extra-legal holdings of the ranchers. Without regulated grazing, the supply of tall grass was soon exhausted, leaving buffalo grass and grama grass, and shortly these also were threatened in many places.

Without provisions for adequate winter feed, the unusually severe winter of 1886-87 spelled disaster for many of the large scale cattle companies. [112] Continued drought from 1886-95, along with the influx of homesteaders, gave rise to smaller operations and the beginning of agriculture in the Great Plains.

As long as the grass of the public domain was the main forage for the grazing stock, whether cattle, sheep, or horses, no thought was given by the owners to range conservation. It was first come -- first served, and stockmen knew little of the needs and requirements for sustained forage plants. Soon the grass was gnawed to the roots and so weakened that they gave way to worthless weeds and annuals or left only rows of dust heaps.

Agriculture was not better, so little did they know of watershed management and soil fertility. The shrubs along the meadows dried out, allowing freshets to tear gashes in the sod and soil.

Early in the 1880's interest was aroused in the conservation of the nation's remaining natural resources, but Congress clung to the idea of the homesteads, adopted in 1862, as the main principle of developing the west. Little was actually done to regulate grazing until the Taylor Grazing Act was passed in 1934. It undertook to stop injury to the public grazing land by preventing over-grazing and soil depletion; to provide for their orderly use, improvement, and development; to stabilize the livestock industry dependent upon the public range. This law required 142,000,000 acres of the public lands to be organized into grazing districts under the control of the Department of the Interior. The Department was also given broad powers to develop water power, to carry on soil erosion control, and to provide for the disposal of land not needed for grazing districts.

The role of grass in conservation is manyfold. The grassland boom has been gaining momentum since the 1930's but grass crops still are not getting the attention they deserve.

A good grass crop protects and improves the soil in several ways: (1) prevents soil erosion, (2) improves soil structure, (3) increases soil productivity, and (4) improves the biological life of the soil. [113] Both the tops and roots of grass plants help do these things.

[112]Ibid., p. 22.
[113]Tom Dale and Grover F. Brown, Grass Crops In Conservation Farming, U. S. Department of Agriculture Bulletin No. 2080 (Washington: Government Printing Office, 1955).

A great part of water erosion starts when raindrops blast loose particles of soil. Without a soil cover, rill erosion begins. A blanket of grass is very effective in checking erosion. The blades or leaves break the force of the falling rain. Large drops are then shattered into much smaller drops that will penetrate the soil, not wash it away. In addition, grass helps prevent raindrop splash from sealing the small capillary pores of the soil, thus permitting the water to soak into the ground more rapidly.

Grass plants, whether living or dead, also slow down run-off. Each blade, leaf, and stem acts as a tiny check dam. They also help catch and hold soil particles that the water may be carrying. The slower run-off permits the soil to soak up more of the water. (See Figure 35)

The blades or leaves of a good grass crop also protect the land from the force of high winds, and thus help prevent wind erosion.

Grass tops add humus, or organic matter, to the soil, if left on the ground or plowed under. The amount may be considerable where the grass crop is grown for several years.

The roots of grass plants are usually fine and numerous. Like the grass tops, they help protect the soil against both water and wind erosion. They improve soil structure and productivity by adding organic matter and by helping to separate soil particles in tight land. They also help create small openings that allow water to soak into the ground.

Like many plants, grasses have the ability to adapt themselves to their particular environment. Each species has its own geographical range, mineral and water requirements. Generally, the percentage of mineral plant nutrients in organic remains from grass is higher than those from forests. Thus, more organic acids result from decomposition of forest litter, even though the total of minerals supplied is somewhat greater. Farmers should make a clear decision between grass and forest. Although wild grass is a good soil building cover in semi-arid and sub-humid regions if protected from over-grazing, it usually is not in humid regions except for relatively unleached soils. Wild, uncared for, frequently burned grassland in humid regions produces little, and the grasslands are better off in forests. [114]

---

[114] Charles E. Kellogg, "Grass and Soil," U. S. Department of Agriculture Yearbook (Washington: Government Printing Office, 1948), p. 54.

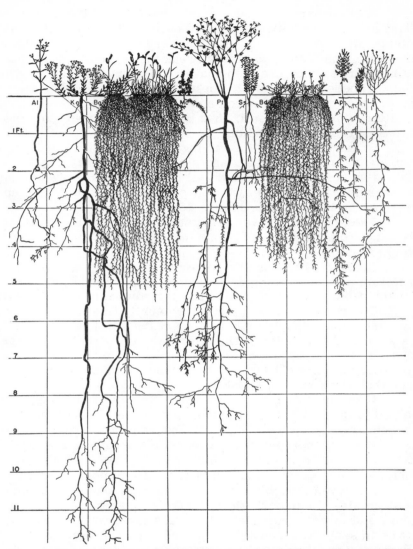

Roots of different grassland plants draw their moisture from different soil layers. Some native plants extend their roots to depths of 20 or more feet. Drawing made at Hays, Kans., before the great drought, by J. E. Weaver and F. W. Albertson (Ecol. Monographs, volume 13, p. 100). *Al*, narrow-leafed 4-o'clock, *Allionia linearis; Kg*, prairie false boneset, *Kuhnia gultinosa; Bg*, blue grama, *Bouteloua gracilis; Mc*, globemallow, *Malvastrum coccineum; Pt*, a legume, *Psoralea tenuiflora; Ss, Sideranthus spinulosis; Bd*, buffalograss, *Buchloe dactyloides; Ap*, western ragweed, *Ambrosia psilostachya*; and *Lj*, skeleton weed, *Lygodesmia juncea.*

Figure 35. 1948 Agriculture Year Book, p. 58.

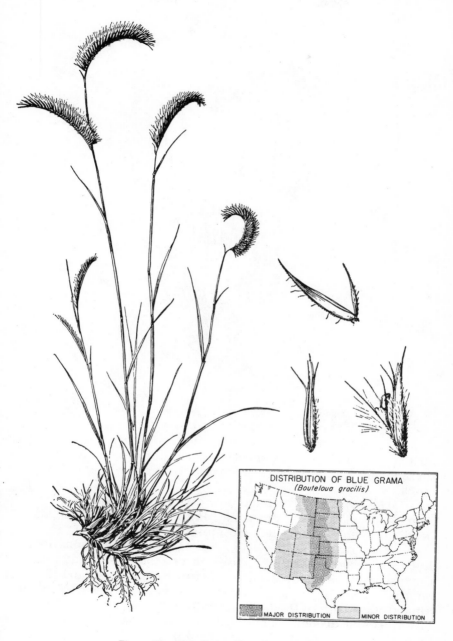

Figure 36. Blue Grama (Bouteloua gracilis)

Figure 37.   Indian Ricegrass (Oryzopsis hymenoides)

Specific species of grasses are used for a variety of purposes.   The cereals, as mentioned earlier, are valuable for
their seeds.   Other species provide forage for grazing livestock.

The prairie grasslands are divided into two divisions,
short and long prairie grasses.   Both divisions overlap, depending on soil, climatic, and moisture requirements.

Blue grama *(Boutelous gracilis)* is a low-growing long-
lived native perennial that grows throughout the Great Plains.
Generally, it is considered a short prairie grass, and is found
on all types of soil, including alkaline soils.   However, it is
almost abundant on the heavier rolling up-land soils.   Its capacity to resist drought permits it to occupy the drier sites
throughout its range.   (See Figure 36)

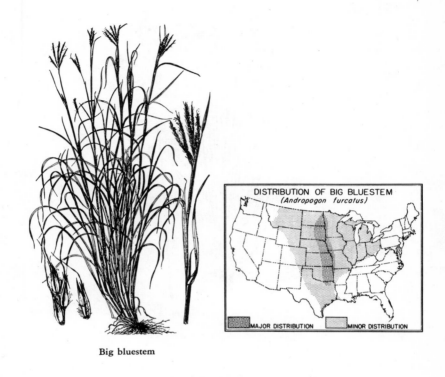

Big bluestem

DISTRIBUTION OF BIG BLUESTEM
(Andropogon furcatus)

MAJOR DISTRIBUTION   MINOR DISTRIBUTION

Figure 38. (Andropogon gerardi) or (Andropogon furcatsu)

Growth begins fairly late in the season and depends on how much moisture is available. The forage is relished by all classes of livestock. Growth ceases during long droughts, but begins again upon the return of favorable moisture and temperature. Because of its wide distribution, high quality, hardiness, and growth habits, it is one of our most important range species.

Indian ricegrass *(Oryzopsis hymenoides)* once was a staple food of the Indians whenever the corn crop failed. The seeds of the ricegrass were gathered in quantity, ground into meal or flour, and made into bread. (See Figure 37)

Indian ricegrass, a densely tufted, native, perennial, bunch grass, is widely distributed over the western states. It occurs mainly on dry, sandy soils and frequently is important

Kentucky bluegrass

Figure 39. (Poa pratensis)

on sand dune areas. It is drought resistant and somewhat tolerant of alkali. Once it was widely prevalent over the western ranges, particularly in the semi-desert areas, but over-grazing on much of the land has made it scarce except in areas inaccessible or under-grazed by livestock. Many specimens may be found on Sentinel Butte, a high ungrazed butte on the western edge of the Badlands in North Dakota.

Indian ricegrass is important for range reseeding because of its drought resistance, palatability, and capacity to grow and spread by natural reseeding on areas where practically no other grasses can be established. Stockmen regard the grass highly as a winter feed for animals, and prize the areas where it grows.

Big bluestem *(Andropogon gerardis)* a coarse, perennial, native, bunch grass that occurs widely over most of the United States, has its major distribution in the tall grass prairie region, but can be found from Ohio to Montana, and from Canada to Texas. Plants will grow to six feet in height under favorable conditions of soil and moisture. (See Figure 38)

Big bluestem was one of the grasses that contributed to the awesome beauty of the Great Plains as the pioneers journeyed west.

Big bluestem has stout, coarse, and solid stalks, while most other grasses have hollow stalks. The extensive root system penetrates deeply, making an excellent watershed cover and the abundant leafy forage is palatable to all classes of livestock. It makes good quality hay, if mowed before the stemmy heads are formed.

Kentucky bluegrass *(Poa pratensis)*, or Junegrass, is used principally for lawn and turf purposes, but is also used for pasture. For a good start, bluegrasses should be planted in the autumn, because temperature and moisture promote germination and growth. (See Figure 39)

If bluegrass is used primarily for lawns, nitrogen is usually added to bring maximum growth and the desirable dark green color. For most lawns, a fertilizer labeled 8-8-8 is used. In order, the numerals indicate the per cent of nitrogen, phosphorous, and potassium used in the fertilizer. It is best to consult an agriculture extension agent or nurseryman for the correct time for lawn fertilization and recommended dosages.

Kentucky bluegrass is believed to be a native of the Old World; it occurs over much of Europe and Asia. Probably, the early colonists brought the seeds to this country in mixtures of other grasses. Apparently the soil and climate of the northern states and the mountainous and cooler localities of some southern regions allowed adaptations, for the species is widely distributed throughout those regions, and its origin is often questioned.

Smooth brome *(Bromus inermis)* is a long-lived, perennial, sod grass with strong creeping rhizomes. It is native to Europe, Siberia, and China. Introduced in the United States in the 1880's, it has spread and is widely grown throughout the country. It is especially adapted to regions of moderate rainfall with low to moderate summer temperatures. (See Figure 40)

Smooth brome will grow to a height of three to four feet and produce an abundance of basal and stem leaves. The root system is extensive, with strong root stocks. The finer laced roots and root stocks form a coarse but dense sod, which resists grazing, and by binding the soil, protects it against wind and water erosion.

Smooth brome

Figure 40. Bromus inermis

Each species of a particular genus can be found within boundaries of a minor range, and in concentrations within the major range. Whether or not a species will prevail within a given area depends on soil, moisture, growing season, and temperature range. Species will migrate from their natural habitat, through seed dispersal, into an area foreign to them, but because of ideal conditions, the species will prevail until such conditions are altered to exterminate them. This is true of other plants as well as grasses.

A large, natural assemblage of plants and animals, extending over large areas, is called a *biome*. The general nature and extent of biomes are determined by factor such as rainfall, temperature variations, soil features, barriers which include high mountains, large lakes, seas, and other biotic factors. [115]

The grassland biome is characterized by the dominance of grasses. Trees may be completely void, as in many parts of the Dakotas, Nebraska, and Saskatchewan, or they may be present as a minor part of the vegetation, chiefly as scattered clumps along river banks and creeks. The grassland biome of the United States is uninhabited by such characteristic plants as buffalo grass, bluestem grasses, and western wheat grass, and such animals as prairie dogs, jack rabbits, antelope, bison, prairie rattlesnakes, and coyotes.

The grassland biome or prairie climax is being threatened on the eastern edge, as deciduous trees penetrate its regions. The short grass prairie is in no danger from progression of deciduous trees, but in areas of over-grazing or poor range practices, grasses are being replaced by broadleafed weeds.

The role of grasses in conservation cannot be over-emphasized. Tests show that the amount of run-off from good grassland is much less than from cultivated fields or bare land.

An experiment at Statesville, North Carolina, showed that nearly thirty per cent of all the rainfall ran off a bare fallowed field; about eleven per cent ran off a field planted to cotton; and less than two per cent ran off similar land that had a good grass cover. [116]

---

[115]Harry J. Fuller and Oswald Tippo, College Botany (New York: Henry Holt and Company, 1954), p. 909.

[116]Tom Dale, op. cit., p. 7.

Minnesota Department of Business Development

Figure 41. Grassland offers wildlife protection

A thick stand of grass is the most effective means of checking run-off. The grass leaves help slow down the runoff, and the roots help keep soil pores open so that water can soak into the soil.

So important are grasses in watershed management and flood control that the Soil Conservation Service and cooperating farmers are using grass crops extensively for watershed treatment. In the Upper Washita Soil Conservation District in western Oklahoma, more than 10, 000 acres of eroding cropland, bare range, and idle land were planted to native grasses in

1951 as part of the flood prevention program. [117]

In summary, the role of grasses in the conservation program and ecological chain is infinite. Grasses provide the grains that furnish the majority of food for the world's massive population. Nearly all the domestic animals require grasses as a main dietary constituent and in turn furnish man with his meat supply.

Wildlife depends on grass for protective covering, nesting facilities, and food. (See Figure 41) Without substantial grassland, such upland game as quail, grouse, and pheasant would soon become extinct. Waterfowl would be without shelter for nesting or feeding. The antelope, elk, bison, and deer would soon vanish, not to mention the rodents, birds, and insects whose existence depends on the grasses that dominate the prairie biome. The symbiotic relationship which is so prevalent in the prairie biome would be void without the grasses. Such importance cannot be denied.

The soil binding quality of grass cannot be overemphasized. Grass roots penetrate from a few inches to many feet aerating the soil and forming a binding power unequalled by any vegetation.

Only through wise management by local, state, and national agencies can our grassland and prairies be preserved to benefit all organisms on earth. It is extremely important not to disrupt the natural balance by farming such land. The dust bowl of the 1930's should serve as a reminder to all to preserve the prairies and let the seed grains feed the masses.

ACTIVITIES

1. Construct a bulletin board showing the foods which come from the grass family. *E-S*
2. Collect samples of the various cereals and make a room display of the seeds and the products made from the seeds or stalks. *E- S*
3. Start a herbarium of the grass family. Correct taxonomic procedures may be found in C. L. Porter's *Taxonomy of Flowering Plants* as listed in the bibliography. *S-C*

[117]Ibid., p. 13.

4. Conduct a nutrient experiment to demonstrate the use of fertilizers in grass production.
   a. Use a fast-growing grass such as rye grass. Plant three boxes using the same type soil for all three boxes. Cut-off milk cartons make fine boxes.
   b. Water each box regularly, but do not saturate the soil.
   c. Add a solution containing potassium to box "A". Potassium nitrate (KNO_3) will dissolve easily in water. Use approximately one teaspoon to a pint of water.
   d. Add a solution rich in phosphorus to box "B". If a soluble phosphorus compound cannot be obtained, bone meal may be spread on the soil.
   e. Plant a bean plant along with the grass in box "C". The legume will have nitrogen fixing bacteria on its roots as a source for conversion of nitrogen.

   The experiment may be continued until a definite variation in the grasses can be seen. *E-S*

5. Conduct an experiment to determine if cutting the grass leaves inhibits root growth.
   a. Fill three soil boxes with rich top soil. Cut-off milk cartons make good boxes.
   b. Plant a fast-growing grass such as rye grass in each box. Water regularly, but do not saturate the soil.
   c. After the grass has grown to about one inch in height, set up a cutting routine.

   Example: Box A -- keep leaf level at one inch
             Box B -- keep leaf level at three inches
             Box C -- let growth continue at will

   After substantial growth and a number of cuttings, rip milk cartons and carefully remove the soil from the roots by washing with water. Compare root structure, length and thickness, and leaf length. *E-S-C*

6. Prepare a list of personnel that could be used by your school as resource people in teaching about grassland conservation. *E-S-C*

7. Conduct a demonstration to show the soil holding qualities of grass in watershed management. Make two trays, filling one with grass sod, and the other with dirt. Trays must be set at the same angle, and equal amounts of water must be used. Pour water on trays, and then check collection pans for silt. *E*

8. Make a report about the Taylor Grazing Act and its effect on grassland conservation. *S-C*

9. You probably have observed the differences in the color and rank of grass. In driving around the community, find some examples of this and determine the causes. Could the variance be due to construction in the area? Soil composition? water content? seed? *S*

10. Write various state conservation departments from different sections of the country asking for grassland conservation materials. Compare the methods of conservation and the species of grasses used. *S-C*

11. Take a class field trip around the school yard. Collect various species of grasses, note color, soil texture, moisture, and topography. *E-S*

12. Read selections from Walt Whitman's *Leaves of Grass* and discuss the passages that relate to conservation. *S-C*

13. Begin collecting resource materials on grassland conservation such as flat pictures, free bulletins, and books. *C*

14. Prepare a bibliography on grassland conservation. *S-C*

15. Take a field trip to the local United States Conservation District Office. Find out how grasses are used in watershed management. *E-S-C*

16. Contact the local nurseryman for information concerning lawn grasses and their care. *S-C*

17. Take photographs of different vegetation climaxes: bare soil, annual weeds, and prairie grasses. Compare progression from weeds to grass. *S-C*

18. Get a variety of grass seeds and plant them to see how the different kinds of grasses vary according to rate of growth and root length. See how quickly the water penetrates the grass covver. *E-S*

19. Plant the same kinds of seeds in a variety of soils. Compare rate of growth and penetration of moisture. *E-S*

20. Investigate how grasses are used in other parts of the world, and construct some of those objects in the classroom (hats, houses, baskets, etc.). *E-S*

21. Using magazines such as *Successful Farmer* and *Farm Journal*, clip pictures of the various kinds of grass and how they are used. Use these materials for your scrapbook. *E-S*

22. Research specific types of grass. *S-C*

23. Prepare an exhibit on grass conservation. *E-S-C*

24. Research question: Why is it not only dangerous, but harmful to burn the grass in an area in the spring of the year? *E-S*

25. Find a place in the community where erosion has occurred. Plant a variety of grasses to see what the outcome is. **S**

BIBLIOGRAPHY

Allred, B. W. *Range Conservation Practices for the Great Plains.* Miscellaneous Publication No. 410. Washington: Government Printing Office, 1940. **S-C**

Cardon, P. V. "Toward a Grassland Agriculture, " *Journal of the American Society of Agronomy,* Vol. 31, 1934. pp. 229-231. **C**

Carter, Vernon Gill. *Man On The Landscape: The Fundamentals of Plant Conservation,* National Wildlife Federation. Washington: Government Printing Office, 1949. **S-C**

Cooper, H. W., James E. Smith, and M. D. Atkins. *Producing and Harvesting Grass Seed in the Great Plains,* U. S. Department of Agriculture Bulletin No. 2112. Washington: Government Printing Office. **S-C**

Dale, Tom and Grover F. Brown. *Grass Crops in Conservation Farming,* U. S. Department of Agriculture Bulletin No. 2080. Washington: Government Printing Office, 1955. **S-C**

DeVoto, Bernard. "The West Against Itself, " *Harper's Magazine,* Vol. 194 (January, 1947). **S-C**

Edwards, Everett E. "The Settlement of the Grasslands, " *U. S. Department of Agriculture Yearbook.* Washington: Government Printing Office, 1948. **S-C**

Flory, Evan L. and Charles G. Marshall. *Regrassing for Soil Protection in the Southwest,* U. S. Department of Agriculture Bulletin No. 1913. Washington: Government Printing Office, 1942. **S-C**

Francis, C. J. *How To Control a Gully,* U. S. Department of Agriculture Bulletin No. 2171. Washington: Government Printing Office. **S-C**

Frandsen, Waldo R. *Grass Makes Its Own Food,* U. S. Department of Agriculture Bulletin No. 223. Washington: Government Printing Office. **E-S**

Fuller, Harry J. and Oswald Tippo. *College Botany.* New York: Henry Holt and Company, 1954. **S-C**

Kellogg, Charles E. "Grass and Soil, " *U. S. Department of Agriculture Yearbook.* Washington: Government Printing Office, 1948. **S-C**

Long, D. D. and R. P. Thomas. *Fertilizer: Food For Plants*.
   Chicago: International Minerals and Chemical Corporation,
   1951. **S-C**

Malin, James C. *The Grasslands of North America*.
   Lawrence, Kansas: James C. Malin, Publisher, 1947. **C**

McCorkle, J. S. *Grass: The Rancher's Crop*, U. S. Department of Agriculture Leaflet No. 346. Washington: Government Printing Office, 1954. **S-C**

Pohl, R. W. *How To Know The Grasses*. Dubuque, Iowa:
   W. C. Brown Company, 1954. **S-C**

Porter, C. L. *Taxonomy of Flowering Plants*. San Francisco:
   H. Freeman and Company, 1959. **C**

Ress, Etta Schneider. "Field and Meadow, " *The Community
   of Living Things*, Vol. I. Mankato, Minnesota: Creative
   Educational Society, Inc. , 1956. **E-S-C**

Riedman, Sarah. *Grass, Our Greatest Crop*. New York:
   Thomas Nelson and Sons, 1952. **S-C**

——————————. *The Story of Grass*. New York: Abelard-
   Schuman, 1962. **S-C**

Stewart, George. "History of Range Use, " *The Western Range*,
   U. S. Forest Service, Senate Document No. 100. Washington: Government Printing Office, 1936. pp. 119-133. **C**

United States Great Plains Committee. *The Future of the
   Great Plains*. Washington: U. S. Government Printing
   Office, 1936. **S-C**

Webb, Walter Prescott. *The Great Plains*. Boston: Ginn and
   Company, 1931. **S-C**

Weaver, John E. and F. E. Clements. *Plant Ecology*. New
   York: McGraw-Hill Book Company, 1938. **C**

White, W. T. "Profit in Range Conservation, " *The National
   Woolgrower*, Vol. 35, No. 11, pp. 16-18. **S-C**

AUDIO-VISUAL MATERIALS

16 mm. FILMS

Above The Timberline - (McG)

This film explores the Alpine tundra zone where plants
and animals are challenged to survive. **S-C**

Gifts of Green - (Sugar Information, Inc.)

All life is directly or indirectly dependent on green plants is the lesson of this film. **S-C**

Grasslands - (U. S. Soil Conservation Service)

Discusses the problem of soil conservation on the grazing lands of the arid southwest. **E-S-C**

Grasslands, The - (EBF)

The film shows some of the world's grasslands and the variety of the animal life. It stresses the fact that grass is the basic energy source for the animal community. The grasslands is that biome where the dominant plants are the perennial grasses. As in the other biome films, a large variety of animals and plants common to the biome are featured. **S-C**

Grass Roots in the Soil - (Iowa State College)

This film tells how grass protects soil, is a good crop, and builds soil. **S-C**

How Plants Help Us - (Cor)

A boy discovers how dependent man is upon plants for food, clothing, etc. **E**

Life In The Grasslands - (EBF)

The color camera depicts plant, animal, and insect life on the grasslands, illustrating the interrelationships of living things and their surroundings. The beautiful photography should lead to appreciation as well as under-standing of the grassland's ecology. **E-S**

Mahnomen -- Harvest of the North - (FEI)

The story of wild rice, probably the oldest harvest on the American continent. Wild rice is found in Minne-sota, Wisconsin, and Michigan. The film shows how wild rice is harvested and what tools are used. **E-S**

Marshland Is Not Wasteland - (RWP)

Shows the role of coastal marshes in the productivity of
the sea. Stresses importance of marsh vegetation.
S-C

Neighbors of the Land - (SCS)

This film was produced under the supervision of the
County Farm Adviser of the Soil Conservation Service.
The film shows sound soil conservation practices. It
also shows how neighbors, as a group, under the direction of the Farm Adviser, can combat soil erosion and
how they can produce better crops on their farms. *S*

Plant Life At Work - (Moody Institute of Science)

By time-lapse photography, the use of energy in movement, manufacture of food, and reproduction are shown.
E-S

Roots of Plants - (EBF)

Different kinds of roots are explained and how they obtain food from the soil and hold the plant in place.

Sea of Grass - (TFC)

Colonel Jim Burton, who pioneered the settlement of
New Mexico Territory, believes that any effort to cultivate the sea of grass as farm land will be fruitless and
will ruin it for grazing. It emphasizes the necessity of
accepting the responsibility of conserving our natural
resources. *S-C*

Story of Soil, The - (Cor)

This imaginative film goes back to the nebulous beginnings of the earth millions of years ago to trace the
story of soil. Full animation, with unusually attractive
renderings, show how man's interference with the vital
partnership between the soil and vegetation has reduced
many areas to desolation. The film emphasizes the need
to restore nature's harmony between climate, soil,
plants, and animals. *E-S*

Succession -- From Sand Dune To Forest - (EBF)

> This film, shot at the southern end of Lake Michigan,
> shows one of the earliest and most thoroughly studied
> examples of succession. **S-C**

Water For The Prairies - (NFB of C)

> This film studies the conservation of watersheds in the
> Rockies. It shows careless exploitation and the positive
> measures that can be taken such as supervision of
> grazing lands, reforestation, etc. **E-S-C**

Vacant Lot - (IFB)

> Ecology of the vacant lot is treated broadly in order to
> relate to other areas, as urban areas. **E-S**

FILMSTRIPS

Animal and Plant Communities: Field - (McG-H)

> The interdependent relationship of the field community
> is illustrated. **S**

Field As A Community, The - (McG-H)

> This filmstrip presents the field as an ecological rela-
> tionship. **C**

Great Plains, The: From Green to Gold - (McG-H)

> This filmstrip stresses natural and cultural phenomena
> that make the area different. **S**

How Animals Live In The Grasslands - (Curriculum)

> Adaptations that animals make to exist are presented.
> This filmstrip shows how they protect themselves,
> build home, and find food. **E**

How Man Destroys Soils - (SVE)

> Various kinds of erosion in grasslands and forests are
> demonstrated. **S-C**

How Nature Defends Soil - (SVE)

Erosion on grasslands and in the forest, as well as the counter forces, are presented. **S-C**

Lamb and the Bluebells, The - (SVE)

This filmstrip shows the effects of over-grazing. **E**

Plant Life and the Soil - (EBF)

This filmstrip shows how plants form soil, as well as their role in preventing erosion. **S-C**

GRENGS

God made all the creatures and
gave them our love and our fear,
To give sign, we and they are his
children, one family here.

Robert Browning

Chapter IX

WILDLIFE CONSERVATION

OBJECTIVES

I. To demonstrate the ecological relationships between wildlife and other conservation areas.
II. To point out the major dangers to wildlife and to indicate ways of preserving wildlife.
III. To call attention to the economic, aesthetic, recreational values of wildlife conservation.
IV. To show how poor or selfish management creates great problems in conserving wildlife.

No other area of conservation has received more publicity -- nor been the object of more concern -- than wildlife conservation in recent months. A headline feature story in the *St. Paul Dispatch* by Irving Lipove went as follows:

"A storm of protest mounted in fury today over oil pollution deaths, reportedly running in the thousands, of ducks, fish and other wildlife in the Mississippi River.

"Two conservation-minded men carried sacks of dead, oil-slicked ducks into the Capitol to complain to Governor Rolvaag about the situation.

"Sportsmen throughout the state were said to be 'up in arms' because ducks were found dying along the shore of Spring Lake near Hastings."[118]

Similar reports could be given from Wisconsin, Indiana, California, and New York.

What is the nature of this wildlife which has become an ever-increasing concern for Americans?

Although wildlife, like worms and insects, may be found in the backyard, most people generally think of wildlife in connection with remote wilderness areas where large animals, such as bear and deer, are common in their wild habitat. Wildlife refers to undomesticated plants and animals: Violets (not

---

[118]*St. Paul Dispatch*, April 1, 1963, p. 17.

geraniums), goldfinches (not parakeets), and carp (not gold-
fish), are examples of wildlife. Wildlife is as small as a
dragonfly or ant, as large as a moose or grizzly bear. However, the wildlife conservation program is concerned primarily with the native animals which have a direct food, fur, or
sporting value. In this sense, wildlife is fish (especially fresh-
water food and game fish), birds (upland game birds, song
birds, and water fowl), and mammals (small fur-bearing and
large game mammals).

In the early days of American history, wildlife was abundant, and the pioneer depended upon the wild game as a part of
the larder. American wildlife played a large part in the westward movement and in the winning of the west. But, since
those early days of plenty, dramatic changes have taken place:

Once the passenger pigeon flew across the heavens in
such masses that they darkened the sky; and when the flocks
swooped to the earth, it was like a small whirlwind, leaving
broken tree limbs in the wake. Yet, in 1913 the last passenger
pigeon died in the Cincinnati Zoo. But, this is not the only example of America's extinct wildlife. Where is the heath hen?
the Labrador duck?

Each year when birds migrate, our news media watch
anxiously the return of the extremely small number of whoop-
ing cranes (thirty-four at last count) to the Texas refuge. And,
the birth of four young trumpeter swans (six hundred estimated
in the United States) in South Dakota rated a feature story in a
major newspaper. [119]

This is news because these few birds are fighting against
extinction: They are on the critical list. Bird life, of all wildlife, seems to suffer most from the perils of modern civilization. The National Geographic Society lists one hundred and
twenty birds (species) apparently on the way to extinction.
Many of them will not be able to make a comeback, no matter
how well conservationists bestir themselves to accommodate
them. On the critical list are the bald eagle, the eastern turkey, Hawaiian goose, Backmans warbler, Everglades kite,
etc.

The list of wildlife species whose ranges have been reduced is almost a listing of all wildlife species. But, a few
species are dramatic examples. Once the bison roamed even
in the forestlands of mid-America, and his rumbling herds

[119]Jim Kimball, "Rare Trumpeter Swans Breed in South Dakota Refuge,"
Minneapolis Sunday Tribune, July 4, 1963.

Minnesota Department of Business Development

Figure 42. No longer nearing extinction

stopped trains and endangered wagon trains: The bison seemed to be unlimited in numbers. Today, they are found in a few scattered herds. (See Figure 42) The puma, the beaver, the black bear are other examples of animals whose range has been reduced.

Why has America's wildlife been reduced? The answer is not simple. It has been a combination of factors.

With the human population growing at an alarmingly rapid rate, vast areas of wildlife land are being altered for man's use, and the birds and mammals inhabiting them are disappearing. Settlement, industry, smoke, the denuding of forests seem to be too much for a large portion of America's wildlife.

The hunting and trapping fraternity, with its pressure for killing, is endangering some wildlife species. Devereux Butcher hits hard at the gunners and trappers. He says, "... gun-toting and killing do not make a man more of a man than he is, or put a single drop of redder blood in his veins. [120] To him, "In all history, the mind of man has not conceived an implement of greater cruelty than the steel trap. " [121] (See Figure 43)

It should be pointed out, however, that disturbance of the landscape by man has favored some game animals, such as the deer, pheasant, and ruffled grouse. [122] Be it admitted, too, that "under the artificial conditions which civilization has produced, it is sometimes necessary for man to take a hand in preserving the balance of nature by removing individuals of a species that locally have become too abundant. " [123]

Man also may be instrumental in the destruction of wildlife when a forest fire runs rampant. Man is definitely to blame when water pollution and poison from badly planned drainage projects kill fish, ducks, and water mammals. Man is responsible for the oil slicks on rivers, the television towers that kill thousands of migrating birds, and for the pesticides.

Sometimes, when nature becomes unbalanced -- with the killing off of natural predators such as cougar, wolf, or fox -- deer or rabbits, for example, become over-populated; and often the result is an epidemic which strikes, and many times affects the human population. Even without over-population, disease attacks birds, fish, and mammals just as it does human beings.

Severe snow storms always take a toll in wildlife, as do floods and other extremes in weather. Specific examples can make the wildlife story more meaningful and dramatic.

Take the case of the television tower at Eau Claire, Wisconsin. Since it was constructed in 1957, it takes a heavy

[120] Devereaux Butcher, Seeing America's Wildlife In Our National Refuges (New York: The Devin-Adair Company, 1955), p. 17.

[121] Ibid. , p. 20

[122] James Kimball, The Game Management Policy, Department of Conservation, Division of Game and Fish, (St. Paul: State of Minnesota, July 14, 1958), p. 4.

[123] Devereaux Butcher, op. cit. , p. 19.

Minnesota Conservation Department

Figure 43. Youth setting traps for muskrat

toll in bird life each year. In 1963, an estimated thirty thousand migrating song birds -- representing sixty-one different
species -- were killed. Dr. Charles Kemper, a director of
the Wisconsin Society for Ornithology describes the most recent slaughter: "The birds fly around and around it, like
moths around a flame. Then they fly into the guy wires and
fall to the ground dead or crippled. " In 1961, Dr. Kemper
described the annual event as follows: "As I approached I
could see, as far as five hundred feet from the tower, birds
lying on the highway crushed by passing vehicles. There were
men, employees of the next door junk yard and neighboring

businesses, raking up dead birds like leaves into piles.   The
carnage was appalling . . . I think twenty thousand dead birds
would be a conservative guess." This is not an isolated inci-
dent.   In October of 1955, an estimated fifty thousand birds
were killed by an airport tower at Warver Robins Air Force
Base in Georgia.   The Tennessee Ornithological Society has
reported that on the nights of October 5 through October 8,
1954, a tremendous number of migrating birds were killed at
a minimum of twenty-seven localities scattered throughout
the eastern and southeastern United States. [124]

Take the mystery of the thousands of dead loons and
gulls on the shore of Lake Michigan.   Dr. Justen Leonard of
the Michigan Conservation Department has said about the
problem: "About all we know for sure is that they are getting
the poison from the environment, but we don't know where. " [125]

Take the case of the sharp decline in the bald eagle young.
There are only about four thousand bald eagles in the United
States and there has been a severe drop recently in the number of young eagles born.   Scientists at the Patuxent Wildlife
Research Center near Laurel, Maryland, are trying to solve
the riddle.   The investigation has centered on pesticides as
the possible cause.   The Patuxent Center proved in research
begun in 1945 that sublethal doses of pesticides lower the capacity of quail to reproduce.   And, pesticides have been found
in varying quantities in the carcasses of eagles. [126]

Why be concerned?   Why should wildlife be conserved?
Mankind probably could not survive if all wild plants and animals were destroyed.   The balance of nature is a very delicate thing; and if even one species is destroyed, the balance
of nature is thrown off.   What would happen if there were a
great decrease in birds of the field that destroy insects?
Would there be an increase in toads, frogs, and reptiles to
eat more insects?   Would the land be over-run with insects,
destroying crops and pasture lands?

Some people are in favor of wildlife conservation simply
for economic reasons.   Minnesota, for example, is a great
fishing and hunting state.   What would happen to the tourist
trade without the walleye, the muskie, and the pheasant?

[124]Lewis Patterson, "T. V. Towers Not For The Birds; Thousands Killed," St. Paul
Dispatch, June 22, 1961, p. 13.

[125]Jim Kimball, "Poisoning of Loons and Gulls Baffles Wildlife Experts,"
Minneapolis Sunday Tribune, December 22, 1963, 5B.

[126]Tom Stuckey, "Sharp Decline in Eagle Young Puzzles Scientists," Associated
Press Special Report.

What would happen to the motel and resort business, especially in the northern part of the state without the wildlife attractions?

Some people wish to protect wildlife because of the recreational value. Camping, hiking, and sightseeing would be rather sterile without an abundant and varied supply of wildlife.

Some people wish to protect wildlife because of its beauty. The beauty of the out-of-doors is a unique kind of beauty that is difficult, if not impossible, to reproduce. Some people wish to preserve for their children, for posterity, the scenes of nature of their childhood.

The interdependence of forests, water, and soil -- the ecological relationships of wildlife to these same factors -- is of utmost importance. (See Figure 44) Durward Allen in his book, *Our Wildlife Legacy,* says the story starts with soil. He says that, "by now most people are acquainted with the well-worn saw that poor land makes poor people -- both in numbers and quality. In time they will learn of such soil also that its deer and turkeys, its rabbits and its quail, its coons and muskrats will be few, and frequently poor."[127]

Olin Kaupanger also calls attention to the inter-relationships that exist. He writes, "All land -- with the water which falls on it or flows through it -- is wildlife land, and all soil and water conservation, when properly planned and carried out, is wildlife conservation. In fact, the unprecedented attention being devoted to soil and water conservation today probably is contributing as much to the welfare of game, fish, and other beneficial wildlife as anything man has ever undertaken in this country."[128]

To be more specific: How can soil erosion cause severe wildlife depopulation in an area? The most obvious cause is that erosion destroys the wildlife habitat. The turbulent unchecked water tears away at cover for small animals, toppling trees and shrubs and leaving rocks and barren land. Erosion sediment can also pollute or fill streams and lakes causing fish, water fowl, and small fur-bearing animals to disappear. "Such soil and water conservation practices as strip cropping, wildlife strips, wetland improvement for

[127]Durward Allen, Our Wildlife Legacy (New York: Funk and Wagnalls Company, 1954), p. 18.
[128]Olin Kaupanger, A Primer On Conservation (Minneapolis: The Colwell Press, Inc., 1952), p. 74.

Minnesota Department of Business Development

Figure 44.   Interrelationship of nature

wildlife, woodland management, tree planting, and farm ponds,
in fact all conservation measures to check erosion and improve
watersheds are wildlife benefiting conservation measures." [129]

Although wildlife habitats vary considerably, they all
must satisfy four fundamental needs: (1) food, (2) cover,
(3) water, and (4) living space.

Food must be abundant and available the year around for
wildlife to survive. Wildlife requires food of high nutritional
quality for health and ability to produce vigorous young. This

[129] Ibid.

relates to soil conservation. The soil must be fertile enough to supply wildlife foods with proteins, minerals and other food elements to meet the wildlife needs. [130] The food supply also must be located in such a way that the animals will be protected while they are feeding.

Cover requirements for the different species of wildlife vary greatly. Cover may be the "housing" of the animals -- a nest of leaves for the squirrel, a deep burrow in the earth for the groundhog, heavy grass for quail. Or, cover may simply be that which conceals the animal from its enemies -- a thicket for the deer, a briar patch for the rabbit, sere leaves for the chipmunk, or sandy beach for the protectively colored water fowl. Cover sometimes is the obstructions which hamper discovery or pursuit -- the great blue herons' nests in swampland, the raccoon favors beech woods or rocky terrain, the fox lives in open places where he can see afar. Cover protects animals from the elements -- snow, sleet, rain, cold -- even the severe heat of summer.

Water is essential in the diet of wildlife. Water also serves as protection and cover for many kinds of wildlife. Fish obtain food and oxygen, as well as cover, from water. Muskrats, ducks, and fish use water as medium of transportation. A well-balanced water area, including the vegetation in or near it, supports a variety of wildlife, *if* the water itself is fertile (as determined by the watershed, including the soil from its bottom and banks), and *if* there is no pollution. [131]

Finally, wildlife needs living space. Even in the same species there is competition for food and cover, and to avoid its deadly enemies, the animal must have freedom of movement. Over-population attracts the hunter. Over-population sometimes brings on disease. And, an area can support only a limited number of each wildlife species at any given time.

Into this delicate balance of nature steps man. Man may simply keep hands off. He may stand back and hope that nature will reestablish a balance and prevent the complete disappearance of many species of wildlife. Or, man may carry out a variety of conservation measures.

1. *He can provide shelter*. In rural areas this can be done by leaving fence rows uncleaned, shocking some of the corn along the edges of the fields, leaving a woodlot area

---

[130] Werner O. Nagel, Habitat Improvement (Washington, D. C.: National Wildlife Federation, 1956), p. 4.

[131] Ibid. , p. 6.

on the farm. In urban areas, planting shrubs and providing bird houses will offer some shelter.

2. *He can provide food.* In rural areas wild berry patches should be left undisturbed in ravines, and the farmer may leave small portions of his corn, oats, or soybeans unharvested for the wild creatures. Some farmers even set out special food plants to attract wildlife to their ponds or woods. In urban areas, bird baths provide water for birds and squirrels, and feeding boxes provided with "goodies" can be a source of delight during the winter months, so great a variety of wildlife will it attract.

3. *Man can set aside refuges or sanctuaries.* Refuges can protect the rare species of birds and animals from hunting or molesting at all times. Refuges also offer protection to the migrating bird -- protection while he rests and feeds.

4. *National and state game laws* can protect wildlife from wasteful destruction. However, there must be strict enforcement of the laws, and the regulations should be well planned. The man who enforces the game laws is the game warden, and he has gone modern. (See Figure 45) Six common regulations often found in state game laws are as follows:

    a. No hunting during the breeding or spawning seasons.
    b. No killing of females.
    c. Limiting the size that can be taken, as in fish.
    d. Limiting of the numbers caught (as a bag limit or a possession limit).
    e. Restricting the hunting or fishing methods, i. e., no explosives or spearing in fishing.
    f. Requiring licenses.

The reasons for game laws can be dramatized by what was done by early hunters. In pioneer days, huge seines were often used in the rivers, and even dynamite was tossed in streams, killing thousands of fish, large and small. Early pioneers often dug fur animals out of burrows or chopped down den trees. Artificial salt licks were made to lure deer into killing range. The roosts of passenger pigeons too were invaded at night and hundreds of these birds were clubbed to death.

5. Wildlife conservation can also be carried out by *restoring or restocking (or even importing) a species.* The smelt and the German brown trout are examples of fish from one part of the country being transplanted to another. The

Minnesota Conservation Department

Figure 45. Game warden goes modern

ringnecked pheasant, the popular game bird of Minnesota
and the Dakotas, was originally imported from the Orient.
However, great care must be taken in planting or importing
so that the balance of nature is not upset. The English
sparrow, for example, from Europe was introduced to
this country, and now many of the native sparrows have
been driven out by the more hardy relative. The English
sparrow is a great pest. The starling and Norway rat are
other examples of foreign pests.

Many states operate fish hatcheries and game farms. The fish (as trout, walleye) and birds (as wild turkey and quail) grown in the hatcheries and game farms are released to populate areas where their species are scarce.

Often animals such as beaver and deer are transplanted from an area where they are too numerous, to an area where there are none or few. This transplanting has been especially effective in the case of the white-tailed deer.

6. *Man can become instrumental in helping to get national legislation passed and in getting international agreements that protect wildlife.* Some strides have been made in this direction, but there is much unfinished business. The Migratory Bird Treaty Act of 1918 was a highlight in this area. This treaty protected migrating birds between Canada and the United States. (A similar treaty with Mexico was ratified in 1937). And, the Convention on Nature Protection and Wildlife Preservation in the Western Hemisphere (1940), an out-growth of the Migratory Bird Treaty, dealt not alone with the protection of nature on this continent, but on both American continents.

Rivers cross man-made boundaries; mammals rove across boundaries; and birds fly across boundaries. This is the heart of the problem. There is great diversity between states in the United States and the countries of the world regarding wildlife protection.

The blue whale points up a recent problem in international agreement. The blue whale, largest living creature, may be faced with extinction if its hunters don't let it propagate, says a United States official: "William C. Harrington, special assistant to the secretary of state for fisheries and wildlife said ... the United States will ask the eighteen-nation international whaling commission to take drastic action to limit catches of the blue whale in Antarctic regions."[132]

7. *Man can become involved in research* in wildlife conservation. This needs to be more than mere population counts. Much observation and research needs to be done in the ecological relationships of many animal communities. Man needs to know more about the migrating habits of wildlife -- feeding habits, courtship habits. Research can be carried out in science departments of secondary schools or colleges, in state departments of conservation, in federal

[132]St. Paul Dispatch, Tuesday, January 1, 1963, p. 40.

agencies such as the Fish and Wildlife Service, by private conservation groups such as the National Wildlife Federation, and the national Audubon Society, the Izaak Walton League of America, the Wildlife Society, or Ducks Unlimited.

8. *Every opportunity should be made to provide informational and educational services* to the public regarding wildlife conservation. As an example: Early attempts at conservation of wildlife often involved an attempt to kill off the predators of the species being protected. Counties and states offered bounties on foxes, wolves, hawks, and owls, for example. But, these measures seemed to have done more harm than good. If foxes are reduced by bounty hunting, rabbits may increase until they become a danger to crops and a great nuisance to the human being. There may not be enough food for all the protected species, if there are not the controls of the predator.

When a predatory animal destroys poultry, livestock, or game, the individual known to be doing damage should be taken by directed predator control. Predatory mammals and birds often play a useful role in the economy of nature by helping to keep population of prey animals healthy and in balance with the environment.

Today it is a rare state park or state fair that doesn't have a conservation exhibit. (See Figure 46) This is but a further attempt to provide the public with information about wildlife and about conservation.

9. Closely related to measure eight is the importance of *providing protection against loss through artificial decimating factors* such as mechanical mowing, spillways, and concrete irrigation canals. These are surreptitious dangers not easily compensated for, or recognized. Seine-like screens at spillways in ponds can keep fish from flowing out into shallow water or onto dry land to become easy prey for a predator or the elements. Mechanical mowers can be provided with safety guards to flush the unwary rabbit, quail, or pheasant. (See Figure 47) To reconnoiter a field before mowing, and then mowing around nests would not be economically disasterous to the farmer -- in fact by the number of weed seeds and insects eaten it may be a profitable investment. A new kind of plant cover planted along concrete irrigation ditches can attract wildlife because of food or shelter.

Minnesota Department of Business Development

Figure 46.   Conservation Department Exhibit

10.   Finally, *careful consideration must be given to the use of pesticides*. As Jim Kimball has recently written in the *Minneapolis Morning Tribune:* "The number of words written and spoken in an effort to discredit Rachel Carson would fill many volumes the size of her famous book, *Silent Spring.* However, in spite of sizable investments on the part of pesticide peddlers to discredit her book, facts from carefully conducted research keep filtering in which seem to prove her right. "[133]

[133]Jim Kimball, "Data Put More Blame on Pesticides," Minneapolis Morning Tribune, December 27, 1963, p. 29.

Minnesota Conservation Department

Figure 47.   Nest destroyed by mower.

Protecting wildlife makes good economic sense.   Unwise drainage is economically unsound.   Pollution is economically unsound.   Over-grazing and burning are economically unsound. It is simply a realistic and practical attitude to conserve wild-life.   When twenty-five million people spend somewhere around three billion dollars a year in activities that are associated with the enjoyment of wildlife, this becomes good business.

Protecting wildlife makes good aesthetic sense.   What would a spring be without the song of the robin or bluebird? What would a visit to the farm be without the flash of color of the cardinal, the meadowlark, or the fox?   What would a city

park be without the squirrel and the pigeon? Wildlife brings a
delicate sound and color -- even a relationship with God, some
will say -- over the roar and clang of the materialistic and industrial world.

Protecting wildlife makes good recreational sense. Why
hike or canoe through the north country if there is no excite-
ment in seeing a fish break the surface of the water, or in seeing a moose crash through the underbrush? Why carry a camera or binoculars into the woods if there are no exciting wildlife scenes to capture or see? Why buy a gun or reel if wings
no longer whir in the wind and the waters are deep and silent?
Some city dwellers still talk of escape to the country. It is not
escape: It is only change, a return to nature, to the landscape
of wildlife.

Man can be very selfish and short-sighted in relation to
habitat management. What he can do in providing food, cover,
water, and living space has already been mentioned. To quickly kill a predator seems to solve a problem; it may only create
long term problems. To clear the farm woodlot or to drain a
swamp may seem a quick way to provide more grazing or plowing land, but what are the long term consequences? Draining
the wetlands can serve as an illustration to the whole problem
of short-sightedness. Originally in the United States there
were about 140,000,000 acres of swampland or marshland;
today, only about half the amount remains. But please note:
About ninety-five per cent of the American fur harvested is
produced on wetlands. About ten per cent of the entire conti-
nental water fowl population is produced on the wetlands of
three states -- the Dakotas and Minnesota. And what of the
great number of fish destroyed by drainage projects?

It is to be noted that some areas cost more to drain than
they yield in crops. Some of the crops grown in these lands
are subsidized -- and we already have a surplus. But at the
same time, producing land is retired in soil banks. Then,
huge sums are spent building dams since we are suffering from
a water shortage. All this hardly makes sense. In the mean-
time, however, there is a great loss of irreplaceable wildlife.

In summary, wildlife conservation represents another
link in ecological chain -- reaching from water and soil conservation to human conservation: Poor land makes poor wildlife. Recent months have brought an increased awareness to
the multitude of dangers facing wildlife -- wetlands destruction, pesticides, oil slicks. But man is not helpless -- he can

investigate, he can educate, he can take direct action on his
own or through a conservation group. Man has come to see
that wildlife conservation is an economic and aesthetic consideration, as well as a scientific and philosophical question.
More immediately, and more graphically, the destruction of
wildlife can reach the heart strings of man.

ACTIVITIES

1. Using glass, wood, metal, or paper, construct mobiles of
    birds, fish, or other wildlife for the classroom or home.
    E-S
2. Make a list of wildlife species that are in danger of extinc-
    tion, or that are extinct. A chart such as the following
    might be appropriate. Organize by fish, birds, mammals,
    etc. *S-C*

Common Name	Range	Approx. No.	Probable Cause

3. Using *Silent Spring* as a talking point, have a student group
    discuss the book for the class -- or a panel of experts can
    be brought for a lyceum or convocation. *S-C*
4. Have a committee survey the school grounds, a local farm,
    or city park and make a report to the school board, the
    farmer, or the mayor as to the steps that can be taken to
    improve the wildlife habitat from existing conditions. *S-C*
5. Discuss: How should unwanted pets be disposed of? *E-S*
6. For a week, have the class scan the mass media to collect
    and/or report on articles, editorials, and reports regard-
    ing wildlife conservation. The class may be divided into
    the following committees: (1) newspapers (national, state,
    local), (2) television, radio, movies, and (3) magazines.
    S
7. Make a scrapbook or notebook of your state's wildlife.
    Drawings, newspaper clippings, summaries from library
    references may be used.
    E-S-C

8. Write several words related to wildlife conservation on small pieces of paper. Put them in a hat, then each student should draw out a name to report on to the class the next day or have him write a paragraph. Sample words: territoriality, mimicry, aboreal, rodent. **E–S**

9. Have a story telling time (Indian legends) involving wildlife: How the rabbit lost his tail, Uncle Remus stories, Wind in the Willows, Aesop's Fables. Primary children may wish to sit in circles on the floor. Either student, teacher, or guest may tell the stories. **E–S**

10. Make a "Who's Who in Wildlife in the Community." What are the most common fresh water fish, the most common snakes, the most common mammals, birds? You may even wish to rank them in order of occurrence. (This can be determined by individual or group field trips. **E–S–C**

11. Make a collection of wildlife tracks (see Boy Scout Handbook) or bird nests (be sure nests have been vacated). **E–S**

12. Make a series of charts showing adaptations of various kinds of wildlife. For example, the bills, feet of birds -- configuration of fish, feet of mammals. **S–C**

13. Make a collection of D.O.R. (dead on road) wildlife. You may wish to start a collection of species for a school museum. **E–S–C**

14. Organize a Saturday hike to observe wildlife. Take a notebook, field guide, and binoculars. A local expert from a college or conservation department may be used as a leader. **E–S–C**

15. Set up experimental situations to discover if (1) toads cause warts; (2) horsehair snakes come from horse hair; (3) snakes won't crawl over a rope. **E–S**

16. Set hen on eggs in the classroom or raise a family of hamsters. Give students an opportunity to care for the animals. Also, observation will bring out questions from students. A diary may be kept: Why some eggs didn't hatch; why she turns the eggs; why she sits on the eggs. **E**

17. Chart the migration routes of several species of birds on a wall map. Yarn, tape, chalk may be used. **S–C**

18. List the good qualities of the following animals that have "bad names": Cooper's hawk, bluejay, coyote, grey fox, great horned owl. **S–C**

19. Obtain a copy of state laws pertaining to hunting and fishing. Discuss the laws with the class. *S-C*

20. How is taxidermy related to conservation -- or is it? Have a taxidermist visit the class. Maybe there is a taxidermist in your school. *S-C*

21. Make a comparative study of what other countries have done to conserve wildlife. Interesting countries to study would be New Zealand, Kenya, Canada, Union of South Africa, and Tanganyika. *S-C*

22. Report on the various kinds of hobbies that can grow out of wildlife study. See E. L. Jordan's *Hammond's Guide to Nature Hobbies* as listed in the bibliography for this chapter. *S*

23. Find drawings or photographs of extinct animals and make a gallery at the back of the room. Talented art students may wish to draw or paint a series for the exhibit. *E-S*

24. Quick answer questions for the class: *E-S*
    a. Why are fish ladders constructed?
    b. Is it against the law to kill a robin? a crow? a vulture?
    c. Why is collecting birds' eggs a poor hobby?

25. What are the regulations for taking wild animals as pets? (research question) *S-C*

BIBLIOGRAPHY

Allen, Durward L. *Our Wildlife Legacy*. New York: Funk and Wagnalls Company, 1954. *C*

American Wildlife Illustrated. New York: William H. Wise and Company, Inc., 1954. *S-C*

Butcher, Devereaux. *Seeing America's Wildlife In our National Refuges*. New York: The Devin-Adair Company, 1955. *S-C*

Douglas, William O. *My Wilderness*. Garden City: Doubleday and Company, 1960. *S-C*

Fitzpatrick, Frederick L. *Our Animal Resources*. New York: Holt, Rinehart and Winston, Inc., 1963. *S-C*

Gabrielson, Ira N. *Wildlife Conservation*. New York: The Macmillan Company, 1959. *S-C*

Gantz, Charlotte Orr. *Discovering Nature*. New York: Charles Scribner's and Sons, 1958. *S-C*

Jordan, E. L. *Hammond's Guide to Nature Hobbies*. Maple-
    wood, New Jersey: C. S. Hammond and Company, 1953.
    S-C

Kaupanger, Olin L. *A Primer On Conservation*. Minneapolis:
    The Colwell Press, Inc., 1952. **S**

Kendeigh, S. Charles. *Animal Ecology*. Englewood Cliffs:
    Prentice-Hall, Inc., 1961. **C**

Kimball, James W. "Data Put More Blame On Pesticides,"
    Minneapolis Morning Tribune, December 27, 1963, p. 29.
    S-C

_____. "Poisoning of Loons and Gulls Baffles
    Wildlife Experts," *Minneapolis Sunday Tribune*. December
    22, 1963. **S-C**

_____. "Rare Trumpeter Swans Breed in South
    Dakota Refuge," *Minneapolis Sunday Tribune*. July 4, 1963.
    S-C

_____. *The Game Management Policy*, Depart-
    ment of Conservation, Division of Game and Fish. St. Paul:
    State of Minnesota, July 14, 1958. **S**

Lipove, Irving. *St. Paul Dispatch*, April 1, 1963, p. 17. **S**

Nagel, Werner O. *Habitat Improvement*. Washington: Na-
    tional Wildlife Federation, 1956. **E-S**

Patterson, Lewis. "T. V. Towers Not For the Birds;
    Thousands Killed," *St. Paul Dispatch*. June 22, 1961. **S-C**

Peterson, Roger Tory and James Fisher. *Wild America*.
    Boston: Houghton Mifflin Company, 1955. **C**

Pinney, Roy. *Vanishing Wildlife*. New York: Dodd, Mead
    and Company, 1963. **S-C**

St. Paul Dispatch, January 1, 1963, p. 40.

Shaftel, George and Helen Heffernan. *The Fisheries Story*.
    Syracuse: L. W. Singer Company, 1963. **S**

_____. *The Wildlife Story*.
    Syracuse: L. W. Singer Company, 1963. **S**

Werner, Jane. *Walt Disney's Living Desert*. New York:
    Simon and Schuster, 1954. **E**

_____. *Walt Disney's Vanishing Prairie*. New York:
    Simon and Schuster, 1955. **E**

Wing, Leonard W. *Practice of Wildlife Conservation*. New
    York: John Wiley and Sons, Inc., 1951. **C**

AUDIO-VISUAL MATERIALS

16 mm. FILMS

Animal Habitats - (Film Associates)

This film illustrates specific adaptations of animals to tundra, desert, prairie, and evergreen forests. *E-S*

Animals in Spring - (EBF)

Common animals are shown making the adjustment to spring. *E*

Animals in Summer - (EBF)

Common animals are shown making the adjustment to summer. *E*

Animals in Winter - (EBF)

Common animals are shown making the adjustment to winter. *E*

Beaver Valley - (Disney)

The relationship of the beaver to the whole wildlife community is shown. *E-S-C*

Deer Live With Danger - (EBF)

The dangers that confront deer are starvation and wolves, not the hunter. *E-S-C*

Duck Hunter's Dilemma - (U of M)

Game biologists are followed in the field as they work on water fowl experiments -- findings and conclusions are indicated. *C*

Field Trip To A Fish Hatchery - (Cor)

Fish eggs are taken from females, fertilized, hatched, and developed from fry into fingerlings. It also shows how fish are planted in streams. *E-S*

Gray Squirrel - (EBF)

The squirrel family is filmed in an interesting manner which the very young will find entertaining, as well as educational. *E*

How Animals Help Us - (Cor)

In a very simple way, this film illustrates how animals help man -- in transportation, protection, in food, in clothing, etc. *E*

How Nature Protects Animals - (EBF)

Natural protection through mimicry, protective coloration, secluded home and others are illustrated. *E-S*

Let's Take A Walk In The High Country - (GPI)

This film emphasizes bird life -- nesting and feeding habits. Ellen is the main character. *E*

Let's Take A Walk In The Meadow To Watch Some Birds - (GPI)

Bird life -- nesting and feeding habits -- is emphasized. Ellen is the main character. This film is especially good for developing observation skills. *E*

Migration of Birds - (EBF)

This film presents the story of the Canadian geese nesting, raising young, defending themselves against enemies, flocking and migrating. *E-S*

Millpond Memories - (ELH)

This film shows rare closeups of wild things that are very wary and wise and seldom seen. *E-S-C*

Minnesota Brown Trout - (U of M)

The research and propagation programs by the Minnesota Department of Conservation are illustrated. *S-C*

Realm of the Wild - (FS)

This film presents scenes of game birds and big game in the National Forests. *E-S-C*

White Splendor - (Pictura)

Indicates how the snowy egret almost became extinct. Also, this film shows the efforts being made to save the bird. **E−S−C**

Wildlife and the Human Touch - (FS)

This film illustrates how improvement of habitats and management of forests benefit wildlife. **E−S−C**

FILMSTRIPS

Aiding Wildlife of Field and Stream - (SVE)

Habitat, food and man are important to wildlife survival, as this film indicates. **S−C**

Aiding Wildlife of Woodlot and Forest - (SVE)

Habitat improvement for animals such as grouse, chipmunk, and deer are shown. **S−C**

Conservation Today, Abundance Tomorrow - (Colonial)

This strip ranges from how wildlife depends on good soil and erosion control, to good hunting and fishing practices. **S−C**

Helping The Birds - (Jane Hardy)

The importance of birds to control insects, weeds and rodents is stressed -- habitat improvement is also outlined. **S−C**

Problem of Wildlife Today - (SVE)

This shows how wildlife can be damaged through bad forest management, lack of water, poor soil management. **S−C**

What Settlers Did To Wildlife - (SVE)

Man's relationship to wildlife is stressed -- food, industrial and recreational value of wildlife. **S−C**

GRENGS

Mingle your cares with
pleasure now and then.

Dionysius Cato

RECREATIONAL RESOURCE VALUES

Chapter X

OBJECTIVES

  I. To delineate the factors which have caused concern about the future of outdoor recreation.

  II. To show the role of legislation and government in promoting outdoor recreation.

  III. To indicate the role and demands of national, state, and local recreation lands.

  IV. To re-emphasize the interrelationships of the various fields of conservation.

The stoplight of public attention is being focused on outdoor recreation to a greater degree than ever before. The late President John F. Kennedy, in his message on conservation, delivered in Congress on March 1, 1962, said: "Adequate outdoor recreational facilities are among the basic requirements of a sound national conservation program." [134] He spoke for a nation.

But, it is only in recent years that the federal government has recognized the value of recreational resources. Recreation, as a facet of conservation, came to the front during the New Deal with its broad and comprehensive approach to conservation. [135] It was only then that conservation was no longer confined to "natural resources" such as soil and water, but was extended to other resources as well, especially human resources.

Several relatively recent federal actions have directly or indirectly aided the development of recreational facilities and interests. In 1954, Congress passed the Watershed Protection and Flood Prevention Act. This legislation provided for greater cooperation between federal, state, and local

[134]Forest Recreation For Profit: Self-Help Suggestions For Rural Areas Development, U. S. Department of Agriculture Bulletin No. 265, Forest Service (Washington: Government Printing Office, 1962), p. 2.

[135]Eric W. Zimmerman, World Resources and Industries (New York: Harper, 1951), p. 802.

governments, especially in reducing flood damage. However,
the law had fringe benefits in so far as recreation was concerned. In 1957, the Forest Service undertook its five year
"Operation Outdoors" program to improve and expand national
forest facilities for outdoor recreation. A further boon to outdoor recreation was the passage of the Federal Aid to Wildlife
Restoration Act, or Pittman-Robertson Act, which permits
each state that uses its hunting license income entirely for the
welfare of wildlife to receive federal monetary assistance. An
additional protection to native birds and animals -- and therefore an aid to developing recreational facilities -- is the federal
Lacey Act which regulates interstate and foreign commerce in
wild birds and animals. These are but a few of the significant
federal bills that mark the short history of conservation in
recreation.

The almost chauvinistic attitude and increased interest
of some states in outdoor recreation can be illustrated by a
passage from the Minnesota's Legislative Manual for 1963-64:
"Perhaps the most distinctive feature of Minnesota life today
is the extent and degree to which those living in the state enjoy
the out-of-doors. More fishing licenses, well over a million
a year, are sold in Minnesota than any other state. In proportion to population, Minnesotans own the most boats. The Fri-
day afternoon and Saturday morning exodus from the state's
cities suggests a mass migration. While commercial forms
of recreation such as major league baseball and football, bowl-
ing and other forms of organized sport have participation at
least equal to that found elsewhere, the organized enjoyment
of outdoor life in fishing, swimming, skating, boating, picnicking, hunting and hiking definitely marks Minnesotans
apart."[136] (See Figure 48)

Almost all Americans take part in outdoor recreation
every year. The participants range from the sight-seer to the
mountain climber. And, the forecasts are that Americans in
ever-increasing numbers will make ever-increasing demands
on the facilities for outdoor recreation.

The relationship of outdoor recreation to conservation is
obvious. The business of participating in high quality outdoor
recreation requires space, unusual types of terrain, cover,
and the environment. "It would be difficult for most people to
use leisure time for constructive sport and relaxation, and

[136]Joseph L. Donovan (compiler), State of Minnesota Legislative Manual 1963-64
(St. Paul; State of Minnesota), p. 16.

Minnesota Department of Business Development

Figure 48.   Everyone enjoys fishing

for obtaining inspiration and adventure that really satisfies, without access to land, water, trees, grass, and wild animal life. " [137]

    There are many factors which have increased concern about adequate needs in the future for outdoor recreation areas and facilities:

1.   Medical science has made tremendous advances against the scourges of disease. As a result, by the year 2000, the

[137]Shirley W. Allen, Conserving Natural Resources: Principles and Practice in a Democracy (New York: McGraw-Hill Book Company, 1955), p. 191.

national population will have doubled.   In addition, the proportion of young and old will increase -- who, because of
youth and vigor, or because of retirement and greater leisure time, will make greater use of outdoor recreation.

2.   There has been an increase in real income, which will allow more occasions for participation in outdoor recreation.
Also, there is a trend for paid vacations for workers, and
for a longer period of time.

3.   Increased leisure time has come through technological advance, and there are predictions that the work week may be
reduced to thirty hours in the next decade.   There is also a
trend toward decreased physical activity at work, which
may turn people to more vigorous outdoor activity.

4.   There is greater mobility -- especially as a result of the
growing use of the automobile.   In summer and fall, the
highways are almost clogged by trailers or automobiles
weighted down with tents and camping equipment.   (See
Figure 49) In the last decade, visits to recreational areas
of all sorts have increased by an average of ten per cent
annually, and evidence points to a continuation of the
trend. [138]

5.   The complexities of urban living with its tensions and
stresses has encouraged escape to the out-of-doors for
relaxing recreation.

6.   Newer kinds of recreational areas are becoming available
for extensive use.   The Corps of Engineers reservoirs,
T. V. A. reservoirs, for example, are providing new opportunities for boating, swimming, fishing.   Even farm ponds
and private utility dam sites can become areas for development of outdoor recreation.

7.   Labor-saving devices in both urban and country homes can
free families for short periods of outdoor recreation during
the day or over the weekend.

In addition to these factors which are increasing the demands on the available facilities and areas for recreation,
there are additional problems.

Much land that is devoted to outdoor recreation is privately owned.   Hunters and fishermen must arrange with the
land owner for hunting and fishing privileges, and often camps
and resorts own only strategically located tracts, and must
depend on surrounding privately owned areas for the recrea-

[138]Richard Highsmith, J. Granville Jensen, and Robert Rudd, Conservation in the
United States (Chicago: Rand McNally and Company, 1962), p. 179.

Minnesota Department of Business Development

Figure 49. Camping has become a family affair

tion of their guests. With an increasing population, this could complicate an already complicated problem. There is ever-increasing concern throughout the country in that private concerns or a few people are leasing large amounts of land for recreational interests. From pioneer days, it has been the philosophy of most people in this country that wildlife, the forests, and the beauty of nature were the property of all the people. But, this comes in direct conflict with another long-standing American ideal: the almost sacredness of man's home and property. As the population increases and greater demands are made on public recreational areas, state legislatures will

find it necessary to come to grips with this emotion laden problem.

With the growth of suburbia and industry, more and more
of the open spaces are being taken up. The expanding highway
network alone each year consumes millions of acres. In the
decade ahead, the middle west and far west will feel the pinch
which the east is already feeling regarding the open land resource.

There is also a geographical maldistribution of outdoor
recreational areas. The east has a small amount of public
lands, while the west has a vast amount of such lands -- and
it is the east which has a disproportionately large share of the
population.

"Recreation -- man's voluntary, satisfying constructive
use of his free time -- restores vitality, refreshes the mien
and spirit, gives expression to creative ideas and feelings, and
helps to provide the proper balance of fitness qualities." [139] It
was in this spirit that President Kennedy in 1962 urged all
Americans to give high priority and support to programs which
contribute to the development of health and strength: "Parents,
schools, public and voluntary recreation agencies, youth organizations, states and local communities -- all must share
in the responsibility of providing both the leadership and the
facilities necessary for those who are willing and able to become active participants in recreational activities which promote physical fitness. [140]

On the surface, there seem to be enough agencies, and
enough land and water areas to provide opportunity for the
present four and a quarter billion recreation experiences
Americans participate in each summer. However, "close
analysis and observation of the crowded conditions and worn
exteriors of the most popular recreation areas show that neither our facilities nor our organizations are equipped to cope
with the coming recreational demand." [141]

The United States is beginning to realize that adequate
amounts of suitable space for recreation must be ranked near
the top of the scale of land-use values, whether in wilderness

[139]President's Council on Youth Fitness, Physical Fitness Elements in Recreation:
Suggestions for Community Programs (Washington: Government Printing Office, October,
1962), p. iii.
[140]Ibid.,
[141]Edward C. Crofts, "A National Recreation Policy: What Should It Consist Of?
What Should It Aim To Accomplish?" Vital Issues (Washington: Center for Information
on America, 1963) Vol. XII, No. 10, p. 2.

areas or in the city. [142] Federal, state, and local agencies have
responded to the increasing pressures for outdoor recreation
with special programs. For example, the National Park Service has initiated "Mission 66" and the National Forests
"Operation Outdoors. " There is increased effort on the part
of the Army Corps of Engineers, Bureau of Reclamation, Tennessee Valley Authority, Bureau of Land Management, Bureau
of Sport Fisheries and Wildlife, among others, to meet the demands of outdoor recreation. [143]

The theme of National Wildlife Week in 1964 is "America
Needs Outdoor Recreation -- Act Now and Provide for the Future. " This theme is symbolical of the great amount of legislative action that is expected to take place in the 88th Congress
-- and other upcoming Congresses -- regarding outdoor recreation. Congress already has passed a bill authorizing the Secretary of the Interior to coordinate federal and state programs
for outdoor recreation. This is considered the organic act
for the new Bureau of Outdoor Recreation. [144]

Secretary of Interior, Stewart L. Udall, established the
Bureau of Outdoor Recreation on April 2, 1962, and assigned
it six major responsibilities:

1. Coordination of related federal outdoor recreation pro-
    grams.
2. Stimulation of and provision for assistance to the states in
    outdoor recreation.
3. Sponsor and conduct outdoor recreation research.
4. Encouragement of interstate and regional cooperation in
    outdoor recreation.
5. Conduct recreation resources surveys.
6. Formulation of a nation-wide outdoor recreation plan on
    the basis of state, region, and federal plans. [145]

Another significant recent governmental development was
the creation on April 27, 1962, of the Recreation Advisory
Council. President Kennedy created the Council by executive
order with cabinet-level status. The Council is composed of
the Secretaries of Interior; Agriculture; Defense; Commerce;

---

[142] Marion Clawson, "Methods of Measuring the Demand For and Value of Outdoor
Recreation," Resources For The Future, Inc. (Washington: Resources For The Future, Inc.,
1958), p. 36.

[143] Edward C. Crofts, loc. cit.

[144] Jack Connor, "Conservation Gains in Congress Seen," Minneapolis Sunday Tribune,
January 19, 1964.

[145] Edward C. Crofts, loc. cit.

Health, Education, and Welfare; and the Administrator of the
Housing and Home Finance Agency. The Recreation Advisory
Council is directed to provide broad policy advice to the heads
of the federal agencies on all important matters affecting outdoor recreation and to facilitate coordinated efforts among the
various agencies. [146]

As early as 1958, Congress established the Outdoor
Recreation Resources Review Commission. In 1962, the Commission submitted its report. It recommended a national outdoor recreation policy. The Commission called on the cooperation of all levels of government and private enterprise in im-
plementing the policy. Individuals and non-profit groups were
also encouraged to participate in developing greater outdoor
recreational opportunities. In addition to the establishment of
a Bureau of Outdoor Recreation, the Commission saw the role
of federal government as cooperating with the states through
technical and financial assistance, as promoting interstate ar-
rangements, as managing federal lands for the broadest possible recreation benefit. The states, along with the federal government, should help in the acquisition of land, the development
of sites, the preservation of areas of great scenic, historical,
or recreational value. Local governments were encouraged
to expand their efforts to provide outdoor recreation opportunities, with particular emphasis upon securing open space and
developing recreation areas in and around metropolitan and
other urban areas. All levels of government were charged
with establishing guidelines, establishing over-all policy, and
providing for coordination. [147]

NATIONAL RECREATION LAND

The national parks and monuments are the best example
of land dedicated primarily to recreation. The National Park
Service is responsible for one hundred and eighty-three units
from Alaska to Hawaii, from Florida to Maine. Bryce Canyon,
Hot Springs, Mammoth Cave, Mount Rainier, Sequoia, and
Zion are good examples of national parks; Muir Woods and
White Sands are good examples of national monuments.

Recreation in the national parks usually centers about

[146]Ibid. , p. 3.

[147]U. S. Outdoor Recreation Resources Review Commission, Outdoor Recreation
for America, Report to the President and to the Congress (Washington: Government Printing Office, 1962).

Minnesota Department of Business Development

Figure 50. Appreciation of natural resources

some historical, geological or scenic attraction, which was the reason for the park's creation. It is a rare park that does not provide for organized nature walks, scenic tours, guided motor trips, or evening lectures with slides or films. (See Figure 50).

Fifty-four of these public reserves contain more than a hundred highly developed camp grounds. Facilities may include boats to rent, museums, guide service, and naturalist services, as well as hot water showers and laundry rooms, supply stores, and restaurants. Because of the great demand for space, most parks place a thirty day limit on occupation of camp sites; but,

Minnesota Department of Business Development

Figure 51.   Recreation in the winter time

no fees are charged for camping, although occasionally charges
are made for ready-cut wood and electricity. [148]

　　The National Forest Service is the other great provider
for the outdoor recreation at the national level. The national
forests can almost be said to have had recreation use thrust
upon them. [149] The principal reasons for their existence are
production of timber, grazing lands, and better watersheds.

[148]George Wells and Iris Wells, The Handbook of Auto Camping and Motorists' Guide
to Public Campgrounds (New York: Harper and Brothers, 1954), p. 38.
　　[149]Shirley W. Allen, op. cit. , p. 202.

There has been an increase in recreational use of national forests in recent years. For example, in response to growing interest in winter sports, especially skiing, the Forest Service has provided the necessary facilities. (See Figure 51) Hunting and fishing are permitted in all the national forests, but governed by state regulations. Picnicking (especially by nearby residents), horse back riding, camping, and swimming have also become important activities in the national forests. Natural forests, too, still provide the opportunity for real primitive adventure for those so inclined. (There are eighty-two wilderness areas in the national forests where camping, roads, and timber harvesting are not permitted.)

The recent movement to establish a number of national seashore recreational areas will have a tremendous impact on outdoor recreational opportunities. In fact, the Select Committee on National Water Resources of the Senate in the Eighty-sixth Congress recommended that fifteen per cent of the ocean and major inland water shoreline be acquired for public recreation purposes. [150] To date, the Cape Hatteras National Seashore has been the only such area established. The potential for developing picnicking, hiking, riding, swimming, tennis, and camping facilities is very great indeed.

Again, it should be noted that reservoirs (such as those by the Bureau of Reclamation and the Corps of Engineers) and wildlife refuges also are potential development areas in outdoor recreation.

STATE RECREATION LAND

State parks are just now coming into their own, due no doubt in large part to the development of the automobile. Today, there are about twenty-five hundred state parks located throughout the United States. About half of the nation's state parks are available for day use only, which means that they have no camp grounds or other facilities for staying overnight. Of the remainder, eight hundred provide developed auto camp grounds and another two hundred permit camping in partially developed grounds or at picnic areas. [151]

There are some state parks that have museums, even hotels. There are nature trails, swimming pools, tennis

[150]U. S. Congress, Senate Committee on National Water Resources, 86th Congress, 2nd session, Print No. 17.

[151]George Wells and Iris Wells, op. cit., p. 25.

courts, softball diamonds. Some states are dotted with way-
sides (generally located at a scenic spot) where the weary
traveler may pause for a cool drink of water or a picnic lunch.
        The states that have provided more or less adequate
areas and facilities via their state park systems, for the recreational needs of their citizens, and the traveler, can be
numbered on one hand. Furthermore, there is no state without beauty spots -- a rushing stream or waterfall, sheer bluff
or escarpment, a fern infested glen, a wide valley of giant
trees.
        The vacationer needs no research statistics to know that
state facilities are overtaxed -- that outdoor recreational demands is unfinished business.
        States that deserve special note as regards a well-
managed, well-used state program are New York, California,
Iowa, Indiana, Minnesota, Oregon, Florida, and Washington.

LOCAL RECREATION LAND

        It is generally assumed that local recreational facilities
are the responsibility of municipal government -- and so it is
generally found to be in practice: It is the city or town which
provides the parks, playgrounds, beaches. But, does this
need to be true? Would it be possible for counties, or counties
in cooperation, to establish recreational areas? Would it be
possible for service groups, industry, even churches and
schools to become more active in providing outdoor recreational facilities?
        Careful consideration must be given in planning, not only
for quantity but quality in the development of local recreation
land. Care must be taken that there is no maldistribution of
recreation areas within a local community. Federal-city cooperation planning as through urban renewal projects has given
city planners a second chance to provide for future recreational demands of its citizenry. Bedroom communities in the suburbs also have a second chance in the breaking of earth for a
sub-city, but too few are planning sufficient space for leisure
time activities.
        If ten acres per one thousand population be the standard,
we are planning half enough recreational areas for the next
generation.
        Many cities are dying in their hearts -- with the sun cut
off and with trees no place to grow -- but this need not be so.

Leadership in the conservation of outdoor recreational areas can begin at the grass roots.

There is something new in outdoor recreation: Many farmers and landowners have found recreation to be a new and profitable crop. Land once farmed is meeting the needs of golfers, fishermen, hunters, campers, and hikers. Land owners are establishing areas for swimming, camping, boating, and hiking. Incidentally, three-fourths of the land area in this country is privately owned.

A Los Banos, California, farmer operates a commercial duck hunting club as part of his dairy ranch. He has six hundred and sixty acres of grazing land that has been developed into a water fowl habitat. The farmer built twenty-seven blinds. He rents them for ten dollars a day to hunters and allows hunting three days a week during the season.

In Virginia, a land owner in the South River Watershed developed recreational facilities around two of the watershed lakes on his property. He built roads, brought in electric lines, and sold lots for cottages. He developed a large area for campers who pay a fee for camping, swimming, and hunting privileges. [152]

Golf courses are among the most important local recreational areas. From the standpoint of man-days of use, golf courses rank high among recreational lands. Also, most courses pay their own way as private clubs, contributing taxes for the support of the local government. Interestingly enough, the federal government now loans money to farmers to build golf courses.

Another significant boon to local recreational efforts was the passage of Public Law 566, in 1954, to provide for small watershed projects. By March 1, 1962, local organizations had prepared applications for assistance under its provisions in some one thousand seven hundred watersheds. A total of seven hundred and twenty have been approved for planning, and three hundred and seventy are in actual operation. These watershed projects provide excellent opportunity for the development of water-based recreational facilities. It is the policy of the United States Department of Agriculture that fish and wildlife and recreational development must be greatly accelerated on small watersheds, if the need for such develop-

[152]Outdoor Recreation on the Nation's Farmlands, Picture Story No. 140, Soil Conservation Service, U. S. Department of Agriculture (Washington: Government Printing Office).

ment is to be brought within reasonable distance and cost to the average citizen. [153]

Brief reference must be made to the economic implications of outdoor recreation. Although it is impossible to make any accurate computation as to the monetary cost of recreation, it has been estimated variously that from between five and twenty-five per cent of the United States national income has been spent on play and recreation.

With increased amounts of leisure time becoming available, it seems likely that the amount spent on recreation will increase. Our present day economy is providing Americans with more money. And, with this greater amount of money, Americans are building better roads for faster cars, so they can go further to explore America's outdoor recreational opportunities. In fact, the United States Forest Service estimates that camp and picnic grounds in the National Forests receive seventy per cent over-use. [154]

To develop and care for the additional recreational sites, a greater number of job opportunities will be available. A land owner whose present business is marginal, or whose earnings are low might find that providing facilities for outdoor recreation would add dollars to his income. Camp grounds and picnic areas can provide useful summer employment for high school and college students. A year around work program patterned after the old CCC program could be of benefit to thousands of American young men. The question may even be asked: Has adequate personnel been employed to care for the national, state, and local recreational areas at the present time?

Certain parts of the United States depend heavily upon the tourist trade, or the recreation business, if you please, in order to keep the regional or community economy healthy. Many communities almost hibernate waiting for the spring thaw -- waiting for the out-of-state hunter and fisherman. Other tourist communities have used ingenious methods to make recreation a year around business -- skiing and ice fishing in winter, deer hunting in the late fall, canoeing and hiking in early spring. (See Figure 52) It should also be noted that motels and restaurants are as much affected by rise and fall

[153]Outdoor Recreation in Small Watershed Projects, U. S. Department of Agriculture Pamphlet 500, Soil Conservation Service (Washington: Government Printing Office).

[154]Forest Recreation For Profit: Self Help Suggestions For Rural Area Development, U. S. Department of Agriculture Bulletin No. 265, Forest Service (Washington: Government Printing Office, 1962), p. 3.

Minnesota Department of Business Development

Figure 52. Canoeing: Popular sport of the north woods

of the tourist trade as is the resort and guide business. Tourists, campers, and picnickers not only buy food and gasoline, they also buy fishing tackle, bait, souvenirs, shells, camera supplies, and postcards. Tourists rent cars, boats, motors, ski equipment, and cabins. They attend festivals and fairs. They go to plays and movies. They play golf and tennis. They bring a new buzz to business in a small resort community. The recreationists are eager to spend: They have been waiting all year to do so.

In addition to the economic benefits of outdoor recreation, the health and hygiene of wholesome recreation are beneficial. Many mental hygienists believe that outdoor interests

can direct those with troublesome feelings into pleasant channels. The out-of-doors, they believe, can be a morale builder -- even a preventive of ill health. Planned recreation can
provide for character development -- hopefully saving some
young people on the road to juvenile delinquency. Although
much can be said for the therapy of the out-of-doors, the case
for recreation should not be over-stated. Outdoor recreation
cannot work miracles.

Recreational resources are a part of the interdependent
conservation world. The state park, for example, may not
only provide a haven for the traveler, it may also be the sanctuary for many species of wildlife. It may serve as a watershed for a stream that could become a turbulent torrent if it
were not held in check. The state park may not only be a place
where children may see woods like the pioneers saw, but it
may also be a laboratory where conservation methods are practiced -- quick plugging of an erosion sore and good forestry
management practices in operation. The state park museum
may be as effective as a classroom for learning about zoology,
botany, or ecology. Those that come to visit a recreational
area may come to see it is one world -- man, bird, tree, and
bee -- and that there is a certain satisfying unity to nature.

This interrelationship is graphically illustrated by a
series of guides prepared by biologists of the Soil Conservation Service entitled *More Wildlife for Recreation*. [155] The
first two land management practices of benefit to white-tailed
deer in the guide are listed as follows:

1. Protection of woodlands from grazing and uncontrolled
    fires. (Is this wildlife conservation? Forest conservation?
    Soil conservation? Human conservation?)
2. Reseeding and renovation of pastures. (Is this soil con-
    servation? Grasslands conservation? Wildlife conserva-
    tion?)

The first two land management practices in the guide for
benefit of bobwhite quail are listed as follows:

1. Crop rotations and good fertilization programs increase
    the amount and quality of quail foods produced. (Is this
    soil conservation? Water conservation? Grasslands
    conservation?)

[155]*More Wildlife for Recreation*, Soil Conservation Service, U. S. Department of
Agriculture (Milwaukee: Soil Conservation Service, 1962).

2. Contour strip cropping provides interspersion of cover types. (Is this recreational conservation? Wildlife conservation? Soil conservation?)

And so the examples could continue with a variety of animals -- each illustrating the coherence of conservation.

In summary, many factors in our modern age have brought attention to the ever-increasing need for bigger and better recreational facilities, both far and near. It has come to be recognized that it is the responsibility of national, state, and local authorities to exert greater effort -- and in more creative ways -- to meet the challenge of the future in recreation. For health and for wealth, all people must become thinkers and doers in providing recreational resources.

ACTIVITIES

1. Make an over-all plan for the development of a recreational area. Make site plan to scale. Relate it to a particular area. (See *Forest Recreation for Profit: Self Help Suggestions for Rural Areas Development* as listed in the bibliography for this chapter.) *S-C*
2. Discuss what your youth or church group could do to improve a local recreational site. Make a list of recommendations to present to a local responsible group. *E-S*
3. Take a survey of your school community to discover how recreational opportunities could be improved. Be sure to prepare a good interview guide or check list. Maybe you would prefer to use a questionnaire. *S-C*
4. Make a series of slides or drawings to illustrate safety rules in hiking, camping, or other recreational pursuits. *E-S-C*
5. Research question: How did the recreational activities in Ancient Greece, the Middle Ages, and the pioneer days differ from today? Presentation can be by paper or by panel. *S-C*
6. Make a miniature of an ideal recreational site in the classroom. Even primary students could participate in this activity by starting with a "sand" table. *E-S-C*
7. Plan an all day field trip by bus to visit a variety of recreational sites. A syllabus and tour plan should be given every participant. The visitation should include everything from a zoo to a farmer's pond. This could be a

culminating activity for the study of a conservation unit. **S-C**

8. Have a physical education teacher visit your class to talk about new ways of participating in outdoor recreation. This is an opportunity for social studies and physical education teachers to do some team teaching. **S-C**

9. Make a large wall map of your community, county, or state, locating all the major recreational areas. This could be a committee project. **E-S-C**

10. Write your national congressman and/or legislator for information regarding new bills or acts concerned with outdoor recreation. Share your information with the class. **S-C**

11. Through your student council or social studies classes, have a "Recreation Week." This may involve a special convocation, the preparation of posters, announcements over the public address system, or the signing of pledges. **S-C**

12. Have a round table discussion of the individual's responsibility for keeping recreational areas healthy and clean. **E-S**

13. Use your imagination: Make a chart showing the relationships between the various aspects of conservation -- soil, water, grasslands, forests, etc. **S-C**

14. Prepare a handbook or guide to local recreational areas. This might be a 4-H, Boy Scout, or other youth group activity -- as well as a classroom project. **S-C**

15. Have a contest to see who can list the greatest number of outdoor recreational activities. **E-S**

16. Take a series of photographs or slides showing misuse or over-use of recreational sites. **S-C**

17. Have guest speakers from the various organizations and agencies speak to the class as to what their group is doing in promoting recreational areas and facilities. Example: Camp Fire Girls, Boy Scouts of America, Garden Club of America, Keep America Beautiful, Inc. **S-C**

18. Keep a record of recreational activities the students participate in during a specific period of time. This may be recorded on a bulletin board or large chart. Stars may be given for every new activity. **E**

19. Debate: Resolved, greater amounts of federal money should be spent on developing recreational sites and facilities. **S-C**

20. Make a seasonal booklet. Students may draw pictures
and indicate what kind of recreational activities are appropriate. *E*

21. Have students pantomime various recreational activities
and see if the class can guess what they are. *E*

22. Make a collage as an art activity, using pictures and
materials related to recreational activities. *E-S-C*

23. Explain an unusual kind of recreation or sport of another
country. The class may even wish to try out the activity. *E-S*

24. Have the students write a story about a little boy who
didn't have a place to play. *E*

25. Have the students clip pictures or draw pictures showing
various types of recreational activities -- using the pictures as a bulletin board type border around the classroom. *E*

BIBLIOGRAPHY

Allen, Shirley W. *Conserving National Resources: Principles
and Practice In A Democracy*. New York: McGraw-Hill
Book Company, 1955. *S-C*

Briggs, Thomas H. (Director). *Time On Your Hands:
Choosing and Using Recreation,* Consumer Education Study,
National Association of Secondary School Principals.
Washington: National Education Association, 1945. *S*

Butcher, Devereaux. *Exploring Our National Parks and
Monuments*. New York: Houghton Mifflin Company, 1949.
S-C

Carson, Rachel. *The Edge of the Sea*. Cambridge: Houghton
Mifflin Company, 1955. *S-C*

Cater, Ruth Cooley. *Tree Trails and Hobbies*. Garden City,
Doubleday and Company, Inc. , 1950. *S-C*

Clawson, Marion. "Methods of Measuring the Demand For
and Value of Outdoor Recreation, " *Resources For The
Future*. Reprint 11. Washington: Resources For The
Future, Inc. , 1958. *S-C*

Conner, Jack. "Conservation Gains In Congress Seen, "
Minneapolis Sunday Tribune, January 19, 1964. *S-C*

Conservation Education In American Schools. Washington:
American Association of School Administrators, 1951. *C*

Crofts, Edward C. "A National Recreation Policy: What
    Should It Consist Of? What Should It Aim To Accomplish?"
    Vital Issues, Vol. XII, No. 10. Washington, Connecticut:
    Center For Information On America, 1963. *S-C*
De Grazia, Sebastian. *Of Time, Work and Leisure.* New
    York: Twentieth Century Fund, 1962. *S-C*
Dickson, James. *Camping In The Muskoka Region: A Story
    of Algonquin Park.* Toronto: Ryerson Press, 1959. *S-C*
Donovan, Joseph L., compiler. *State of Minnesota Legislative
    Manual, 1963-1964.* St. Paul: State of Minnesota. *S-C*
*Forest Recreation For Profit: Self Help Suggestions For
    Rural Area Development,* U. S. Department of Agriculture
    Bulletin No. 265, Forest Service. Washington: Govern-
    ment Printing Office, 1962. *S-C*
Highsmith, Richard, J. Granville Jensen, and Robert Rudd.
    Conservation In The United States. Chicago: Rand
    McNally and Company, 1962. *C*
Mason, Bernard S. *The Junior Book of Camping and Wood-
    craft.* New York: A. S. Barnes and Company, 1943. *E-S*
President's Council On Youth Fitness. *Physical Fitness
    Elements in Recreation: Suggestions for Community
    Programs.* Washington: Government Printing Office,
    October, 1962. *S-C*
Reben, Martha. *The Healing Woods.* New York: Thomas K.
    Crowell Company, 1952. *S-C*
Shankland, Robert. *Steve Mather of the National Parks.*
    New York: Alfred A. Knopf, Inc., 1950. *S-C*
Swanson, William E. *Camping For All It's Worth.* New York:
    The Macmillan Company, 1952. *E-S-C*
Tilden, Freeman. *The National Parks -- What They Mean To
    You and Me.* New York: Alfred A. Knopf, 1954. *E-S-C*
U. S. Congress. *Senate Committee on National Water Re-
    sources,* 86th Congress, Second Session, Print No. 17. *S-C*
U. S. Outdoor Recreation Resources Review Commission.
    Outdoor Recreation For America, Report to the President
    and Congress. Washington: Government Printing Office,
    1962. *C*
Wells, George and Iris Wells. *The Handbook of Auto Camp-
    ing and Motorist's Guide To Public Campground.* New
    York: Harper Brothers, 1954. *S-C*
Wolfe, Linne Marsh. *Son of the Wilderness: The Life of
    John Muir.* New York: Alfred A. Knopf, 1945. *S-C*
Zimmerman, Eric W. *World Resources and Industries.*
    New York: Harper and Brothers, 1951. *S-C*

AUDIO-VISUAL MATERIALS

16 mm. FILMS

Adventure at Day Camp - (GS of A)

Conservation and service projects are emphasized in the summer. *E—S*

America For Me - (GBS)

A group tours the United States by Greyhound Bus -- Gallop, Montana; Key West, Florida; San Antonio, Texas, etc. *S—C*

America The Beautiful - (Treasury)

A panorama of scenic and power-laden resources in the United States is shown. *E—S—C*

Camping for Girl Scouts - (GS of A)

Community-minded citizens plan a camp for their town. Structures as well as health and safety factors are shown. *S—C*

Colorado River - (Cor)

This film contrasts beauty of region with the influence of dams which control the flow of the river providing electric power and water for irrigation and other uses. *E—S*

Fun That Builds Good Health - (Cor)

This is a story about the importance of balanced healthful activities. *E*

Geography of Your Community - (Cor)

The film illustrates how children may collect and organize data about their local community. *E*

Happy Fishing Grounds - (NFB of C)

This film is of interest to all fishermen and those interested in outdoor activities. It shows fishing in the lakes
of Manitoba, Canada. **S-C**

Holiday in Manitoba - (NFB of C)

The facilities and the great variety of sports provided
in Riding Mountain National Park for the whole family
are shown. **S-C**

Hunting With A Camera - (NFB of C)

This film is concerned with the photographs of a field
naturalist -- rodents, water birds, buffalo, etc. **S-C**

Let's Go Troop Camping - (GS of A)

A troop's step-by-step preparation to go camping is
portrayed. Brings out discussion. **E-S-C**

$1,000 For Recreation - (MSHSL)

Suggestions for setting up a community recreation program as illustrated. **S-C**

Our Community - (EBF)

This film illustrates community institutions and their
services -- including health safeguards and park and
recreational facilities. **E**

Playground in the Wilderness - (La Reina)

Scenes of hunting and fishing along the Canadian border
are presented. **E-S-C**

Playground of the Nation - (La Reina)

This is a film illustrating northern Minnesota's scenic
trails and waterways with emphasis upon local fish and
game. **E-S-C**

Playtown, U.S.A. - (MSHSL)

The "why" and "how" of community organization are presented for a year-round, all-age public sponsored recreation program. A specific example of Decatur, Illinois is given. **S-C**

Three Little Bruins Go Camping -(Castle)

This is a comedy which young children will enjoy -- showing baby bears wrecking a camp. **E**

Wardens of Waterton - (NFB of C)

This film not only illustrates the warden's work, but shows activities of tourists and beautiful scenes of Waterton, Glacier Park, and Canada. **E-S-C**

We Explore The Beach - (Cor)

A presentation of a visual background and appreciation for life in and near the sea. **E**

We Explore the Woodland - (Cor)

The children learn that the woodland is a kind of home shared by many different animals and plants. **E**

Wilderness Canoe Country - (Quetico-Superior)

A plea is made for the preservation of the wilderness nature of Quetico-Superior -- telling the story of the region. **S-C**

Wilderness Day - (Quetico-Superior)

This film shows what canoeists need to know about camping, portaging, handling of canoe and safety precautions while living in a wilderness area. **S-C**

Wilderness River Trail - (Audubon)

Camping, fishing, rapids-shooting in the Green and Yampa Canyons of the Dinosaur National Monument area are explored. **S-C**

Winter Carnival - (NFB of C)

The highlights of a Canadian winter holiday are presented
-- ski trails, ice carnivals, sleigh rides, and dog der-
bies. *S-C*

Woodland Manners - (Forest Service)

This film illustrates how good manners can keep the
National Forest recreation areas in good condition.
E-S-C

GRENGS

...And there came a creeping death, carried by the wind and scattered by the seven seas...

Chapter XI

CHEMICAL POLLUTION

OBJECTIVES

  I. To present the beneficial and detrimental effects of
      agriculture chemicals.
 II. To show the dependency of modern society and agricul-
      ture on chemical deterrents.
III. To investigate the corrective measures being used and
      those proposed to regulate chemical pollution.
 IV. To call attention to the recommendations of national
      committees and governmental regulations.

    Man takes his environment for granted and strives to im-
prove all facets, if it can be justified in his eyes, as beneficial
to mankind.
    To define chemical pollution, both water and air pollu-
tion must be included. This chapter, however, will be confined
to an investigation of agriculture chemicals.
    Agriculture chemicals include: [156]

Insecticides -- to control injurious insects which affect
               plants, animals, and human beings.
Fungicides --- to prevent or cure plant diseases caused
              by fungi.
Herbicides --- to eradicate unwanted weeds.
Rodenticides - to control rodent populations.
Antibiotics --- to cure virus and bacteria caused by
              plant diseases.
Plant regulators - to make plants grow faster, or
              slower, or in some way more beneficial
              to man.
Defoliants and Desiccants - to speed the drying of
              plant tissue or cause leaves and foliage
              to drop from plants to facilitate harvest-
              ing.

---

[156] From a list prepared by the National Agriculture Chemicals Association.

It is extremely difficult to establish a balance among maximums: agriculture production, comfortable recreation, abundant wildlife, and the beauty of wilderness.

Rachel Carson's best seller, *Silent Spring*, aroused the slumbering populace to the detrimental effects of large-scale semi-regulated pest and insect control. Her evidence is certainly awesome, and her point is well taken.

Pest control has been with us for sometime. In 1000 B.C., the Greek poet Homer wrote of "pest-averting sulfur," and in 270 B.C., Democritus suggested using a product of olives to cure blight. [157] In those days, the only tools man had at his command were magic spells and slave-wielded fans and flails.

Major disasters attributed to pests include the bubonic plague (spread by fleas of infected rats), the Great Potato Famine in Ireland (a fungus disease), and in 1874, grasshoppers which caused such a great food shortage in the mid-western section of the United States that Congress called it a national disaster. [158]

From an ecological standpoint, we could say that man has brought these disasters upon himself, through increased population and migration. Nature, if left untouched, would develop an ideal balance among plant and animal. The survival of the fittest would prevail and natural selection would exist. Natural enemies would prey on the weak or mutant leaving only the strong to propagate the species. However, man is also a species and unlike other organisms alters his environment and controls his natural enemies. There are some who say man will probably destroy himself, either through over-population or mass destruction by the nuclear weapons he himself has created.

Human nature or the desire for more comfortable ways of life has given us the slogan, "better living through chemistry." We cannot deny this, because the chemical industry has developed many products beneficial in daily life from the water soluble paints to the conglomerate of antibiotics used by the medical profession.

Many of the pests responsible for untold destruction of plants and animals have in turn triggered large-scale use of insecticides. The production of synthetic pesticides in the

---

[157]*Open Door To Plenty* (Washington: National Agriculture Chemicals Association, 1959), p. 4.
      [158]Ibid., p. 5.

United States climbed from 259,000 pounds in 1947, to 637,666,000 pounds in 1960. [159]

It is proclaimed by many that man has imported thousands of these pests himself. The Dutch elm disease, that is raising havoc with the American elms that shade the endless boulevards of the mid-west, was brought to this country in the 1930's when elm burl logs were imported for the veneer industry. The disease is actually a fungus, whose spores are carried by the elm bark beetle from infected to healthy trees. Once infected, the trees are usually doomed for the fungus attacks the vascular system of the trees, causing wilting, defoliation, and death. Control has consisted mainly of cutting and burning the infected trees or large-scale spraying to eliminate the spore carrying beetles. Other measures such as forest genetics offer possibilities in developing a hybrid more resistant to the fungus. The European elm seems to be highly resistant, and many have already been planted in Washington, D. C.

To the elm loving home owner, with his majestic shade tree in his backyard and the song of the robin to soothe his troubled mind, neither method seems very enhancing. Further study and investigation must be continued to insure safety to the wildlife and to maintain the beautiful trees we have grown to love.

The long awaited pesticides report of the President's Science Advisory Committee (P. S. A. C.) was issued in 1963. The report substantiated much of the evidence and carefully balanced in its assessments of risks versus benefits. It pointed out that the United States alone used 350 million pounds of pesticides in 1962, and estimates that one out of twelve acres in the forty-eight mainland states were treated with pesticides in that year; that 45 million pounds are used each year in urban areas and around homes; and the aerosol "bug bomb" was common in most households.

One of the most highly used insecticides is D. D. T. (dichloro-diphenyl-trichloro-ethane). It was first synthesized by a German chemist in 1874, but until 1939 it was not known for its insecticide properties. Paul Mueller of Switzerland, won the Nobel Prize in physiology and medicine for discovering the insect-killing properties of D. D. T.

D. D. T. first became well known in February, 1944,

[159]Rachel L. Carson, Silent Spring, (Cambridge: Houghton Mifflin Company, 1962), p. 17.

Minnesota Conservation Department

Figure 53. Rotenone poisoned fish

when the United States Army used it to halt an epidemic of
typhus fever in Naples. The powder was dusted over all the
inhabitants to destroy body lice, which carried the disease.
When used as a solution, D. D. T. will keep clothing free from
lice for as long as two months; it remains effective even after
the clothes are laundered. D. D. T. will kill a large variety of
insects. The United States Department of Agriculture estimates it is successful against forty to fifty different kinds,
including Japanese beetles, bedbugs, livestock lice, flies,
mosquitoes, and termites. Flies could not live in a room
for three months after D. D. T. had been used on the walls.

Minnesota Department of Business Development

Figure 54. No chemical pollution

It is also poisonous to fish and various other cold-blooded
animals, and even to warm-blooded animals, if they consume
too much. (See Figures 53 and 54)

The P. S. A. C. report states: "In recent years, we have
recognized the wide distribution and persistence of D. D. T. It
has been detected at great distances from the place of applications ... D. D. T. has been found in oil of fish that live far at
sea, and in fish caught off the coasts of eastern and western
North America, South America, Europe, and Asia... Residues

of D. D. T. and certain other chlorinated hydrocarbons have
been detected in most of our major rivers, in ground water,
in fish from fresh waters, in migratory birds, in wild mammals and in shellfish. Small amounts of D. D. T. have been
detected in food from many parts of the world, including processed dairy products from the United States, Europe, and
South America. " Although these levels are very low, and
rarely above the tolerance limit for products in interstate commerce, and people ingesting large amounts of D. D. T. usually
suffer no apparent ill effects, the tolerances are backed by
seemingly inadequate research on long term effects.

One of the most sinister features of D. D. T. and related
chemicals is the way they are passed on from one organism to
another through all the links of the food chains. [160] An example of this might begin with the spraying of an alfalfa field or
pasture with D. D. T. dust. Cattle feeding in the pasture or
consuming the alfalfa pass it on to human beings in the form
of milk or butter.

The poison may also be passed on from mother to offspring. Insecticide residues have been recovered from human
milk in samples tested by Food and Drug Administration scientists.

The P. S. A. C. report goes on to report some startling
facts. "Pink shrimp have been experimentally poisoned by
0. 9 parts per billion of heptachlor... The growth of young
oysters has been inhibited by concentrations as low as three
parts per million of chlordane, heptachlor, or rotenone. Five
other commonly used pesticides inhibit oyster growth in concentrations of one part per ten million.

"An entire year's production of young salmon was nearly
eliminated in the Miramichi River in New Brunswick in 1954,
and again in 1956. ... from D. D. T. applications of one half
pound per acre for control of spruce budworm. Stream insects, which are a most important food for young salmon,
disappeared and failed to return within two years. Surviving
young salmon were very thin. In British Columbia, mortality
of coho salmon approached one hundred per cent in at least
four major streams after the surrounding forests were sprayed
with one pound of D. D. T. per acre for control of the black-
headed budworm. "[161]

[160] Ibid. , p. 22.
[161] "News and Comment," Science, Vol. 140, May 24, 1963, pp. 878-879.

With these facts -- storage at even low levels, subsequent accumulation, and records of some liver damage at levels that may easily occur in normal diets -- the Food and Drug Administration scientists declare as early as 1950, that it is "extremely likely the potential hazard of D. D. T. has been under-estimated. " Only time will tell of the ultimate consequences derived from such wholesale use of insecticides.

Dr. Byron T. Shaw, Administrator of the United States Agriculture Research Service, was asked if chemical insecticides were used as a mainstay in agriculture production. [162] He stated, "We in the Department of Agriculture, as a first step in control of any one of these insects, try to bring in their natural enemies -- the other insects that will prey upon them, and the diseases to which they are subject. A good illustration involves weed control. Ranges of the west were invaded by the so-called Klamath weed. It's a weed that livestock will not eat. The weed rapidly took over, pushing out the grasses. Ranges in California, Oregon and Washington were becoming worthless. There was a beetle found in Australia that, so far as we could learn, ate only this particular weed. We went down there, got the beetle, and adapted it to a new environment because their winter months were our summer months. Finally, about 1954 or 1955, we got the beetle established on those ranges, and we've completely controlled the Klamath weed.

"While we've had some success with predators and parasites, we still have to say that most insects that we must deal with can't be controlled that way at this time. So, we are forced to use chemicals. "

The effectiveness of widespread use of insecticides, as in aerial spraying, is often questioned. (See Figure 55) Laboratory tests verify that flies develop resistance against insecticides.

In the first spraying, ninety-eight per cent of the flies were killed. Using the same dosage in the second spraying killed eighty-five per cent. The survivors of the first application bred a resistant generation. The third spraying, using the same dosage as the first two sprayings, resulted in fifty per cent fatalities, proving that resistant generations multiply. [163] Further statistics show that within seven years after

[162]Dr. Byron T. Shaw, "Are Weed Killers, Bug Sprays, Poisoning the Country?" U. S. News and World Report, November 26, 1962, pp. 86-87.

[163]David B. Peakall, "How Insects Resist Insecticides," Audubon, January, 1964, pp. 33-34.

Minnesota Conservation Department

Figure 55.   Spruce budworm spraying

the corn rootworm in Nebraska had been sprayed with aldrin
and heptachlor, its descendants had developed a stubborn resistance to the same amount of insecticide.   The sprayer had
to use one hundred times the dosage to be effective as when
first used.

More than thirty species of malaria carrying mosquitoes
have developed insecticide resistance.   Figure 56, which was
prepared from World Health Organization reports, shows the
accelerated resistance after dieldrin was substituted for
D. D. T. in 1957.

The evidence against concentrated mass spraying can be
exemplified further from studies showing that doses which may

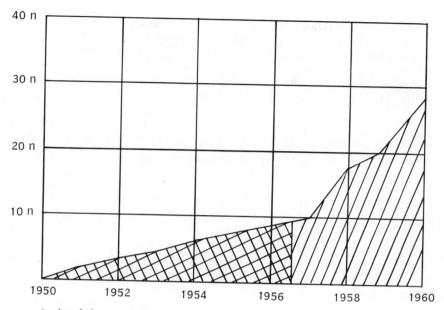

* Anopholen: malaria carrying mosquito.
(n) Number of mosquito species.

D.D.T. Resistant

Dieldrin Resistant

Figure 56.   Increase in number of Anopholen*
mosquito species resistant to insecticides

not be fatal to all of the insects (sublethal doses) are actually
more effective than massive application one hundred per cent
effectiveness.   There is much experimental evidence covering
a wide range of species to prove that an insect can not acquire
resistance to an insecticide if successive generations are subjected to sublethal doses. [164]

Much has been said against widespread use of agriculture
chemicals, especially insecticides, but evidence equally as
startling can be presented to prove the effectiveness and need
for such chemicals in our modern society.

The story of the "good old days, " when Mr. Homeowner
merely planted his shrubs, seeded his lawn, and let mother

[164] Open Door To Plenty, op. cit. , p. 42.

nature take charge are gone. The patio era is here, and with
it comes city-wide spraying for mosquitoes, demanded by the
citizenry. Without spraying, the cankerworms would defoliate
our elms, maples, and birches; the aphids would curl our
flowering crabs; and the dandelions would replace the green
carpets with a sea of yellow gold.

While farmers raise crops for profit, home gardeners
raise flowers, vegetables, and ornamental trees for pleasure.
More than 30,000,000 Americans garden for recreation and
pleasure. [165]

In recent years, gardeners have been turning the heavy
garden chores -- weeding, protecting plants against insects
and diseases -- over to pesticide chemicals.

Hundreds of insects, diseases, and weeds threaten gardens, lawns, and ornamental trees. Grass, for example, is
susceptible to grubs, cutworms, chinch bugs, and webworms.
These and other similar pests chew off grass roots. Diseases
damage some types of desirable lawns. There are many weeds
from plantain to crabgrass which destroy beautiful lawns.

Insecticides, fungicides and herbicides can protect lawns
against all of these pests. When a flower, such as a rose, or
even a group of flowers or garden vegetables are susceptible
to a variety of pests, mixtures of insecticides and fungicides
are made available. With single treatments, all common pests
for a particular group of flowers or vegetables can be controlled.

Owing to the wide variety of garden, lawn and tree care
chores chemicals can do, modern gardeners usually keep a
special cabinet for garden chemicals, and spray and dusting
equipment. These materials should be stored away from plant
materials, and safely away from children or older people. Directions and warning on container labels should be followed
exactly for best results.

Every eleven seconds there is a new mouth to feed in the
United States. Each year we add enough people to equal three
new cities the size of Washington, D. C., and by 1975, we expect a population of 220,000,000, or about 50,000,000 more
than we have today. Nearly thirty per cent greater production
of most foods will be needed to feed our population adequately
in 1975.

Food authorities view the population's growing demand
for food and fiber with concern. Cities, suburbs, factories,

---

[165]Ibid.

airports, and highways are taking about 1, 000, 000 acres of
good land out of farm production every year. New land is being reclaimed by irrigation and brush clearance; however,
most of the reclaimable land is expensive to farm and is of
poor quality. The answer has been to concentrate on further
boosting of farm efficiency.

Pesticide chemicals, fertilizers, farm equipment, new
and better crops, and cultural practices are the keys to increased farm efficiency and productivity. Some scientists
now predict that if all the knowledge and materials for scientific pest control, now on hand, were used to maximum advantage, crop production could be increased by fifty per cent.

When a veterinarian discovered in 1892 that the cattle
tick carries Texas cattle fever, he opened a door to vast progress in the control of many serious animal and human diseases. Since then, dozens of insects, rodents, and weeds
have been identified as carriers or causes of disease. Malaria,
typhus, Rocky Mountain spotted fever, plague, yellow fever,
dengue, filariasis, sleeping sickness, poison ivy, and hay
fever are among human ills carried or caused by pests.

A most dramatic public health achievement was the control of louse-borne typhus. After World War I, when there
were no chemical controls of this disease, 5, 000, 000 cases
were reported in Russia alone. During World War II, chemical controls held the number of cases in the Near East, North
Africa, Italy, Germany, Korea, and Japan to less than
500, 000.

Malaria, a destructive disease carried by some mosquitoes, was once prevalent in our southern states. Spraying
conducted by the United States Public Health Service and the
states' authorities begun in 1947 has eliminated malaria from
the United States. A world-wide program in which many health
groups are cooperating is now under way to eradicate malaria
from the earth by 1967.

Destructive pests are not solely a problem in farming
and outdoor living. Millions of dollars are plucked from
American pocketbooks every year by pests which attack our
clothes, property, and even our health inside our own houses.

Not long ago, a truck drove into a gasoline station in
Los Angeles. As it rumbled up to the gasoline pumps, the
station's wooden columns collapsed and the whole structure
crumbled to the ground. Unseen by human eyes, termites had
honeycombed the station's wooden columns and the vibration

from the truck was enough to bring the building crashing to the ground.

This example is typical of the destruction pests bring to our properties. The powerful jaws of termites attack woodwork, beams, flooring, clocks, pianos, boats, even baseball bats. In the process, they cause an estimated damage to one hundred million dollars a year in the United States.

Carpet beetles, clothes moths, and silverfish carry the destructive pest attack against our clothes. Each year these pests destroy from 200 million to 500 million dollars worth of blankets, sweaters, scarves, suits, carpets, furs, and feathers.

While improved packaging of foods has greatly reduced kitchen losses to food pests such as the flour weevil, foods stored too long or too carelessly are subject to infestation and damage. It is estimated that stored food pests cost American housewives about 200 million dollars a year in infested or damaged food stuffs on kitchen shelves.

Forest insects and disease are causing far greater timber losses today than are caused by forest fires and all other agencies combined. They kill an estimated seven billion board feet of timber a year, nearly nine times the timber killed by fire.

No official list of the ten most dangerous forest pests has been made to date. The destructiveness of any variety of pests varies from year to year. Bark beetles such as the Englemann spruce beetle and Douglas fir beetle, western and southern pine beetles, and defoliators such as the spruce budworm, tent caterpillars, sawflies, and the gypsy moth have caused tremendous damage.

Among the diseases, chestnut blight wiped out an entire species of trees. White pine blister rust, oak wilt, Dutch elm disease, heart rots, are destructive diseases. Equally damaging are the dwarf mistletoes, tip moths and weevils.

In recent years, improvements in direct pest control with chemicals has brought important progress in the control of the spruce budworm, gypsy moth, Douglas fir tussock moth, ambrosia beetles, termites, and many other species of defoliators and bark beetles. Direct chemical control has been found for many diseases, also. The United States Forest Service cooperates with the state and private forest owners in surveying forests to detect insect or disease outbreaks, and conduct control operations. Action against forest pests has

increased since the Forest Pest Control Act of 1947 was
passed by Congress.

Agriculture chemicals are beneficial as well as detrimental, but to dictate absolute abolishment or wholesale use
would be fool-hardy and premature; however, further investigation is necessary.

The President's Science Advisory Committee report
pointed out the shortcomings of divided power among regulating bodies of the federal government. The report found that
the "present mechanisms are inadequate" and that "the existing federal advisory and coordinating mechanisms (should) be
critically assessed and revised as necessary to provide clear
assignments of responsibility for control of pesticide use. "
Regulations governing the use of pesticides are administered
by the United States Department of Agriculture (USDA). If a
proposed pesticide is not intended for use on food crops, USDA
is authorized to certify it for use on the basis of experimental
data submitted by the manufacturer. If it is intended for food
crops, however, and its use leaves a residue on the product,
the Food and Drug Administration (FDA) must establish a
tolerance. When a tolerance has been set by the FDA, it is
then certified by the USDA for interstate and foreign commerce,
but there is a loophole that could easily accommodate a squad-
ron of crop dusters: If the manufacturer protests a USDA
refusal of certification, USDA must grant certification, and
as the PSAC report points out, "At present, the purchaser cannot distinguish such a product from one which has been accepted for registration because the label does not carry an
indication of its unsanctioned status. " The "protest" registrations remain in effect for five years, unless USDA successfully assumes the burden of establishing that the substance is
unacceptable. In actual practice, the protest registrations
are relatively insignificant, at least in number. According
to USDA, they now total fewer than 25 out of 54, 000 registrations. [166]

In rebuttal, many feel the present legislation is adequate.
The Federal Insecticide, Fungicide and Rodenticide Act of
1947 is administered by the United States Department of
Agriculture. It requires manufacturers to prove that pesticide chemicals are effective against destructive pests. It

[166]D. S. Greenberg, "Pesticides: White House Advisory Body Issues Report Recommending Steps To Reduce Hazard To Public, " Science, CXXXX, No. 3569 (May 24, 1963),
pp. 878-879.

further requires labeling of pesticides to show which pests the chemical will control, the crops on which it can be used, the proper method of application, and warning or caution statements concerning any hazard that might be involved in handling or using the material.

The Miller Pesticide Residue Amendment to the Federal Food, Drug and Cosmetic Act of 1938 was added in 1954, and is administered by the USDA and by the FDA. The law requires the thorough pretesting of a pesticide chemical before it can be packaged or sold. The manufacturer must provide detailed scientific data to demonstrate to the USDA how much pesticide residue, if any, will remain in or on a crop after application. The manufacturer must further supply detailed data on the degree of toxicity of pesticides to human beings and warm blooded animals. From this data, the Food and Drug Administration establishes a tolerance or maximum amount of residue of a chemical which may legally remain in or on a food crop when it enters interstate commerce. This level is scientifically determined to be safe for human beings. Food crops bearing residues above the established tolerances are seized, kept off the market, and in addition, the person responsible for the excess residue may be fined.

Laws and regulations in more than forty states either duplicate the same federal requirements within the state, or establish similar requirements to protect the safety of consumers. State laws require labeling to warn users of any possible hazards in using the chemicals, and licensing of professional pesticide applicators.

When all the pros and cons of insecticide regulation have been discussed, the need for further guidance is indicated to assure the federal government supported programs (which involve application of pesticides to more than four million acres of land at a cost of about twenty million dollars) are adequately handled. The PSAC group recommends the following:

1. Development under the Department of Health, Education and Welfare, a comprehensive data gathering program and a continuing network to monitor residues (See Figure 57)
2. Federal funds to assist states in monitoring pesticide levels in intrastate products
3. Rapid completion of the Food and Drug Administration's current review of residue tolerances, to be followed by

Minnesota Conservation Department

Figure 57. Testing for pollution

a re-evaluation of toxido-logical data (For this purpose, it was recommended that the National Academy of Sciences nominate a panel.)

4. Improved coordination among federal agencies
5. An expansion of research on specific controls, and a shift away from broad spectrum chemicals
6. More research on toxicity, especially on reproduction, chronic effects, and synergism and potentiation with such commonly used drugs as sedatives, tranquilizers, analgesics, anti-hypertensive agents, and steroid hormones

7. Expanded research, by the Department of Interior on toxic effects of pesticides on wild vertebrates and invertebrates
8. A general expansion of training and research financed with grants to universities and other non-governmental research organizations
9. Elimination of protest registration

Some risks remain, and will always compel caution from the customer and the onlooker, as well as the manufacturer and the distributor. Certainly, no one chemical company can assure safety of users and handlers who fail to read carefully and follow the manufacturer's instructions on labels and in descriptive literature. Professor Rene Dubos of Rockefeller Institute, stated "Our society will, of course, continue to strive for comfort and for protection from threats of health... However, a society that does not continue to grow through adventure and willingness to take chances is not likely to survive long in the modern world. With regard to health as to all other fields, society must be willing to take educated and calculated risks inherent in a technological civilization. " [167]

Modern society requires a careful and sober judgment of benefit versus damage in the use of new chemicals or in new uses for familiar ones. Universities, industry, and government agencies all have their part in meeting this need.

In summary - agriculture chemicals might be thought of as offsprings of a progressive society. Nature's balance is unique and as man invades nature he drives out natural predators and upsets the balance.

The pros and cons of agriculture chemicals are many and only intelligent reasoning can cultivate a program which will serve man and preserve the wildlife we cherish.

One point, recently brought to focus, is the long term persistence of chemicals on vegetation and contents in foodstuffs. Further investigation and research is needed to determine their effects on human health.

Only through research and controlled application can an effective program be established. Such a program will give maximum protection from insects, pests, and fungi, provide a better crop yield and preserve our wildlife.

---

[167]Chemicals and Public Health (Wilmington: E. I. du Pont de Nemours and Company, 1963), p. 12.

ACTIVITIES

1. Make a bulletin board showing pictures of beneficial and harmful insects found around the home or yard. *E- S*
2. Make a list of resource personnel who could be contacted to talk to your class about chemical pollution. *E- S*
3. Make a list of insecticides, herbicides, fungicides, etc. used in your home to control insects, weeds, and other pests. Make a master list from individual list of students in the class. Do not duplicate chemicals. *E- S*
4. From the above mentioned activity, make a bar graph showing the ten or five most used chemicals. *E-S-C*
5. Contact the local nursery man to find out the correct procedures for using agriculture chemicals. This could be given as a class report or made into a bulletin board. *E-S*
6. Make a resource unit pertaining to federal legislation on uses of agriculture chemicals. *S-C*
7. Collect labels or directions from insecticides to show manufacturers' safety precautions. *E-S*
8. Make a scrapbook or bulletin board of recent articles concerning dangers of agriculture chemicals. *E-S*
9. Make a bulletin board showing the diseases caused by pests and how these are controlled. *E-S*
10. Write to various chemical manufacturers for information concerning their testing and certifying for safety of agriculture chemicals. *E-S-C*
11. Contact a United States Department of Agriculture agent and ask him to speak to your class about the use of chemicals in the conservation program. *E-S*
12. Contact the Department of Health for information on poisonous household chemicals. What are the safety precautions which are recommended? *E-S*
13. Discussion: The harmful versus the beneficial uses of insecticides. *S-C*
14. Contact the municipal or commercial mosquito control bureau. Have a representative talk to your class about mosquito control. What chemicals are used? How are they applied? What effects will they have on wildlife? *E-S-C*
15. Make a bibliography of sources in your school library concerning chemical pollution. *S-C*

16. Write an essay on your feelings about the use of agriculture chemicals. *S–C*

17. Select significant passages from *Silent Spring* to project by overhead projectors. This will provide a discussion format. *S–C*

18. Write a skit, make puppets and put on a color show about Wilbur Worm and the Chemical Man. *E*

19. Have a chemist and biologist from a nearby college discuss the problem of insecticides and chemical pollution with the class. *S–C*

20. In your home (or school) garden, grow several rows of beans. Treat some of the rows with a variety of chemicals to control bugs. Some rows will be left completely free of chemical controls. Evaluate quality and quantity of the beans grown. *E–S–C*

21. Research problem: Can chemicals obtained through use of herbicides and insecticides have genetic effects on human beings? What is the effect of D. D. T. and related chemicals passing from organism on to organism through the food chains? *S–C*

22. Take a dish washing detergent and mix it with water. Run the mixture through several filter devices, such as sand, disc filters, and zeolite. What do you discover? *E–S*

23. Make a list of all the different kinds of things that would ordinarily be dumped into rivers, thus causing the death of fish and water fowl. *E*

24. Buy a classroom set of *Silent Spring* and have the entire class read the book. Have panel discussions on particular chapters in the book. *S–C*

25. Write a precis of one of the films listed at the end of this chapter. *S*

BIBLIOGRAPHY

"Aroused Spring, " *Time*, May 24, 1963. *S–C*

Breidenbach, Andrew W. and James L. Lichtenberg. "D. D. T. and Dieldrin in Rivers, " *Science*, CXXXXI, No. 3584 (September 6, 1963). *S–C*

Brown, A. W. *Insect Control by Chemicals*. New York: John Wiley and Sons, 1951. *S–C*

Carson, Rachel L. *Silent Spring*. Cambridge: Houghton Mifflin Company, 1962. *S–C*

Chemical Control of Brush and Trees, U. S. Department of Agriculture Bulletin No. 218. Washington: Government Printing Office, 1961. **S-C**

Chemicals and Public Health. Wilmington: E. I. du Pont de Nemours and Company, 1963. **E-S-C**

Counter Attack - 1962: The Fight Against Forest Insects and Diseases, U. S. Department of Agriculture Pamphlet 499, Forest Service. Washington: Government Printing Office, 1962. **S-C**

Elton, Charles S. *The Ecology of Invasions by Animals and Plants.* New York: John Wiley and Sons, 1958. **S-C**

Flanagan, Dennis. *New Chemistry.* New York: Simon and Schuster, 1957. **C**

Greenberg, D. S. "Pesticides: White House Advisory Body Issues Report Recommending Steps To Reduce Hazards To Public, " *Science,* CXXXX, No. 3569 (May 24, 1963). **S-C**

Hargraves, Malcolm M. "Chemical Pesticides and Conservation Problems. " Address to 23rd Annual Convention of the National Wildlife Federation, February 27, 1959. (Mimeographed.) **C**

"If You Didn't Have Poison Sprays, " *U. S. News and World Report,* June 3, 1963. **S-C**

"News and Comment, " *Science,* Vol. 140 (May 24, 1963). **S-C**

Open Door To Plenty. Washington: National Agriculture Chemicals Association, 1959. **E-S**

Peakall, David B. "How Insects Resist Insecticides, " *Audubon,* January, 1964. **S-C**

"Pesticides: The Price for Progress, " *Time,* September 28, 1962. **S-C**

Rudd, Robert L. and Richard E. Genelly. *Pesticides: Their Use and Toxicity in Relation To Wildlife,* California Department of Fish and Game, Bulletin No. 7. Sacramento: State of California, 1956. **C**

Shaw, Dr. Byron T. "Are Weed Killers, Bug Sprays, Poison, ing The Country?" *U. S. News and World Report,* November 26, 1962. **S-C**

"The Pesticide Report, " *Scientific American,* July, 1963. **S-C**

The Pesticide Situation for 1960-61, Commodity Stabilization Service, U. S. Department of Agriculture. Washington: Government Printing Office, 1961. **S-C**

"The Pest-Ridden Spring, " *Time,* July 5, 1963. **S-C**

U. S. Congress, Senate, Committee on Appropriation. *Report on Environmental Health Problems*. Hearings before Sub-Committee, 86th Congress, March, 1960. Washington: Government Printing Office, 1960. *C*

Use of Pesticides, A Report of the President's Science Advisory Committee. Washington: Government Printing Office, 1963. *S-C*

Waller, W. K. "Poison on the Land, " *Audubon*, March-April, 1958. *S-C*

Worrell, Albert C. "Pests, Pesticides, and People, " *American Forests*, July, 1960. *S-C*

AUDIO-VISUAL MATERIALS

16 mm. FILMS

Biological Control of the Oriental Fruit Moth - (NYS Col. of Ag.)

> This film gives a picture of the work necessary to produce the parasite that controls the oriental fruit moth better than present-day sprays and dusts. *S-C*

Case of the Disappearing Poison - (Eastman Chem.)

> Problems encountered through use of poisonous materials, particularly toxic residues, which linger on crops after harvesting, are reviewed. *C*

Chemical Conquest - (Can. NFB)

> This film reports on how chemical research is allied on the side of the farmer in his battle against the plagues which threaten his crops. *S-C*

Chemistry - (Gateway)

> Chemistry is shown as responsible for many of the things we see and use in every day life. *E*

D. D. T. - (UW Gov't.)

> The use of D. D. T. is explained as an insecticide and larvicide, how mixed effects are obtained, precautions to be observed, and dispersal methods in emulsion, oil or dust solutions. *S-C*

D. D. T. As A Mosquito Larvicide - (US Gov't.)

Hand spraying D. D. T. in mosquito larviciding mixture of solution, equipment, its functions, care and precautions in use, approved application practices, and advantages of D. D. T. are illustrated. *S-C*

Housefly and Its Control, The -(Cor)

Views of a large scale model and close-up photography of the egg-laying, hatching and emergence of the adult from the pupa give us an understanding of the anatomy, life-cycle and feeding habits of the common housefly. This film shows how this harmful insect contaminates food and spreads disease, and recommends methods for combatting it. *E-S*

Housefly, The - (EBF)

Makes use of unusual techniques of microphotography and magnification to portray the habits and life history of the common housefly and the ways in which it is a menace to health. Suggests practical control methods. *E-S-C*

How To Use Parathon - (Am. Cyanamid, Ag. Chem. Div.)

Portrays the methods suggested for the safe use and handling of parathon insecticides. *S-C*

Insect Enemies - (Inst. Inter Am. Affairs)

This film illustrates practical measures any farmer may use to control the insects. *E-S-C*

Insects Astray - (Public Service Network, Inc.)

Even before the earth stopped spitting smoke and fire, insects were rampant. Capable of living in the heat of the desert and the cold of ice and snow, insects seem to be indestructible. In the biological cycle of life, nature intended insects to be the scavengers that would clear away dead matter. But, when man started tilling the soil, and clothing himself with fur and wood, he upset nature's balance and created a paradise for insects. This film shows the species of moth and beetle which damage any wool material and what scientists have done to render wool unpalatable to wool-eating insects. *E-S*

Magic In Agriculture - (Ethyl Corp.)

The story of farm chemurgy. Describes the industrial uses for new crops and the more profitable utilization of present crops and their waste by-products. **S-C**

Man In The Doorway - (Modern TP)

The story of the modern chemicals industry and the amazing accomplishments of chemists in conserving our resources for a happy, abundant future is portrayed. **S-C**

Preface to Chemistry - (EBF)

A brief description is provided of our chemical heritage. The work of modern chemists contributes to a high standard of living. **S-C**

Prelude To Plenty - (Modern TP)

Insect control, modern insecticide, agriculture chemicals, and our food and fiber are presented. **S-C**

Regulation of Growth - (McG-AiBS)

Hormones are chemical regulators produced in one part of an organism that have an effect on some other part. Many plant hormones are growth substances; indoleacetic acid (IAA) was the first to be introduced. If an unpollinated flower is treated with IAA, fruit will develop, but without seeds. The film shows some of the aspects of hormones in plant development. **C**

Rival World - (Shell Oil)

An account of the war between man and insects with close-ups of the enemy and its attack. **E-S**

Story of D. D. T. - (BIS)

This is a good film to show the methods of applying D. D. T. to control flies, lice, mosquitoes, and the laboratory procedure in determining the value as an insecticide, as well as its effects on man and animals. **S-C**

Taking Care Of Our Garden - (EBF)

In this film we see the kinds of damage done to vegetable plants by various insect pests, and we learn how these pests can be controlled. We also learn about certain helpful insects, and about how the soil of the garden can be kept in condition. ***E-S***

Wheat Rust - (EBF)

Provides an excellent basis for understanding the complex life history of a parasitic plant -- in this case, stem rust of wheat, the fungus which must live on two host plants. The film also shows how man works to control the fungus -- with the goal of eliminating the menace altogether. ***S-C***

Wonder of Chemistry - (Young America)

The contributions that chemistry and the chemist have made to a better way of life are stressed. ***E***

FILMSTRIPS:

Backyard Insects - (SVE)

Reveals the activities and marking of insects of the grass, sand, shrub. ***E***

Insect Pest and Diseases - (McGH)

Points out the five main insect pests and that insect control is a concern of everyone. ***E***

Man Against Insects - (McGH)

Shows the structure of insects and some typical life cycles. ***E-S***

Some Useful Insects - (Eyegate)

Describes anatomy and habits, life cycles of useful insects. ***E-S***

GRENGS

From the depths of the atom
comes a power strong enough
to save us from our wastes.
God Almighty first planted a
garden. And, indeed, it is
the purest of human pleasures.

Francis Bacon

THE ROLE OF NUCLEAR SCIENCE IN CONSERVATION

Chapter XII

OBJECTIVES

   I. To point out the need for nuclear science in our present civilization.

  II. To investigate the uses of nuclear science in our conversation program.

 III. To evaluate the progress being made in nuclear science.

 IV. To project future needs of nuclear science.

      Mankind faces two great needs in the future. The foremost need will be for enough food to support a vastly increasing population. The second great need will be for enough energy to keep man's industries running.

      Through his own ingenious discoveries, man has progressed from the wood age to the coal age to the petroleum age, and now on the threshold of the nuclear age. Few of us can remember the wood stoked locomotive that brought civilization to the west. Many of us remember the fireman who shoveled coal into the steam engine that seemed to puff smoke like some mythical monster. But, the present generation recalls only the streamlined diesel or gas turbine-electric locomotives.

      Yes, truly, man has progressed, at least in his own eyes. But, can the end justify the means? Of all the sources of energy, wood has the power of regeneration. Through scientific forestry, we can be assured of lumber and wood products for generations to come. Considering all the sources of energy available to man on earth, wood is the only renewable natural resource, and until the renaissance among conservationists, our great forests were threatened by human scavengers.

      Once considered nearly inexhaustible, the world's coal reservoirs of high grade coal are rapidly being depleted. North America is blessed with nearly 46 per cent of the world's reserves and the United States has reserves estimated at nearly 3,000 billion tons. This may seem to be enormous and almost inexhaustible, but thirty per cent of our high quality coal

(anthracite) has been mined and now new deposits must be discovered.

Through engineering efficiency we may be able to decrease
the waste in mining and develop new uses for our low grade coal.
However, developing such low grade deposits is a matter of
economics: mining costs, transportation, and prices competi-
tive with other fuels. The conservation of this valuable resource is, therefore, a problem that concerns everyone today.

Petroleum, like coal, is a "one crop" resource. Once
tapped, it cannot be replaced. Although new reservoirs have
been found, which more than make up for the consumption at
the present time, this cannot continue indefinitely. The time
will come when new fields cannot be found and consumption
will steadily shrink our reserves. It is therefore imperative
that strict conservation practices be enforced. Most of the oil
producing states have conservation laws designed to prevent the
waste of oil and gas. Drilling is regulated so that wells will
not be placed too close to each other. The production of the
fields and of individual wells is limited by law. The oil industry is constantly investigating new drilling methods to make
sure they are getting the maximum amount of oil out of the
ground. Through these sound practices, we can at least fore-
stall the inevitable.

Although nuclear energy, produced from fissionable uranium, is not renewable, it gives great hopes to mankind.

Increased populations have, in turn, demanded more
products through a mechanized industrial output. If we look
at the over all goals of conservation in saving our natural resources to benefit mankind, it is an awesome sight. Such
populations will demand increased food production and maximum industrial production. From the billowing smoke stacks
and the tail pipes of the millions of automobiles comes an ever-
increasing air pollution problem.

Mankind will have to find some source of energy that will
not add to the magnitude of the already present problems.
Such a source may be here, if we can put it to use.

Little did the world know that in 1942, beneath Stagg Sta-
dium at the University of Chicago, Enrico Fermi and his associates achieved the first self-sustaining chain reaction and
thereby initiated the controlled release of nuclear energy.

Accelerated by the thought of ending World War II, the
Manhattan Project was organized to develop the atomic bomb.
In 1945, atomic bombs were exploded releasing the destructive

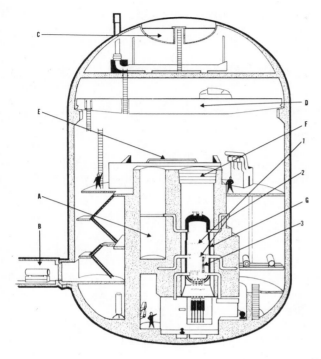

SUPERHEATER

The superheater receives turbine steam from the heat exchanger and increases the temperature of the steam. This creates a dry steam which contacts the turbine blades to run the generator. The superheater is housed in a building separate from the containment shell and will be fired by coal or natural gas.

A—Fuel Element Storage Well	F—Reactor Plug
B—Air Lock (Personnel)	G—Reactor Vessel
C—30,000 Gal. Water Tank	1—Shroud
D—Bridge Crane	2—Control Rods
E—Heat Exchanger	3—Fuel Elements

Figure 58. Rural Cooperative Power Association

forces that leveled Hiroshima and Nagasaki. But, not until 1951 did man harness nuclear energy for peaceful means by generating electricity from atomic power. Since then, nuclear energy has opened up a new world to mankind. Controlled reactors have been developed to produce electrical energy and propel sea going vessels.

Nuclear reactors built to produce electrical power are very similar to conventional coal or diesel powered electrical generating plants. Most plants use steam turbine generators or direct drive generators. In the conventional coal generated plant, the coal is used as a source of heat energy producing steam to drive the steam turbine generators. Diesel operated plants use diesel engines in direct drive with generators to produce electrical energy. (See Figure 58)

The nuclear powered plants replace the coal stoked boilers by using a nuclear reactor to produce heat energy which, in turn, converts water to steam that propels the steam turbine generators.

Nuclear powered electric generating plants will be especially beneficial to areas lacking conventional power sources. The reactors are clean, since combustion is not necessary, and will therefore lessen one of the sources of air pollution. Safety is extremely important so that no radioactivity is released to the surrounding environment or to personnel involved in the operation of the plant. (See Figure 59)

Nuclear powered submarines have already proven their superiority over diesel electric conventional vessels. Atomic powered submarines need not surface to charge batteries as their diesel electric ancestors did. The nuclear reactors are self-sustaining and do not depend on combustion as a source of energy. The United States Navy's first atomic submarine, the Nautilus, traveled 56 thousand miles without recharging its nuclear enriched fuel. Nuclear powered submarines have circumnavigated the globe and passed under the polar ice cap without surfacing.

Surface vessels are also being equipped with nuclear reactors, and in the future an atomic sea-going navy is predicted.

More startling than nuclear reactors or atomic propelled submarines is the field of radioisotope application. One area of radioisotope research is biological chemistry. Little did Becquerel know that his discovery of the atomic radiations effect on photographic film would develop into the tool of science that it is. The ability of an isotope to form a self-portrait

Rural Cooperative Power Association

Figure 59. Elk River Reactor

(radio-autograph) has been used by many researchers to determine the localization of a radioactive substance. Scientists in-
ject a radioactive drug into an animal, sacrifice it after a period of time, make very thin slices of various organs or whole
animals, and lay the slices on a sensitive film. Exposure time
may vary depending on the concentration of radiations. The
film is developed in the ordinary way, while the tissue slice
can be colored with histological stains, and the two can be
viewed with one on top of the other. The darkened areas on
the film show where the labeled drug -- and its degradation

products -- are concentrated. [168]

Probably the most spectacular of the high-resolution radiographs made so far are the ones which show individual labeled chromosomes. The autographs show how each chromosome for cell division acts as a template for copying. From this a basic theory of genetics was confirmed by direct observation.

In biochemistry, it is particularly important to learn what each organism does with each chemical it meets. If a radioactive chemical is fed or injected into an animal or plant, the tissue and excretions can be examined for the presence of the original compound or its metabolic transformation products.

The rate or kinetic approach has been strikingly successful in studying photosynthesis. When illuminated in the presence of $C^{14}O_2$, plants form radioactive organic compounds which are converted eventually into every compound in the plant. Carbon-14 is a radioactive isotope of carbon, formed when cosmic rays bombard nitrogen atoms in the upper atmosphere. The cosmic rays knock a proton out of the nitrogen nucleus, thus forming Carbon-14.

The Carbon-14 combines with oxygen to form a special carbon dioxide, $C^{14}O_2$ which circulates in the atmosphere and eventually reaches the lower limits where it is absorbed by plant and animal. Carbon-14 has a half-life of approximately 5,720 years as it spontaneously changes back to Nitrogen, $_7N^{14}$. [169]

In plant kinetics, it is extremely important to find out which substances are formed. First, one kills the plants at very short intervals after exposure and make paper chromatograms of the cell juices. Such studies have shown that the first step is a reaction of carbon dioxide, CO_2, with a phosphate ester of a sugar and that light is not involved in this step. [170]

Many people are aware of the medical research accomplished with nuclear energy and radioisotopes. The use of radium, X-ray, and Cobalt-60 in the treatment of cancer is extensive. Radioactive iodine has been used in thyroid and metabolic regulation.

In the area of forestry, nuclear radiation is beginning to make enormous headway. Mapping root systems is one tech-

[168]Nuclear Science Study Guide, (Des Plains: Nuclear Power Corporation, 1964), p. 4.

[169]L. Don Leet and Sheldon Judson, Physical Geology (New York: Prentice-Hall, Inc., 1954), p. 374.

[170]Nuclear Science Study Guide, loc. cit.

nique used. A grid system is set up around the tree. As
radioactive material -- injected into sap streams -- circulates
through the root system, its course is charted with a special
Geiger counter called a scintillator. Root patterns are important in planning the spacing of trees on government and commercial tree farms and to developing fertilization systems. [171]
 Radioactive isotopes have been used to detect river silt
migration. Tagged silt or dirt is deposited either on a nearby
watershed or in the stream itself. Later, with a specially
equipped Geiger counter lowered directly into the stream, the
migration pattern of the silt is formed as the tagged silt is followed down the stream. Such a system will aid in the construction of dams and flood control. Watershed treatment and run-
off can also be studied.
 Ground water patterns may also be studied by injecting
a radio-tagged water soluble solution into the particular aquifer to be studied. Test wells can be dug or known wells can
be tapped to reveal the distance and pattern that the water follows.
 The mobility of such pests as the mosquito, weevil, bark
beetle, and cutworm can be followed. For example, bark beetles dosed with radioactive strontium and placed in pill boxes
are attached to the bark of a laboratory tree stump. The beetle's activities can then be carefully traced.
 Tagged atoms are used in testing chemical insecticides
and herbicides. The particular chemical to be tested is radi-
ated and then used in the field. Insects used, as well as the
plants, are examined to determine the effect and reliability
of the chemical tested. Close examination of the insect's organs reveals exactly what organs are affected by the chemical.
From this will come better agriculture chemicals and methods
of application.
 Before radioactive isotopes used as tracers came into
use, scientists had always thought that plants drew all their
nutrients through their roots. They thought that the epidermis
or outer layer of plant leaves served only for transpiration of
water vapor and oxygen gas, that such parts as bark and leaves
were impervious skin and could not absorb food.
 The use of tagged atoms or tracers proved that this was
not true -- the leaf is actually a living blotter for absorption
of plant nutrients. Plants of all kinds -- vegetables, fruit
trees, evergreens, and flowers were sprayed with solutions
containing valuable plant nutrients such as nitrogen, phospho-

[171]James N. Miller, "The Atom Taps The Forest's Secrets," Popular Mechanics,
September, 1961, p. 144.

rous, and potassium in the desired amounts. The fertilizing elements were tagged with radioisotopes and could be traced easily as they were absorbed by the plants. The experiment showed that plant nutrients applied in this manner were absorbed faster and more efficiently than those applied to the surrounding soil.

The leaf surface of a twelve year old apple tree, for instance, provides an absorption area of one-tenth of an acre, while the tree itself only occupies one-hundredth of an acre. Such a surface area provides for maximum absorption of the necessary plant nutrients and will provide better fertilization than the old style method of ground application. [172]

Dr. H. B. Tukey, head of the department of horticulture at Michigan State University, has stated, "This is the most efficient method of applying fertilizer to plants that we have discovered. If we apply these materials to the leaves in soluble forms, as much as 95 per cent of what is applied may be used by the plant. If we apply a similar amount to the soil, we find about ten per cent of it is used."

Many previous theories in horticulture and animal husbandry have been disproven by the aid of radioisotopes. For example: Scientists had long assumed that sulfur, unless it were contained in a food compound, could not be utilized by animals which do not chew their cuds, such as pigs and chickens. To check the theory, radioactive sulfur in an organic compound was fed to chickens. The chickens used the inorganic sulfur to make the amino acid cystine, which forms protein. Such an experiment proved the theory to be false. [173]

Another area which lends itself to nuclear science is the field of plant genetics. Plant scientists have always been aware of mutations within a given species. Possibly 99.9 per cent of all mutations are unsuccessful because mutants cannot reproduce themselves or, in some cases, will revert back to the recessive characteristics of the parents. But, occasionally a mutation will prove to be beneficial to the line. Many hybrids result from cross-breeding from a mutation. Some expensive furs -- silver fox, platinum and blue mink -- are obtained from careful breeding of lines originating from a mutation.

Mutations will occur naturally at infrequent intervals, possibly due to the constant bombardment of the earth by cosmic rays. But, the rate of mutations can be increased

[172] Martin Mann, Peacetime Uses of Atomic Energy (New York: Thomas Y. Crowell Company, 1957), p. 82.

[173] Ibid., p. 84.

by the use of radiation, applied artificially, and will increase the rate nearly one hundred times the rate which occurs naturally. Atomic rays from X-ray machines, radioactive materials, or nuclear reactors disrupt the hereditary carrying chromosomes and cause mutations. Such induced mutations are just like natural ones; the irradiated material does not become radioactive itself. This enables scientists to work out beneficial characteristics without having to wait for the one in ten thousands mutation which will improve the line.

Much of this work on plant genetics with the aid of atomic energy is being done at Brookhaven National Laboratory near New York City, but many agriculture departments of the various universities and colleges are doing careful research along this same line.

Hundreds of examples of beneficial applications of nuclear science can be given, but all research must be conducted with reservation and respect for the unknown. As man unlocks the atom and releases the mysterious nuclear energy that binds all matter together, he must do so with wisdom and foresight.

Natural radioactivity gives off two particles and one high energy radiation wave. The alpha particle has a positive two charge and can be artifically made by stripping a Helium atom of its electrons. It has an atomic mass of four and an atomic number of two, meaning the nucleus consists of two protons and two neutrons. The symbol for an alpha particle is α or artificially as a Helium nucleus $_2He^4$. Alpha radiation is not considered very dangerous to man because it can be stopped by a thin piece of paper. However, continued exposure is not recommended.

The beta particle has a negative one charge and is considered to be a high energy electron. Beta radiation is not deeply penetrating, as it can be shielded by cardboard or aluminum foil. The symbol for a beta particle is β.

The real danger of radioactive materials is gamma radiation (α). Gamma rays are high energy deep penetrating radiation and cannot be shielded by ordinary clothing or simple shelters. It does not carry an electrostatic charge and is therefore not influenced by a magnetic or electrical field. Gamma rays are used extensively in the treatment of cancer. Radium, X-ray, and now recently Cobalt-60 are good sources of gamma radiation.

One extreme caution must be observed while working with or being near gamma radiation and that is to respect it

at all times. Be sure proper shielding is available and exposure is not extended. Gamma radiation is absorbed readily by
the gonads or reproductive organs of human beings, as well as
those of animals. This causes great alarm because of the possibility of radioactive induced mutations in man.

Radiation is cumulative in the body and continued exposure over a long period of time will eventually lead to radiation sickness. However, the amount of radiation from dental
X-rays or chest X-rays does not come anywhere near the human dosage limit.

From the point of human survival, each family should
take the necessary steps in the case of nuclear attack. Information concerning recommended fallout shelters and family
provisions may be obtained from the local or state Civil
Defense Department. It is the obligation of every citizen to
acquaint himself with proper first aid, evacuation procedures,
and survival techniques, in the case of nuclear attack.

The atom will continue to serve man, to better his life,
and to advance his civilization. With increased efficiency of
nuclear reactors, electrical power may be available to make
desalting of sea water economical and feasible.

In summary, the role of nuclear science in conservation
is paramount and extremely diversified.

The feasibility of nuclear powered electrical generating
plants that were once science fiction are now reality. Such
plants are especially beneficial in areas lacking an abundant
power source such as coal, petroleum, or water power. Nuclear plants have yet to be economical in respect to other
sources, but future technological advances may make it com-
petitive. The availability of fissionable material far outreaches
the supply of oil or coal and is nearly void of atmospheric pollution because no oxidation takes place. From this standpoint,
we can predict a great future for nuclear generated power.

Nuclear powered submarines and ocean going vessels
have proven far superior to their diesel cousins, both in range
and speed. Such power plants eliminate the need for surfacing
by submarines and also allows more cargo space due to the
reduction of huge fuel tanks. Again the conservation of ex-
haustible resources such as petroleum and coal comes into
focus. With nuclear stockpiles we can look forward to reserve
energy far greater than that of either coal or petroleum.

Radioisotopes or tagged atoms have opened the door to
numerous biological processes that were pondered but never

solved.   Fertilizer uptake and usage by plants can be traced.
Root systems can be plotted without the need of disturbing the
plant.   The feeding habits of many animal species can be established.   The list of possible uses is nearly inexhaustible as
science and technology advance.

The use of radioisotopes in medical research has gained
recognition in cancer detection and treatment.   Many serious
illnesses are found by the use of radioactive tracers.   High
energy X-rays and cobalt-60 are used for treatment of malig-
nant tumors.

Whenever nuclear energy is used there is always the
danger of exposure and contamination to all.   Extreme care
must be taken to regulate and safeguard all personnel involved.

We are certainly in the nuclear age and the future is almost impossible to predict.   The awesome power of the atom
can serve man to bring undreamed of marvels, but lurking in
its shadows is the threat of world contamination and destruction if reasoning and safety are neglected.

ACTIVITIES

1.   Prepare charts, pictures, or models showing the basic
     structure of atoms and of several kinds of molecules.
     E-S
2.   Prepare a flow chart showing the process of converting
     fuel to electricity in an ordinary steam plant, and another
     showing the process of converting nuclear energy into
     electricity.   Notice the similarities.   What is the basic
     difference? *E-S-C*
3.   Prepare a picture or a model of a nuclear reactor showing
     the fuel rods, moderator, cadmium rod and any other
     parts deemed necessary. *E-S-C*
4.   Write to some experimental plants asking for literature
     concerning the operation of plants.   Prepare an exhibit
     utilizing the information gained from responses. *E-S-C*
5.   Prepare reports on each of the following: The Interna-
     tional Atomic Energy Agency, The United Nations (in
     reference to atomic energy), Euratom, and the Atomic
     Energy Commission of the United States. *S-C*
6.   Prepare a current events bulletin board showing newspaper
     and magazine articles about nuclear energy, along with
     commentaries from the class as to the significance of
     each item. *S-C*

7. Class demonstration: Set a number of mouse traps close
   together, each holding two ping-pong balls. Trigger one
   of the traps by releasing a ping-pong ball into the area.
   The result is a chain reaction. Explain how this chain
   reaction is similar to that of a nuclear chain reaction. *E-S*

8. Discussion: In terms of the world's need for energy
   sources, which would seem the most desirable to use up
   first -- oil or uranium? Why? *S*

9. React to the following statement: Since there is enough
   uranium fuel to last mankind for at least 1,000 years,
   there is no need for this generation to worry about the
   use of oil, gas, and coal. *S*

10. Prepare a bibliography of books and magazines found in
    your school library concerning nuclear energy and radio-
    isotope applications. *S-C*

11. Experiment: Transportation of phosphates in plants.
    Using radioactive phosphorous-32 (P^{32}) in solution, take
    a slip of a plant and place in solution. After a few hours,
    take the slip out of the solution. Check progress of isotope
    with Geiger counter. P^{32} may be obtained from most
    isotope suppliers without a license. P^{32} is a beta emitter.
    S-C

12. Prepare a list of resource people that your class could
    ask to speak to your group concerning nuclear energy.
    E-S

13. Experiment: Radiograph of plant leaf. (Used in conjunc-
    tion with activity number 12). Take a leaf from the plant
    slip and place over photographic film. Care must be taken
    not to expose film before placing the leaf on it, and time
    should be allowed to be sure of radioactive exposure. The
    film may be developed commercially or by someone with
    dark room experience. *S-C*

14. Construct a model of a nuclear reactor or nuclear sub-
    marine. This may be done individually or as a class pro-
    ject. *E*

15. Contact a local United States Conservation agent and ask
    him to speak to your class on the subject of nuclear science
    in the conservation program. *E-S-C*

16. Make a chart showing some of the most common radio-
    isotopes, their chemical form, half-life, radiation emitted
    and some of their applications. *S-C*

17. Make a bulletin board showing some of the uses of radio-
    isotopes in conservation. *E-S-C*

18. Write to some of the chemical insecticide or herbicide manufacturers for information on how nuclear energy is used in their chemical testing programs. **S-C**
19. Contact the State Fish and Wildlife Department for information on the role of nuclear science in their program. Take a field trip to their laboratories, if feasible. **E-S-C**
20. Make a bulletin board concerning nuclear energy and medical science. **E-S-C**
21. Contact the Civil Defense Department in your area and invite a representative to speak to your class on nuclear safety. **E-S**
22. Discussion: Nuclear energy has done more good than harm. **E-S-C**
23. Construct models or graphs showing the difference between uranium-235 and uranium-238. **S**
24. Make a list of safety precautions concerning nuclear energy and radioisotopes. **E-S-C**
25. Write to the U. S. Forest Service for information concerning nuclear energy in their research program. A display board may be made of the materials. **E-S-C**

BIBLIOGRAPHY

Abarbanel, Albert. "Iodine: Much More Than A Germ-Killer," *Today's Health,* November, 1961. **S-C**

"Advanced Radiotherapy," *Time,* October 6, 1961. **S-C**

Asimov, Isaac. *Inside The Atom.* New York: Abelard-Schuman, 1956. **S-C**

Beeler, Nelson F. and Franklyn M. Branley. *Experiments With Atomics.* New York: Thomas Y. Crowell Company, 1954. **S**

Dean, Gordon. *Report on the Atom.* New York: Alfred Knopf, 1954. **S-C**

Dunlap, Henry A. and Hans N. Tuck. *Atoms At Your Service.* New York: Harper and Brothers, 1957. **S-C**

Fermi, Laura. *The Story of Atomic Energy.* New York: Random House, 1961. **E-S**

Glasstone, Samuel. *Sourcebook on Atomic Energy.* New York: D. Van Nostrand Company, 1950. **C**

Goodnight, Clarence and Arthur G. Johanningsmeier. "Use of Iodine-131 To Measure Movements of Small Animals," *Science,* October 12, 1962. **S-C**

Hyde, Margaret O. *Atoms: Today and Tomorrow*. New York:
McGraw-Hill Book Company, Inc. (Whittlesey House), 1955.
E-S

Jaworski, Irene D. and Alexander Joseph. *Atomic Energy:
The Story of Nuclear Science*. New York: Harcourt, Brace
and World, 1961. *S-C*

Jukes, J. D. *The Story of Zeta: The Man-Made Sun*. New
York: Abelard-Schuman, 1959. *S-C*

Lang, Daniel. *The Man In The Thick Lead Suit*. New York:
Oxford University Press, 1954. *S-C*

Lapp, Ralph E. *Atoms and People*. New York: Harper and
Brothers, 1956. *S-C*

_____. *Roads To Discovery*. New York: Harper and
Brothers, 1960. *S-C*

Leet, L. Don and Sheldon Judson. *Physical Geology*. New
York: Prentice-Hall, Inc., 1954. *S-C*

Lewellen, John. *You and Atomic Energy and Its Wonderful
Uses*. Chicago: Children's Press, Inc., 1949. *E*

Leyson, Burr W. *Atom Energy in War and Peace*. New York:
E. P. Dutton and Company, 1952. *S-C*

Manchester, Harland. "New Uses for Neurotic Atoms,"
Reader's Digest, August, 1961. *S-C*

Mann, Martin. *Peacetime Uses of Atomic Energy*. New York:
Thomas Y. Crowell Company, 1957. *E-S-C*

Miller, James N. "The Atom Taps The Forest's Secrets,"
Popular Mechanics, September, 1961. *S-C*

Nuclear Science Study Guide. Des Plains: Nuclear Power
Corporation, 1964. *S-C*

Shaftel, George and Helen Heffernan. *The Energy Story*.
Chicago: The L. W. Singer Company, 1963. *S-C*

Stokley, James. *The New World of The Atom*. New York:
Ives Washburn, Inc., 1957. *S-C*

Yates, Raymond F. *Atomic Experiments For Boys*. New
York: Harper and Brothers, 1952. *E-S*

AUDIO-VISUAL MATERIALS

16 mm. FILMS

A For Atom - (Gen. Elec.)

An explanation in lay terms of what an atom is, how
energy is released from certain kinds of atoms, and
the peacetime uses of atomic energy. *S-C*

Atom and Agriculture - (EBF)

Reveals the legitimate areas in which radioactivity can
be expected to produce practical results for agriculture.
Tells the important story of radioactive tracers applied
to different agriculture problems including photosynthesis. *S-C*

Atom and Biological Science - (EBF)

Describes some of the biological effects of high energy
radiations on plants and animals. Points out some possible applications of nuclear radiation to problems of
human health, emphasizing work already under way in
the study of cancer. *S-C*

Atom and Industry - (EBF)

Reveals how radioisotopes are providing new techniques
of measurement and quality control in a wide variety of
industries. Indicates how radiation symbol is becoming
a common sight in factories and laboratories. *S-C*

Atom and Medicine - (EBF)

Dramatically shows how, by taking radio-iodine internal-
ly, one man's condition was diagnosed and cured. Describes the increasingly important role of radioisotopes
in hospitals, clinics, and doctors' offices. Shows clearly the respect with which radiation must be treated and
reveals some of the instruments and devices used to
handle it. *S-C*

Atomic Age Farmer - (Handel Film Corp.)

Three applications of atomic energy in agriculture:
mutation of corn, animal studies, atomic tracers. *S-C*

Atomic Energy As A Force For Good - (Christophers)

Shows the change in a rancher's attitude regarding the
bringing of an atomic energy plant to his area. *E-S-C*

Atomic Energy Can Be A Blessing - (Christophers)

Atomic energy can benefit man rather than destroy him.
S-C

Atomic Power - (EBF)

Shows by means of animation how nuclear synthesis is accomplished, how radiant energy is released, and how nuclear fission and the chain reaction are affected. **S-C**

Atomic Power - (McGH)

Explains the nature of atomic energy and includes re-enactments of the scientists' current campaign to tell the full meaning of atomic power. **S-C**

Atomic Radiation - (EBF)

Explains the fundamentals of atomic radiation: The dramatic story of its discovery, what it is and does, and why it must be respected rather than feared. Explains the roles of alpha, beta, and gamma and neutron particles in radioisotope research. **E-S-C**

Atomic Research - (Cor)

Using authentic footage of actual atomic research installations and operations, the film surveys three large areas of atomic research -- energy applications of nuclear fission, the structure of the atom, and the by-products of nuclear fission. **S-C**

Miracle Makers - (TFC)

Stresses the potential importance of the atom as a source of future power. **S-C**

Nuclear Radiation: Fallout - (CSC)

The film goes into the type of fallout and sources of contamination on earth. **S-C**

Nuclear Radiation: In Earth Studies - (CSC)

The film shows how a material's age can be judged to a span of 50,000 years by the amount of radioactive decay using Geiger-Muller and scintillation counters. **S-C**

Nuclear Radiation: In Outer Space - (CSC)

The film shows the Van Allen Belts centering on 2,500 and 10,000 miles off the equator and at high altitudes. Radiation hazards will be a major consideration when designing and building man's space vehicles of tomorrow. **S-C**

Radiation in Biology: An Introduction - (Cor)

How high-energy radiations affect living plants and animals is graphically demonstrated through laboratory experiments in one of the nation's leading research laboratories. The film shows the use of radioactive materials in treating cancer and in studying the process of growth, nutrition and reproduction in living things. **E-S**

Report on the Atom - (McGH)

Shows the non-military uses of atomic energy. Indicates uses already made of radioactive materials in medicine, biology, and industry. **S-C**

The Strange Case of The Cosmic Rays - (Bell Telephone)

Story of how scientists track cosmic rays and establish their mysterious character and behavior. **E-S-C**

Unlocking The Atom - (UW Educ)

Background information is given on the early knowledge of the atom and the contributions of the leading scientists. **S-C**

FILMSTRIPS

Atomic Energy - (Visual Sciences)

Shows the basic structure of matter and develops the concept that there is a variety of atoms. Introduces some of the sub-atomic particles that students will encounter in their reading. Illustrates a few uses of radioactive isotopes. **E-S**

New Power From The Atom - (NY Times)

Deals with the latest advancements in the use of atomic power. **S**

Putting Atomic Energy To Work - (McGH)

How atomic piles are used, applications of radioisotopes in industry, medicine, etc. are illustrated. **E-S**

Radioactive Atoms - (Chas. Scribner & Sons)

Describes and shows uses of radioactive atoms. **E-S**

Using Isotopes To Improve Health - (Chas. Scribner & Sons)

Describes and shows how isotopes are used to improve our health. **E-S**

The angry buzz of a multitude
is one of the bloodiest noises
in the world.

Lord Halifax

Chapter XIII   POPULATION DYNAMICS

OBJECTIVES

I. To discuss the factors of population depletion and growth
    -- using man as an example.
II. To point to the complexity of the "population explosion"
    -- politically, economically, and socially.
III. To relate human population to conservation -- and to an
    ecological framework.
IV. To project future developments and consequences
    of the increasing rate of growth in the human popula-
    tion.

Elihu Root, Jr. has said: "I think the population problem
is really the world's number one puzzle -- tougher and poten-
tially more dangerous than even the danger of nuclear war. [174]
Each year more than fifty million people are added to the
3,115,000,000 people already on the planet (mid-1962 esti-
mate) -- as many individuals as live in the world's tenth largest nation, the United Kingdom. In all human history, world
population has never grown so fast as today. Analyzing trends
in human population growth and predicting future developments
are the special province of a special branch of the social sciences, demography. The growth rate is 1.8 per cent per year
-- almost twice the rate of two decades ago. If the present
growth rate continues, the number of people on earth will double to over six billion in forty years. To illustrate the spectacular growth rate, it is estimated that about one third of the
world's population has been added since World War II.
    Significantly, it is among the restless, impoverished
people of the world that the population is growing at the greatest rate. (The highest growth rate in the world is turning up
in Latin America.) United Nations statistics reveal that over-

[174] The Population Bomb, Population Policy Panel of the Hugh Moore Fund (New
York: Hugh Moore Fund), p. 22.

- 293 -

Minnesota Department of Business Development

Figure 60. More people mean more areas for recreation

population in relation to resources already exists in some
areas to an alarming degree as in Asia, Latin America, and
in parts of Africa. Only in part can this difficulty be attributed
to under-development of resources. In a larger measure, the
difficulty exists simply because there are too many people when
measured against the availability of food and other needs. (See
Figures 60 and 61) It is to be noted that in per capita food some
countries are behind where they were before World War II.
Even in the United States, many observers say present population growth indicates that before long the strain on our supplies

Minnesota Department of Business Development

Figure 61. City parks are especially important in the population boom

of raw materials, water and other resources will begin to tell. [175]

Population experts cite problems already developing in the United States -- traffic congestion, classroom shortages, a shortage of jobs for youths coming out of school, and water development -- as a sample of what to expect. Experts warn that the United States, near a growth rate of 1.5 per cent annually, will have 716 million people by the year 2050. The United States, then, would be almost as crowded as Red China is now. [176]

[175]"Each Day 130,000 More People," The Minneapolis Star, November 7, 1960, p. 1B.
[176]"Too Many People In The World?" U. S. News and World Report, September 16, 1963, p. 62.

There is little history to sketch in the study of population dynamics, as it relates to the human being. Strange as it may seem, it was not until 1948, with the publication of William Vogt's *Road To Survival*, that much attention was given to the problems of population. But, even then, the predictions of Malthus were recalled and the people said surely something would "turn up" like the Industrial Revolution or the growth of the New World to make the prophets of doom look foolish again. As Raymond Dasmann points out though: "The present world situation is entirely new. The population problem is nothing like anything that we have experienced before. The only unexpected something that can 'turn up' is disaster."[177] Dasmann takes little comfort in the speculation that people can eat algae and yeast and can make greater utilization of nuclear and sun sources. [178] Perhaps optimists will whisper: What about the unexplored galaxies of space?

Why has the population explosion developed? Basically, how quickly or how slowly the population grows depends on the number of births and deaths taking place. Medical discoveries and wide-spread advances in sanitation have improved health and prolonged life spans and thus have lowered death rates. For example, Ceylon cut its mortality rate forty per cent in one year after World War II by spraying the island with D. D. T. in an anti-malaria campaign. Birth rates have not gone down proportionately.

New advances in technology have opened up new areas for settlement such as the cold lands of Alaska and Siberia and the hot lands of Brazil and mid-Africa for settlement, but the empty spaces today that have rich soil and good climate are very limited. Although the agricultural revolution in many countries has made it possible for fewer and fewer farmers to produce more and more food on less and less land, the earth is only so large -- and hundreds of millions of people in the world are hungry.   (See Figure 62)

Today, one American farm worker feeds twenty-seven people. Rising productivity and efficiency on farms and ranches will make it possible to feed 230 million people in 1975 from less total acreage than is now used. [179] Further, today's farm-

[177]Raymond F. Dasmann, The Last Horizon, (New York: The Macmillan Company, 1963), p. 214.
[178]Ibid. , p. 220.
[179]The Food We Eat, Miscellaneous Publication No. 870, U. S. Department of Agriculture, (Washington: Government Printing Office, 1962), p. 15.

Minnesota Department of Business Development

Figure 62. Mechanization alleviates food problem of greater population

ers increasingly are applying the soil and water conservation measures needed to protect land for maximum safe use in 1975 -- and far beyond that date. But, the United States is only one of more than one hundred countries in the world. "Actually -- apart from transportation and other problems -- the annual U. S. food surplus would supply the equivalent of just one cup of rice a week for each of the under-nourished people of the world." [180] Obviously, U. S. taxpayers cannot feed the world. And, this is an interdependent world -- whether we speak in terms of health, politics, or economy.

[180]The Population Bomb, op. cit., p. 7.

How can population and resources be brought into balance? The most obvious and direct way of meeting the problem is limiting the number of people. This can be done through birth control. But, "no controversy during the last several decades has caused more tension, rancor and strife among religious groups in the country than the birth control issue."[181] Significantly, a noted gynecologist and Catholic layman, Dr. John Pock, has urged acceptance of contraceptive pills, and other Catholics are suggesting broad-scale interfaith discussions on the subject of birth control and the population problem. The controversy has flared up over regulations in municipal hospitals and health and family welfare agencies. It has erupted over including birth control information and material in foreign aid to under-developed countries. But again, significantly, President Kennedy -- a Roman Catholic -- early in 1963, affirmed United States willingness to offer information on birth control to other nations. In addition to the religious objections is the simple fact that no one yet has developed a means of birth control which is inexpensive, readily available and understood by the masses of people who are illiterate and naive. However, it is to be noted that some countries have been able to reduce birth rates by birth control -- notably Japan, where birth control is officially approved.

A variety of birth control measures are practiced. The so-called "rhythm method" (periodic abstention) is practiced by many Catholics. Some countries resort to legalized abortions. In Hungary in 1959, the number of abortions exceeded live births.[182] In some parts of the world, such as India, Japan, Sweden, voluntary sterilization is gaining wide acceptance by both men and women.[183] A wide variety of contraceptives are now available in Europe and America and in the larger cities throughout the world.

There are a number of limited, short-term alternatives to birth control, but these alternatives wreak of problems. Migration of people from densely settled areas to thinly settled areas -- such as Australia, South Africa -- would have to overcome political immigration barriers as well as the fact that most people are happy living where they are. The number of people that could be moved would probably be less than the

---

[181]Rev. John A. O'Brian, "Let's Take Birth Control Out Of Politics," Look, October 10, 1961, p. 67.

[182]"Too Many People In The World?" loc. cit.

[183]The Population Bomb, op. cit., p. 10.

population growth. The United States serves as a case in point: In the 135 years between 1820 and 1955, the United States took in 34 million immigrants -- about a single year's population in Asia today.

Increasing world food production seems at first blush to negate the importance of increasing population. New food resources can be brought from the sea. New synthetic foods can be developed. New food producing areas can be opened in Africa, South America, and the islands of the Pacific. New and better ways of irrigating, fertilizing, and managing farmlands through scientific research offers much promise. But, without sufficient capital, without a sufficient industrial economy, without a certain stability of government, without a literate citizenry, increased food production through new means is hopeless.

Better distribution of food resources is extremely complicated and would have only a slight hand and a temporary effect, as mentioned earlier. Even increased trade has overwhelming political complications -- as the recent wheat sale to Russia or the "poultry war" with the Common Market so vividly illustrate.

Shirley Allen uses the term *human powers*, rather than *human resources* in her book about natural resources, because "the use of human beings for the benefit of themselves and other human beings is a use of services which flow from human powers, and because there is nothing unnatural about human beings. "[184]

Richard Ely has classified human powers into those of the body (power to reproduce, strength, and dexterity) and those of the spirit (power to think and reason, imagination, power to distinguish between right and wrong, and the power to inspire and to lead). [185]

The use of human powers is analogous to that of mineral resources and wildlife resources, in that human powers may be wasted, depleted, unwisely used, inequitably distributed or they can be efficiently and effectively used, reallocated and redistributed, or wisely hoarded. The factors which waste and deplete human powers (or resources) are disease (How much time is still lost through the common cold?); accidents

[184]Shirley Allen, Conserving Natural Resources: Principals and Practices in a Democracy (New York: McGraw-Hill Book Company, 1955), p. 327.
[185]Richard T. Ely and Associates, Foundations of National Prosperity, (New York: The Macmillan Company, 1923), p. 48.

(How many Americans are killed each year in automobile accidents?); vice and crime (How many reformatories and prisons dot this land?); war (Almost every day human life is lost on some battle field, somewhere in the world.); and over-population (How many people go to bed hungry every night?). And the list could go on -- idleness, disasters, dishonesty.

In conserving human powers, something is being done. A National Institute of Child Health and Human Development has been founded. The government is contributing about six million dollars annually to research on human production. The United Nations is dedicated to preserving the peace and promoting health throughout the world. The American Cancer Society and U. S. Public Health Service, among a multitude of organizations, wage an unending battle against disease. President Johnson has made the battle against poverty one of the keystones of his administration. And, it should be noted that the President of the Population Reference Bureau, Robert C. Cook, has hailed 1963 as the year when the idea of population control finally gained world-wide acceptance among political, religious, scientific, and educational leaders.[186] Cook cites the change of outlook of Dwight Eisenhower who, in 1959, rejected government participation in seeking solutions to population problems, but who wrote in 1963 about "the responsibility we have for finding some realistic means of containing this human explosion.[187]

In his book, *Why Not Survive?*, Michael W. Straus hits on a key point in population dynamics and the relationship to natural resources. He says: "Man is myopic. In the modern pattern and pressure of industrial life, he becomes of necessity more remote from the resources that sustain him. Consequently, he becomes less conscious of his dependence for survival on resources he rarely sees or contacts.[188] Minnesotans don't get hot and bothered about the water problem in California. The people of Ohio are relatively unconcerned about Washington timber. People of Maine are not up in arms about the "tidelands oil" controversy. Kentucky's citizens do not explode over the fishing rights off Newfoundland. People seem to be concerned only when the problem is immediately under their noses -- of concern to them.

[186]Editorial in the Minneapolis Morning Tribune, January 8, 1964.
[187]Ibid.
[188]Michael W. Straus, Why Not Survive? (New York: Simon and Schuster, 1955), p. 20.

It may be appropriate to say that from the conservation-ists point of view, man is the control focus -- the environment is examined from man's frame of reference, but obviously the environmental or community relationships can be examined from the ecological frame of reference -- from the plant and animal perspective: In any one place, the populations of different plants and animals are interrelated to constitute a biotic community. Each member of the population has its ups and downs, and these changes influence other parts of the community. But generally, an equilibrium (or carrying capacity) is reached and the population fluctuates around this level. Even so, the population changes from season to season, year to year, due to biotic and climatic changes; therefore, even the so-called "balance of nature" is a dynamic one. (See Chapter II.)

Each year, for example, new individuals are born in the community -- immediately there is population pressure. There will be competition not only within the species, but among other species for food and space. The community will become more or less balanced as a result of migration to other areas, loss by predation or climatic conditions, or loss by disease or starvation.

A classic example of the oscillation in population density is that of the lemming, the arctic fox, and the snowy owl. Every three or four years, over the enormous area of the tundra, lemmings become extremely abundant, only to "crash" -- sometimes within a single season. The result: Owls and foxes, which increased as a result of the food increase, decrease very soon afterward. Owls migrate south in great numbers; foxes starve in great numbers. In fact, this oscillation is so regular that ornithologists can count on a snowy owl invasion every three or four years. [189]

Another example of the biotic relationships that exist in the plant and animal kingdom occurs when, through a bounty system, or other unnatural means, predators are killed off. Suppose a county government offers a five dollar bounty on foxes. Farmers quickly queue up at the county clerk's office with fox tails hanging at their waists like bloody ribbons. Soon, the farmer's wife conversing to another farmer's wife during the Saturday shopping complains about the sudden influx of rabbits -- how they have girdled their favorite fruit

[189] Eugene P. Odum, Fundamentals of Ecology (Philadelphia: W. B. Saunders Company, 1953), pp. 193-195.

trees and completely destroyed the garden. And suddenly, for
some unknown reason, there is an epidemic of "rabbit fever"
in the county.

Or, take the case of the lowly English sparrow or the
Norway rat. Both were immigrants to this country -- one an
invited guest, the other a stowaway. In the beginning, they
beget and beget untrammeled. They spread across the country
like a whirlwind. The English sparrow drove out the native
sparrows, and became a close companion of man -- building
his fire-trap nests in rafters, often spreading diseases such
as cholera among beasts and man, and aesthetically scarring
buildings and monuments with excrement. The Norway rat,
with sharp teeth, cuts into man's very abode -- raiding the
pantry, as well as the corn crib. He has become a plague.

Dr. Hudson Hoaglund, in the *Bulletin of the Atomic
Scientists*, suggests that nature has its own subtle systems
for stopping excessive breeding. Population among animals
declines when over-crowded -- cannibalism develops, abnor-
mal sexual patterns set in, physical changes occur in the
glands, particularly the adrenal gland. Although there is no
known relationship to humans, social stress does exist in the
over-crowded slums. Hoaglund fears that nature may strike
man with as yet unpredictable perils. [190]

In the early days, man was an intimate part of the biotic
community. He was a competitor of the wolf and bear; he
lived off the land -- hunting the deer and the duck. As time
passed, seemingly man has been less directly involved in the
community of nature. But, man's indirect ecological manipulations may be of even greater significance. When man drains
a swamp, many creatures die or move; when move removes
a forest, animals are forced to find a new home or make most
difficult adjustments; when man builds a pond or plants a
hedgerow, he encourages new wildlife to move to the area.

Population study began with Malthus. It was his theory
that population multiplies in geometric ratio -- i. e., 1, 2, 4,
8, 16 -- while man could only add to his resources by arithme-
tic progression -- 1, 2, 3, 4, 5. The result is constant pressure on resources, which results in disease, war, and starvation. Today, biologists discuss the "biotic potential" of an
organism; that is, the possible reproductive rate. But, this
potential can never be fully reached:

[190]"Sociology," Time, February 28, 1964, p. 56.

Famine and war, parasites and predators stand in the way. These causes of death are summed up in the concept of "environmental resistance." [191] The formula for the existing population may be diagramed as follows: $P = BP/ER$.

"Environmental resistance" for man, however, has a different meaning from that for other organisms: He is a rational being, and he has developed many aids for his survival.

Man, too, is a necessary resource in the community of needs and wants. Man is an essential ingredient in the development of resources. "He initiates and plans their uses, he engages in the actual production, and he benefits from the product or suffers from the mistakes made in using them." [192] Man is not a separate, an omnipotent factor of the environment: He is of the land.

In summary, man is multiplying until there is strain and stress upon food and resources. Man has become concerned with controlling and balancing the factors of his existence. Man can look to the cruel world of nature to science to find the means to cope with the problem. Man can discover anew his relationship to the good earth -- and to all things that inhabit it.

ACTIVITIES

1. On an outline map of the world, indicate the areas having the greater population density. Colors can be used to specify degree of density. *S-C*
2. Obtain water from a pond. Examine the microscopic life under the microscope -- listing varieties and estimating numbers. Then, place a tablespoon full of the same pond water in a number of other containers which have equal quantities of water obtained from a variety of other sources -- large river, spring, from a faucet at school, well, etc. Let the containers set in warm lighted room for a few days, then examine the water from each container under a microscope. Can any generalizations be made? *S-C*
3. List the population of the United States for every decade beginning in 1790. Determine the rate of growth. Try to determine the differences for different rates by events

[191]Marston Bates, Man In Nature (Englewood Cliffs: Prentice-Hall, 1961), p. 58.
[192]Henry F. Becker, Resources For Tomorrow (New York: Holt, Rinehart, and Winston, 1964), p. 6.

taking place in American history at the time. Especially
note economic conditions, political conditions such as wars,
and increasing area of the United States. **S-C**

4. How may experiments be set up to discover population
dynamics? Try to set up some research designs. See
Basic Ecology as listed in the bibliography, pp. 80-82.
S-C

5. Discuss the ethical and religious aspects of population control -- such as mercy killing of old, infanticide, sterilization, etc. A panel preceding the discussion with members
representing different cultural or religious points of view
would be appropriate. **C**

6. There is a wide range of opinion on the question of just how
many people the world can support. Get opinions of various
authorities -- pointing out the assumptions and implications
of their estimates. **S-C**

7. Make a line graph showing the most populous countries of
the world. Compare this line graph with a line graph
showing the largest countries in square miles. What effect does climate, natural resources, and general location
have on the differences? **E-S**

8. Talk to your grandparents or older members of the community about how your community has changed in the last
fifty years. Share your stories with the other members
of the class. **E-S**

9. Show the shift in United States population by showing on an
outline map of the U. S. those states which have gained
more than the average, gained less than the average, or
lost population over the last ten years -- compare 1950
with 1960. The same principle can be demonstrated by
simply listing the top 25 cities in population in 1950 and
1960. (*Time* magazine is a good resource for this activity.) **S-C**

10. Report to the class on "The Population Explosion And Your
Taxes or Business." Pamphlets are available from Hugh
Moore Fund, 51 East 42nd Street, New York 17, New
York. **S-C**

11. Have committees report on the changing population of the
United States and the effects on schools, jobs, and government. (*See U. S. News and World Report*, October 22,
1962 and September 18, 1961, also *Urban Development*,
by David E. Christensen as listed in the bibliography for
this chapter.) **S-C**

12. Have a social worker, a sociologist, or an economist appear before the class to answer questions about the effects of the changing and growing population on the local community. Preparation should be made before the guest's appearance regarding good questions, appropriate and significant. *S-C*

13. If there is an urban development or new housing development nearby, visit the area; then have the students write a theme or paragraph about the field trip. Stress should be given to accurate observations. *E-S-C*

14. Prepare a series of transparencies for the overhead projector for a unit of teaching about "human conservation." *C*

15. Debate: "The Population Explosion: Can We Survive It?" *S-C*

16. Some peoples are in danger of becoming extinct -- the "white people" of Japan, the aborigines of Australia, certain tribes of Indians. In a taped "bull session" -- after some research -- discuss the why and the applications for modern civilization. The "bull session" should be taped in an informal give-and-take atmosphere and then brought to the class for reactions. *C*

17. Develop a related resource unit -- including a research paper that can be duplicated as a student resource on "Under-developed Potentials of the Sea," "Under-developed Resources of the Arctic or Tropic Regions," or "Hydroponics." *C*

18. Read a story to the class. Examples: Robert Lawson's *Rabbit Hill;* Clare Newberry's *April's Kitten;* Wanda Gag's *Millions of Cats,* or Robert Browning's *The Pied Piper of Hamelin.* The books, of course, can be related to population dynamics. *E*

19. Make a picture album of contrasting pictures showing "The Good Life" population in control, and "The Bad Life" over-population, and their consequences. *E-S*

20. Discuss "Demographic Transition." (See Dasmann's *The Last Horizon* as listed in the bibliography for this chapter.) Is it occurring now? Where? Why? *S-C*

21. Research problem: Distinguish between "ecological death" and "physiological death." *S-C*

22. Add these words to your vocabulary. Specific attention should be given to increasing vocabulary in each area of study by writing words on the chalkboard and discussing them. Examples:

E	S	C
urban	hinterland	megolopolis
slum	cosmopolitan	Malthusian theory
subsistence	provincial	Lebensraum
starvation	distribution	vasectomy

23. Write and produce a skit telling about America one hundred or two hundred years from now. What will they eat? Where will they live? How will they work and play?
    E-S-C
24. Have a round table discussion on George Orwell's *1984,* Aldous Huxley's *Brave New World,* and Nevil Shute's *On The Beach.* The same or different books may be used. *S-C*
25. Trace your family history using newspaper files, courthouse records, and census records. Has there been a difference in number of children in your father's, grandfather's, and great grandfather's generations? *S-C*

BIBLIOGRAPHY

Allen, Shirley W. *Conserving Natural Resources; Principles and Practices in a Democracy.* New York: McGraw Hill Book Company, 1955. *S-C*

Bates, Marston. *Man In Nature.* Englewood Cliffs: Prentice-Hall, 1961. *S-C*

_____. *The Prevalence of People.* New York: Charles Scribners and Sons, 1955. *S-C*

Becker, Henry F. *Resources For Tomorrow.* New York: Holt, Rinehart and Winston, 1964. *S*

Brown, Harrison, James Bonner and John Weir. *The Next Hundred Years.* New York: The Viking Press, 1957. *S-C*

Buchsbaum, Ralph and Mildred. *Basic Ecology.* Pittsburgh: Boxwood Press, 1957. *S-C*

Christensen, David E. *Urban Development.* New York: Holt, Rinehart and Winston, Inc., 1964 *S-C*

Dasmann, Raymond. *The Last Horizon.* New York: The Macmillan Company, 1963. *S-C*

"Each Day 130, 000 More People, " *The Minneapolis Star,* November 7, 1960. *S-C*

Ely, Richard T. and Associates. *Foundations of National Prosperity.* New York: The Macmillan Company, 1923. *C*

Fagley, Richard M. *The Population Explosion and Christian Responsibility.* New York: Oxford University Press, 1960. *S-C*

Hyde, Margaret O. *This Crowded Planet.* New York: McGraw Hill Book Company (Whittlesey House), 1961. *S*

Maury, Marion. *Birth Rate and Birth Right.* New York: Macfadden-Bartell, 1963. *S-C*

Minneapolis Morning Tribune, January 8, 1964. *S-C*

O'Brian, Rev. John A. "Let's Take Birth Control Out of Politics, " *Look,* October 10, 1961. *C*

Odum, Eugene P. *Fundamentals of Ecology.* Philadelphia: W. B. Saunders Company, 1953. *C*

Population Is The Problem of Our Age, Package Library Briefs, Vol. XVI, No. 4. Bloomington: Indiana University Bureau of Public Discussion. *S-C*

"Sociology, " *Time,* February 28, 1964. *S-C*

Straus, Michael W. *Why Not Survive?* New York: Simon and Schuster, 1955. *S-C*

The Food We Eat, Miscellaneous Publication No. 870, U. S. Department of Agriculture. Washington: Government Printing Office, 1962. *S*

The Population Bomb, Population Policy Panel of the Hugh Moore Fund. New York: Hugh Moore Fund. *S-C*

Thompson, Warren S. *Population Problems.* New York: McGraw Hill Book Company, 1953. *S-C*

"Too Many People in the World?" *U. S. News and World Report,* September 16, 1963. *S-C*

Vogt, William. *People.* New York: William Morrow Publishers, 1960. *S-C*

_____. People, *Challenge to Survival.* New York: William Sloane Associates, 1960. *S-C*

AUDIO-VISUAL MATERIALS

16 mm. FILMS

And So They Live - (New York Univ.)

The poverty of the land in a rural southern community is shown -- lack of sanitation, proper housing, food. **S-C**

Battle For Bread - (U. N. , Film Div. , Assn. Films, Inc.)

The FAO is shown at work -- problem of food needs increased due to normal population growth and declining death rates. **S-C**

Big City, The - (British Information Service)

This film indicates how Londoners live -- transportation, work, and recreation. **E-S**

City, The - (Museum of Natural History)

This is a documentary film showing five stages in development -- demonstrates what can be done through city planning. **S-C**

Eternal Fight, The - (U. N. , Film Div. , Assn. Films Inc.)

The eternal struggle against plague, hunger, and war points out the importance of the World Health Organization. **S-C**

Food and People - (EBF)

The world food problems are presented contrasting between people who have plenty to eat and those who have little. **S-C**

Forty Million People - (International Film Bureau)

This is a general survey of life in Great Britain. Hospitals, playgrounds, housing, schools are all a part of this film. **S-C**

Giant People - (EBF)

Watussi of Africa are shown in their way of life -- food, clothing, home furnishings, family relationships. **S**

Golden Door, The - (Brandon Films)

Highlights of the U. S. immigration history and policy are illustrated. **S-C**

Improving America's Health - (Cor)

This film points to individual responsibility and education in improvement in health. **S**

Inside Story - (EBF)

Penal rehabilitation through vocational therapy and recreation play is presented. **S-C**

Living City, The - (EBF)

The growth, decay, and renewal of a city is explained. **S-C**

Man and His Culture - (EBF)

This film shows how cultures are constantly changing through interaction, through new inventions and discoveries. **S-C**

Mars and Beyond - (Walt Disney)

The theory about Mars is explored -- ways plants and animals may have adapted to conditions there. An imaginary flight to Mars in an atom powered space ship is undertaken. **S-C**

Place to Live - (Dynamic Films)

This is a documentary story of the aged and their social needs. **C**

Remnants of a Race - (Instruction Films)

The Bushman's struggle for survival is illustrated. **S**

Roots of Happiness - (Mental Health Materials Center)

The film shows the contrasts in family living. It also promotes respect for people, irrespective of their cultural or economic backgrounds. *C*

Shelter - (EBF)

A variety of homes are shown: Eskimo, desert people, pioneers. *E*

Story of Prehistoric Man - (Cor)

The Old and New Stone Age man are described -- tools, paintings, habitat. *E-S*

Wastage of Human Resources - (EBF)

Attention is called to the wastage through war, alcohol and drug addiction, mental disease, crime, unemployment. *S-C*

We, The People - (Young America Films)

This film pictures the beginning of the U. N. -- considerations of human rights, welfare, security, and justice. *C*

You, the Human Animal - (Walt Disney)

Differences between men and animals are presented. *E*

FILMSTRIPS

Human Resources - (Curriculum)

This filmstrip shows how the people of the four great geographical areas make a living. *E*

People, Our Most Valuable Resource - (Popular Science)

The problems of keeping man healthy and happy -- also relations of other resources to man are demonstrated. *S-C*

Urban Conservation Today - (SVE)

The interrelationship of problems of both central city and outlying areas due to increasing population are illustrated. *S*

God Almighty first planted a
garden. And, indeed, it is
the purest of human pleasures.
Francis Bacon

Chapter XIV

HOME AND YARD CONSERVATION

OBJECTIVES

I. To point out proper materials and landscaping techniques used by home owners.

II. To investigate the species of plants and grasses recommended for home use.

III. To point out the need for conservation around the home.

IV. To develop an awareness for active conservation practices by everyone.

Landscaping may be called the art of adapting nature to your own home yard. With the proper use of trees and shrubs, a well cared for lawn and the addition of a few flowers, you not only make your surroundings more pleasing, but also create the impression that your home is an integral part of a naturally beautiful site.

Landscaping the home can be a cooperative family effort. The finest of plans do not always take into account the particular preferences of individuals in the family. It is, therefore, very important for the family to plan the landscape, keeping in mind future plans. Without careful considerations of family needs and desires, a landscape plan may have little value. The family with pride in its home will be more enthusiastic in working out a plan of its own making.

When you are building a home, the location of the house and garage has a great deal to do with the development of a good landscape plan. Remember, when building, plan your house with the landscape in mind.

It is important to allow for a large, usable living area at the rear of the lot. It is, therefore, important to place the house properly, allowing for an adequate play area, and a short, economical driveway and sidewalk.

With the house located toward the front of the yard, the lot naturally divides itself into two or three major areas. These are the approach, the living area, and the work area.

The approach area is the street side of the property. It should be devoted to a good setting for the house with simple, restrained plantings and an adequate, uncluttered lawn area.

The living area is usually located to the rear of the home. It should be accessible from the house living area. Plantings will be developed to increase privacy and provide enjoyment for the family members as an outdoor living room.

The work area may include a children's play space, clothesline area, and a small vegetable or flower garden. A small work area on a city lot or urban lot is essential and should provide room where leaves, lawn clippings and similar refuse from yard work can be temporarily stored.

Exactly how these areas are separated will depend on both the size of the yard, and the degree of privacy the home owner desires. The major areas may be divided by shrubs and trees, or fences. A combination of both is often most effective for the contemporary home. In many cases, trees, when properly placed, may suggest area divisions without actually separating them. This treatment is especially effective for small properties.

The first step is to draw a top view of the lot, placing the house, garage, and approach area as close to scale as possible.

Use graph paper for your plan, and a scale of one inch to eight or sixteen feet. Follow the scale in locating permanent yard features. Remember, it is easy to change a tree or shrub that is planted on graph paper, but it presents somewhat of a problem when it weighs five hundred pounds.

Trees frame the house and provide a background. Properly placed, trees provide shade at strategic locations, without breaking up the lawn area. Low branching or shrubby trees -- spruces, cutleaf weeping birch, or flowering crabs -- along area boundaries help separate areas and increase privacy.

In general, areas outlined by curves on your plan should be lawn. Locate trees near area boundaries. Front yard trees near boundaries of the approach area will frame your house. Trees near the private or work area boundaries contribute to the background. (See Figure 63)

Balance in tree placement is necessary, but identical trees need not be used on opposite sides. A large tree on one side, balanced by two small trees or a clump of tall shrubs, create a more interesting contrast. Informal balance is best suited to rural homes and to most urban homes of contemporary architecture.

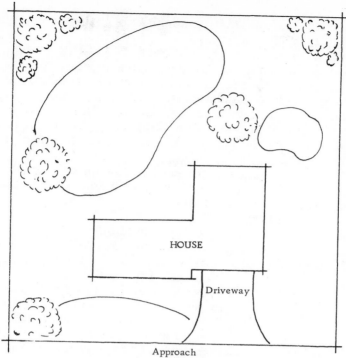

Figure 63. Pre-planning for best landscape.

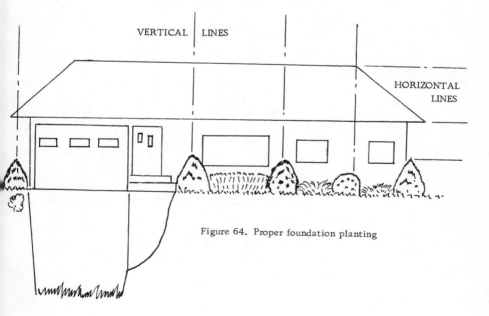

Figure 64. Proper foundation planting

The foundation planting consists of those shrubs planted immediately along the foundation of the home. To many people, the front or public foundation planting is most important. The functions of a foundation planting for the modern home are: Soften lines of the house, minimize certain essential but unattractive features of foundation structure, and make the transition from house to lawn more gradual and pleasing to the eye. Proper placement of foundation plants may give the optical illusion of changing the size or dimensions of the structure. (See Figure 64)

The strongest and harshest lines seem to focus on the vertical lines of the outside corners of a house. For this reason, the heaviest plantings should be located near the outer corners of the structure.

A lone shrub on the corner would only emphasize the line of the corner. Use a group consisting of one tall or medium shrub with several of lesser height to make the transition to ground level more gradual. (See Figure 65)

In planning shrub groups, allow the following recommended distances between shrubs: Low shrubs -- $2\frac{1}{2}$ to 3 feet; medium shrubs -- 3 to 4 feet; tall shrubs --5 to 6 feet. Exceptions to the rule include the junipers, since tall growing pyramidal junipers may attain a diameter of only three to four feet, while the low spreading types like Pfitzer or Savin junipers may have a mature spread of five to six feet. A rule of the thumb method of planting shrubs a specific distance from the foundation recommends that shrubs be located at least one-half of their mature diameter from the foundation or wall of the building.

Plants for the foundation plan can easily be selected on the basis of two rules: (1) Vertical lines in architecture are complemented by shrubs having a vertical habit of growth. (2) Horizontal lines in architecture are complemented by plant materials having a low horizontal habit of growth.

The living area consists of shrubs, mainly as boundaries, and trees which are located partly to provide background and partly for shade. Although the boundaries may be planted in several ways, the extent of the plantings will depend on the degree of privacy desired.

Hedges, as well as fences, may be used for boundaries, but should be accented by shrubs. Shrubs soften the lines and restore curves to the plan. Avoid changing from fence to shrubs at a point where there seems to be no reason for such

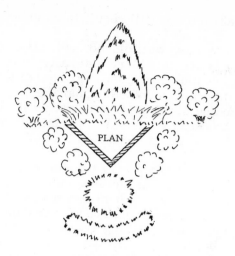

Figure 65.   Corner foundation planting and plan.
             Small shrubs may be eliminated if
             space is not available.

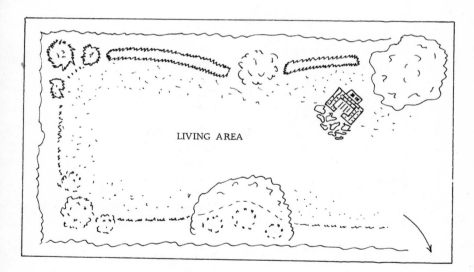

Figure 66.   Hedge and accent shrubs:
             Shrubs soften the lines and restore
             curves to the plan.

change. Such abruptness will result in an unplanned, disorganized effect.

Shrubs and trees, well placed, will allow privacy to the
members of the family and blend naturally from lawn to sky.
Shrub boarders should be planted in groups of three or more
of a kind to avoid a disorganized appearance. A particularly
large or outstanding shrub may be used singly, but in most
cases a softer line may be achieved by using a medium or low
shrub to blend in and make the transition less severe. (See
Figure 66)

Many shrubs and trees may be acceptable to the home
owner, but due to ecological factors, certain species are recommended for a given area. Such factors as moisture requirements, temperature range, and growing season must be taken
into consideration when selecting trees and shrubs.

The following lists are shrubs and trees recommended
for the upper mid-western states, prepared by the State University of North Dakota and the University of Minnesota Agriculture Extension Service.

SHRUBS FOR FOUNDATION PLANTING:

Low Shrubs -- 1 to 3 feet

Japanese Barberry   Pfitzer Juniper
Shrubby Cinquefoil   Savin Juniper
Dwarf Gooseberry   Mugho Pine
Common Juniper   Froebel Spirea
Creeping Juniper   Dwarf Viburnum
Common Snowberry   Littleleaf Mockorange

Medium Shrubs -- 3 to 6 feet

Globe Arborvitae   Pfitzer Juniper
Globe Caragana   Dwarf Ninebark
Pygmy Caragana   Garland Spirea
Alpine Currant   Threelobe Spirea
Snowhill Hydrangea   Dwarf Arctic Willow
Flowering Almond   Lemoine Mockorange

Large Shrubs -- 6 feet and up

Pyramidal Arborvitae   Peking Cotoneaster
Eastern Red Cedar   Rocky Mountain Juniper
European Cotoneaster   Van Houtte Spirea
Hedge Cotoneaster   Japanese Yew*

* Requires a moist, protected spot

CONIFEROUS EVERGREEN TREES:

Eastern Red Cedar	Black Hills Spruce
Rocky Mountain Juniper	Colorado Spruce
Western Yellow Pine	Ponderosa Pine

DECIDUOUS TREES FOR SHADE:

American Basswood or Linden	Green Ash
Silver Maple	Norway Maple
Black Walnut	American Elm

TREES FOR SHADE AND ORNAMENTAL VIEW:

European Birch	Ohio Buckeye
Cutleaf Weeping Birch	Mountain Ash
Flowering Crab	Bolleana Poplar

The lawn is the most important landscape feature, and should be in before the shrubbery is attempted. There are a number of important facts to remember when putting in a lawn. Here are just a few:

1. Plan a large, sweeping, open lawn.
2. Don't clutter the middle of the lawn with ornaments.
3. Lay out graceful curving lines for flower beds, drives, or walks. These lines can be made with a hose or rope.
4. Plan a secluded outdoor living room. Lawn furniture and a barbecue pit will add to its usefulness.
5. Avoid steep terraces. Graceful slopes are beautiful and easy to maintain.
6. Consider the esthetic possibilities of a gently sloping lawn as compared to a flat one.
7. Grade the lawn downward from the house to allow drainage and avoid a wet foundation.

When seeding, the soil quality must be considered. Lawns grow best on sandy loam and loam soils. A loam soil is made up of 40 to 65 per cent sand, not more than 20 per cent clay, and 10 to 15 per cent organic material. Loams are usually fertile, hold moisture well, drain well, and are easily tillable. [193]

[193] All About Your Lawn (Minneapolis: Northrup, King and Company, 1962), p. 9.

Mucks and peats are not suitable for lawns. Peats can be easily distinguished when dry, because of their light weight. Mucks and peats are high in organic matter and make excellent sources for mixing with those soils that lack sufficient organic matter.

Clay soils drain slowly, stay wet and soft for long periods of time, and soon become rough and uneven. Such a soil should be removed. Remove the top three or four inches, grade and replace with two to three inches of sand or sandy loam and one to two inches of organic matter. The organic matter should be thoroughly mixed with underlying soil to a depth of six to eight inches.

For best results, seed in the early spring or fall. In most areas, mid-August through early October is the best seeding time. Annual weeds are much less agressive and the small grass seedlings get a better start. Spring seeding should be done as early as possible. Early planting gives the grasses a head start on annual weeds and allows them to make considerable growth before the warm weather sets in.

The "pH" of a soil should be considered to bring out the maximum color and growth of a particular grass species. A pH of 7. 0 is neutral, while a pH higher than 7. 0 indicates alkalinity. Values lower than 7. 0 indicate acidity. Most lawns prefer a pH of about 6. 5. Kentucky bluegrass does not grow well below 6. 0 and Bent grass and Fescues do not grow well below 5. 5.[194] Most nurserymen can supply you with an inexpensive kit to check the pH of your soil. Lime can be added if the pH is acidic, and gypsum can be added if the soil is alkaline.

In most cases, a grass turf is preferred, rather than other soil covers, such as Lippia, Dichondra, Ivy, or other viney plants. Most people who use ground cover plants do so with the idea that they take less care than a lawn, but the interminable hand weeding while they are getting started, and the later work in keeping them out of flower beds, drives, and walks can amount to some real chores. There are many good ground cover plants, but they have their place and are most useful where it is difficult or impossible to grow a good lawn.

Selecting the right seed for your locality is important. Most nurserymen recommend a mixture of lawn grasses, because they will give you more wear resistance. Each kind of lawn grass grows best and looks best during certain times

[194]Ibid. , p. 10.

during the growing season. The planned succession of these
growing periods means that with a mixture of lawn seeds,
there will be at least one vigorously growing grass at all times
to cushion and protect less strongly growing species. [195]

After the lawn has been graded and raked to remove any
large stones or hard clumps of soil, the seed and fertilizer
can be spread. Use a mechanical spreader and follow the
manufacturer's recommendations on coverage rates for both
seed and fertilizer. Fertilizer applied at the time of seeding
will not burn, and your lawn will start much faster. The lawn
should be raked lightly to cover the seed, but not more than
one quarter inch. Water with a fine spray, keeping the seedbed constantly moist until the grass is two or three inches tall.
Again, most commercial lawn seed mixtures have definite directions recommended by the manufacturer for seeding and
watering.

Many new home owners prefer to sod rather than seed.
Sodding will bring an almost instantaneous lawn, but caution
must be taken to produce a sod lawn as good as a seeded lawn.

Sod may be obtained from most nurseries or commercial
sod dealers. It usually comes in cut strips eighteen inches
wide and six feet long, with a sod thickness of $1\frac{1}{2}$ to 2 inches.
The price will vary from dealer to dealer, and the buyer is
wise to shop around before he purchases his sod. Pasture sod
will cost from five to ten cents less per roll than cultured sod,
but will contain more weeds and less good strains of grasses
than cultured sod. However, with adequate weed control and
supplement seeding, a pasture sod lawn can be developed into
a fine green carpet.

Preparation for sodding is similar to seeding and caution
must be taken to lay out the lawn properly. Grading and raking
are extremely important. For best results, sodding should be
done in early spring or fall, but can be accomplished anytime
during the growing season, if watered sufficiently.

Watering any lawn is important and bears some mention.
It is best to water in the early morning or late evening so that
evaporation is kept to a minimum. Don't spare the water.
Adequate watering will develop strong, healthy, deep penetrating roots, while too little or light watering will cause a
shallow root system that cannot withstand dry periods.

Conservation is a living activity for every member of

[195] Ibid., p. 12.

the family. Each person should acquaint himself with conservation practices that he himself can follow.

Conservation in the home covers many facets, including
conservation of food, health protection, food for birds and
wildlife, and over-all safety practices around the home.

Caution in handling food is only wise management, and
requires no extra work, just common sense. Proper storage
of leftovers to avoid spoilage and possible food poisoning can
be accomplished by placing the leftovers in a suitable container
and covering it with a plastic cover or aluminum foil. After
covering the container, place it in a refrigerator for storage.
Systematic usage of leftovers will save on the food budget and
avoid spoilage of valuable food. Open cans of vegetables or
meat should not be left uncovered at room temperatures for
any length of time. Bacteria, which are always present in the
air, will soon attack the food and cause spoiling.

Drugs, household insecticides, or other poisonous mixtures should be properly labeled and kept in a safe place out of
the reach of small children. Under no circumstances should
small children be left unattended at home. Hundreds of fires
and household accidents have resulted from parental neglect
or lack of safety in the home.

Lawn herbicides and insecticides should be kept in a
locked storage cabinet out of the reach of small children. Containers used for application should be thoroughly washed and
separated from other containers. Gasoline and other flam-
mable mixtures should be safely stored and smoking prohibited
in a closed area where fumes may be concentrated.

Rotary type lawn mowers are extremely dangerous.
Stones, sticks, and other foreign materials should be picked
up before mowing. Little children should be indoors or out of
the vicinity when mowing is being done. Caution should be
taken not to leave a running lawn mower unattended and to
avoid cleaning debris away from the whirling blades. Many
a toe, hand, and even life has been lost because of rotary
mower misuse.

Young members of the family will enjoy building bird
feeders that will, in turn, provide many moments of pleasure
for the entire family. Birds, that winter in your area, are
in desperate need of food, which is covered by snow during the
winter months. Bread crumbs and prepared bird feed should
be placed in the feeder and the feeder located out of reach of

prowling cats or dogs.   Bird feeders properly placed and
stocked will provide food for many species of birds and bring
countless moments of enjoyment to the family as they watch
them feed.

In summary, conservation around the home is a family
affair.   Neither the leaky faucet nor the scattered highway litter should go unnoticed.

Home landscape planning should be in organized sections
which should provide functional living and scenic beauty.   Such
planning allows room for the small children to play, a clothes
drying area for mother to hang the wash, the family play or
barbecue area, and the ornamental or scenic front yard.   It
should not be something that cannot be used by all members
of the family.   The investment may, at first, seem substantial, but careful early planning will mean untold enjoyment for
the entire family.

When planting shrubbery, sharp lines must be avoided
that would accentuate the transition from lawn to house.   A
gradual contour is needed using low shrubs first and the taller
varieties as the vertical lines of the house are approached.

Many new home owners prefer to plant their own lawn,
while others will use cut sod purchased from nurseries or sod
growers.   In either case it is best to seek professional advice
as to the method of preparation and the type of lawn best for
the geographical location.

Household safety is of great importance to all, but extreme care must be taken when small children are involved.
They are particularly adept to investigation and household or
garden chemicals lend to their curiosity.   Such harmful chemicals should be kept out of their reach in a locked cabinet.
Other hazards around the home include gasoline cans and
rotary type mowers.

Conservation is truly a family affair, and should not be
left to the local, state, or national conservation departments.

Be proud of your home, your state, and your country:
guard it, watch over it, keep it clean, and conserve it, so
those to come will appreciate your efforts and strive to maintain its usefulness and beauty.

ACTIVITIES

1. Make a plan of your home and check to see if proper care was taken to plan the landscape. **S-C**
2. Class project: Prepare an area for seeding. Follow correct procedures and select the proper seed for the soil. **E**
3. Make a bulletin board showing pictures or photographs of different species of shrubs grown around your home. **E-S-C**
4. Make a list of resource personnel that might be contacted to speak about home safety. **E-S-C**
5. Set up a list of home safety and conservation practices that should be followed. Such a list should become a class and even an entire school project. **E-S**
6. Make a bulletin board of news clippings about accidents contributed to neglect around the home. **E-S-C**
7. Develop an interest in conservation by noticing highway litter and fire hazards. **E-S**
8. Make a resource unit about conservation in the home. **S-C**
9. Make a bibliography from resources in your school library about home conservation. **S-C**
10. Make a list of leftover foods at your home. How is it stored and when is it used? **E-S**
11. Discussion: How can we become conservation minded? **E-S-C**
12. Make a bulletin board or display that will show ways of conserving water around the home. **E**
13. Make a display of various species of grasses used for lawn seeding. Give the growing habits and needs of each species. **E-S**
14. Make resource unit or report on types of fertilizers used for lawns and shrubbery. **S-C**
15. Write to various agriculture extension services for information concerning landscaping, lawn care, and gardening. **E-S**
16. Obtain a soil kit from a nurseryman to evaluate the soil's needs. Kits will have simple directions to follow. **S-C**
17. Make a scale drawing of a "dream house" with lawn and garden. **S-C**
18. Make a scrapbook using *Better Homes and Gardens*, *Successful Farming*, and seed magazines to illustrate the possible "dream home" of the future. **E-S-C**

19. Make an evaluation of the school grounds, lawns, and land-scaping to submit in written form to the superintendent of schools with recommendations for improvement. **S**
20. Have the art teacher act as a resource person regarding art in home landscaping. **S**
21. Make a miniature country home or urban dwelling with surrounding lawns and gardens. **E-S**
22. Make a survey of the immediate neighborhood on tips for better lawn care and landscaping. Several teams may undertake the survey -- reporting back to the class. **E-S**
23. Research question: How would landscaping and lawn care differ in southern Arizona, southern Florida, and Iowa?
24. Research project: You would like to have flowers bloom-ing in your yard all through the spring, summer, and fall. Discover what flowers would give you this continuity of color. **S-C**
25. Architects are concerned that the house fits the site. Ex-plain how a house built on flat land would differ from one on rough terrain. Gardens can also become pictures. See *Art For Young America* as listed in the bibliography for this chapter. **S-C**

BIBLIOGRAPHY

All About Your Lawn. Minneapolis: Northrup, King and Com-pany, 1962. **C**

Booth, Charles O. *An Encyclopaedia of Annual and Biennial Garden Plants.* London: Faber and Faber Limited, 1952. **C**

Bronson, Wilfrid S. *Freedom and Plenty Ours To Save.* New York: Harcourt, Brace and Company, 1953. **E**

Camp, Wendell H., Victor R. Boswell, and John R. Magness. *The World In Your Garden.* Washington: National Geo-graphic Society, 1957. **S-C**

Clark, William H. *Gardening The Small Place.* Boston: Little, Brown and Company, 1952. **S-C**

Cox, E. H. M. and P. A. Cox. *Modern Shrubs.* New York: Thomas Nelson and Sons, Limited, 1958. **S-C**

Crockett, James Underwood. *Window Sill Gardening.* Garden City: Doubleday and Company, 1958. **S-C**

Free, Montague. *Plant Propagation in Pictures.* Garden City: The American Garden Guild, Inc., and Doubleday and Com-pany, 1957. **S-C**

Hard, G. Gustav. *Landscaping the Home,* Extension Bulletin
    No. 283, Agricultural Extension Service. St. Paul:
    University of Minnesota, 1958. *S-C*

Heyne, Carl J., et. al. *Art For Young America.* Peoria:
    Charles A. Bennett Company, 1960. *S-C*

Hoag, Donald. *Landscape Your Home,* Bulletin No. 407,
    North Dakota Agriculture Experimental Station, May,
    1957. *C*

Howard, Frances. *Landscaping With Vines.* New York: The
    Macmillan Company, 1959. *S-C*

Howland, Joseph E. *The House Beautiful Book of Gardens
    and Outdoor Living.* New York: Doubleday and Company,
    Inc., 1958. *E-S-C*

Kinney, Richard R. *A Guide To Gardening With Young People.*
    New York: Prentice-Hall, Inc., 1955. *E*

Luxton, George E. *Flower Growing In The North: A Month-
    by-Month Guide.* Minneapolis: University of Minnesota
    Press, 1956. *S-C*

Melady, John Hayes. *The Home Owner's Complete Garden
    Handbook.* New York: Grosset and Dunlap, 1954. *S-C*

Rockwell, F. F. (ed.) *10,000 Garden Questions Answered By
    Fifteen Experts.* Garden City: The American Garden
    Guild, Inc., and Doubleday and Company, Inc., 1953. *S-C*

Rockwell, F. F. and Esther C. Grayson. *The Complete Book
    of Bulbs.* Garden City: The American Garden Guild, Inc.,
    and Doubleday and Company, Inc., 1953. *S-C*

_____. *The Complete Book
    of Lawns.* Garden City: The American Garden Guild, Inc.,
    and Doubleday and Company, 1956. *C*

Shoemaker, James S. and Benjamin Teskey. *Practical Horti-
    culture.* New York: John Wiley and Sons, 1955. *S-C*

Smith, F. C. *The First Book of Conservation.* New York:
    Franklin Watts, 1954. *E*

Spencer, Edwin Rollin. *Just Weeds.* New York: Charles
    Scribners Sons, 1957. *S-C*

Stradtherr, Richard J. *The Home Lawn,* Agricultural Exten-
    sion Service Folder 16S. St. Paul: University of Minne-
    sota, 1958. *S-C*

Weiser, V. L. *Lawn and Garden Fertilizers,* Extension
    Service Circular A-293. Bismarck: North Dakota State
    University, April, 1958. *C*

Zaylskie, John J. *Fertilization of Trees,* Extension Service
    Circular A-362. Bismarck: North Dakota State University,
    January, 1962. *C*

AUDIO-VISUAL MATERIALS

16 mm. FILMS

Adventuring in Conservation - (Ind. U.)

This film combines the values of outdoor life and camping with the responsibilities for conservation of our resources and shows boys and girls many ways in which
they can take an active part in the whole program. *E*

City Water Supply - (EBF)

Animated drawing describes the relation between rainfall
and life. The source of city water supply -- wells, rivers,
lakes, and watersheds -- is shown. *E*

Conserving Our Soil Today - (Cor)

Latest techniques and experiments in soil conservation
are shown in this film, such as the use of plastic sheets
to retain moisture, subsoil mulching, new fertilizers,
and experiments with artificial rain to determine patterns
of erosion. *E-S*

Constructing Landscape Features - (Michigan State U.)

Explanation of design details for walls, steps, walks,
and fences with emphasis on practicality, proportion,
and appearance. *S-C*

Contamination of Water Supplies By Back Siphonage -
(U of M)

Bad-tasting drinking water in a public school is found
upon investigation to be contaminated by a faulty plumb-
ing arrangement, which results in back siphonage. The
film shows corrective measures used to overcome the
difficulty. *S-C*

Developing The Space Near Buildings - (Michigan State U.)

Suggestions for different types of buildings. *S-C*

Gardening - (EBF)

Attention is given to aspects of soil, growth, role of
the sun and insect pests. *S-C*

Garden Plants and How They Grow - (Cor)

Shows factors necessary for good growth of plants -- soil and sunlight. *E*

How Birds Help Us - (Cor)

Jack believes all birds are pests, like the crows in his garden. Looking around, however, he observes that birds help us in many ways, such as providing us with food, destroying harmful insects and rodents, eating weed seeds, and giving us pleasure with their bright colors and happy songs. *E*

How Green Is Your Garden - (American Ag. Chemical Co.)

Useful how-to-do-it information on lawn and garden care is shown. *S-C*

Landscape Designs For The Home Property - (Michigan State U.)

Methods for designing home property; purposes of plot development, grading, drainage, planting plan, and construction detail. *S-C*

Landscape Materials - (Michigan State U.)

Useful components of landscape; relationship of shrubs, trees, evergreens, stone and fences. *S-C*

Landscaping For The Future - (Cornell U.)

Shows techniques in transplanting shrubs and trees for successful growth and lasting beauty around the home. *S-C*

Lawn Beautiful - (Assn. Films, Inc.)

Color film shows how effective a little know how and a planned lawn program can be to produce that luxurious green lawn. *S=C*

Lawns - (Hayes Spray Gun Company)

This color film shows the necessary steps in building and maintaining a successful lawn. It includes preparation of the soil, selecting and planting of seed, proper watering, mowing, fertilizing, insect and fungus control, and remedies for other lawn problems. *S-C*

Man's Problem - (EBF)

This film points out that man needs great quantities of water and that water is of vital importance to people on the farms. *S-C*

Nature's Half Acre - (W. D. P.)

This film shows all of the millions of inhabitants of the tiny grass-roots world in any half acre and how the balance of nature is maintained. Sequences in nest building, feeding the young, and the activity during the four seasons of the year are interestingly presented. *E-S*

Our Soil Resources - (EBF)

Animation as well as live photography are used to show the formation of soil, the factors that lead to the formation of different soil zones, and the conservation aspects of soil control. *E-S*

The Truck Farmer - (EBF)

Planting, irrigating, spraying, harvesting, packing, and shipping truck crops are detailed. *E-S*

The Water We Drink - (Cor)

This film depicts the importance of proper drinking habits for good health and illustrates the many body functions which water serves. *E*

What Is Landscape Design? - (Michigan State U.)

This film reviews the history of landscape architecture. It also shows how logic is applied in designing outdoor space for human use. *S-C*

FILMSTRIPS

Making Water Safe To Drink - (SVE)

This filmstrip covers the sources of community water supplies to the essential steps of water purification. **E- S**

Plants in Home and School - (Eyegate)

Describes the care of plants at home, the type of plant which grows in homes, and the work that is done in school gardens. **S- C**

Plants In My Garden - (Eyegate)

Describes the care of a garden -- weeding, watering, and destroying pests. **S- C**

Testing Soil - (SVE)

Explains the necessity for testing soil and shows how it is tested. **E- S- C**

GRENGS

Burn down your cities and leave
our farms, and your cities will
spring up again as if by magic;
but destroy our farms, and
the grass will grow in the streets
of every city of the country.

W. J. Bryan

Chapter XV   AGRICULTURE CONSERVATION

OBJECTIVES

   I. To call attention to recent legislation that has had an effect on agriculture conservation.

  II. To point to significant technological advances which have had impact on agriculture conservation.

 III. To indicate the important research and education groups in agriculture conservation.

 IV. To note the economic implications of the changing population as they relate to agriculture conservation.

     Agriculture conservation is many faceted and inter-related to all other aspects of conservation, and in many ways may be said to be the capstone in the study of conservation. The farmlands and the rural areas are the hinterlands which literally feed the cities and towns of this country -- with raw materials, with human resources, and with a market place. Agriculture conservation cuts across the broad framework of conservation in that the dynamics of population growth is as essential in understanding this aspect of conservation as is the impact of mechanization on farming and the rural community. Agriculture conservation must be concerned with the economic aspects of farming such as the cost-price squeeze and farm price supports as well as with the ecological ramifications of soil, water, forests, and wildlife.

     President Eisenhower hit at the population dynamics of agriculture conservation in his message to Congress. He said, "A century ago an American farm worker fed himself and three others. Today he feeds himself and twenty others." [196]

     Since 1920, the farm population has been declining. From 1933 to 1957, the number of farmers decreased from 32, 393, 000 to 20, 396, 000 -- dropping from 26 per cent to

---

[196]"What is Happening to American Farmers?", Christian Science Monitor, March 21, 1958.

- 333 -

12 per cent of the national population . Young people reared
on the farm are moving to urban centers in droves. Many, although they find many features of rural life attractive, cannot
find jobs on the farms, or find the salaries so meager they
cannot afford to stay down on the farm. Fewer and fewer workers in mechanized farming can do more and better work than a
multitude of hands -- and at less cost. So, the following comment may be symbolic. Speakers at the American Institute of
Cooperation in Fort Collins, Colorado, in August, 1957, even
discussed the possibility that 500,000 commercial farmers
may one day meet the agricultural needs of the United States. [197]

The implication is clear: "As land becomes constantly
more valuable under pressure of population and the costs of
farming in terms of labor, machinery, and fuel, increase
steadily, the bad farmer and a wasteful agriculture are steadily being forced out of existence. " [198]

The Committee for Economic Development, a non-profit
economic research foundation, among its several proposals
listed the following: Retirement of a large amount of land so
as to reduce both the number of people and the amount of land
devoted to farming. [199] There are those who disagree. Among
them is Dr. Philip M. Raup, professor of agricultural economics at the University of Minnesota. He thinks that the assump-
tion that the farm problem will solve itself once the land is
freed of marginal farmers may be the most tragic kind of wish-
ful thinking. [200] It is to be recalled, too, that purely economic
reasons drove the miners of the fields forever westward as
they sapped the soil in their avarice, wearing out farm after
farm. Only when there was nowhere else to move did farmers
look back over their shoulders and think of conservation -- for
purely economic reasons. The problem of population dynamics
and agriculture conservation is not simply an economic consideration. It is a sociological problem -- involving people --
a political problem -- involving government and law-making --
and it is an ecological problem -- involving man: his environment of plants and animals, water and air, soil and forests.

The federal government began to play a very significant
role in agriculture conservation during the Franklin Roosevelt

[197] Ibid.
[198] "Conservation, " Colliers 1954 Yearbook, (New York: P. F. Colliers and Sons,
1954), p. 150.
[199] Carl Rowan, "Should the Marginal Farmer Quit the Soil?", Minneapolis
Morning Tribune, March 8, 1958.
[200] Ibid.

administration with the beginning of cash-subsidy to farmers.
When the Supreme Court declared that the authority under which
the Agricultural Adjustment Administration operated was uncon-
stitutional, the A. A. A. was reorganized to operate under the
basic Soil Conservation Act. Since the reorganization, the
A. A. A. has paid farmers for the establishment of soil conservation practices. The cash-subsidy program has operated
closely with the soil conservation district program in some
parts of the nation, but has worked quite independently of the
districts in other parts. [201]

The Agricultural Act of 1956, passed during the Eisenhower administration, provided for a soil bank in two phases.
First, the acreage reserve program authorized payments to
farmers for reducing production of the six basic crops (corn,
wheat, cotton, tobacco, peanuts, and rice) by reducing crop
acreage below the farm acreage allotment. The program was
voluntary except for corn. The second phase provided for the
conservation reserve. The Secretary of Agriculture was authorized to enter into contracts with agricultural producers for
a minimum period of three years and a maximum period of ten
years. The producers would devote a designated part of his
crop land to conserving uses, trees, grass, or water facilities,
agreeing not to pasture or harvest any crop therefrom except
under certain emergency conditions. The Secretary, in turn,
would agree to pay a fair share of the costs of establishing the
conservation use and, in addition, make an annual payment to
the producer to provide a fair and reasonable annual return for
the land diverted to conservation uses. [202]

The immediate effects of the soil bank were not as effective as had been hoped. It was only natural for farmers to put
their poorer acres into reserves, and despite a reduction of
about three per cent in cropland use because of the soil bank,
in 1957 increased yields kept crop production about equal to
that of 1956. [203] But significantly by 1960, a total of about 23
million acres were in the Conservation Reserve. [204]

Specific conservation practices in land cover and water

[201]William A. Rockie, "Soil Conservation," Conservation of Natural Resources,
edited by Guy-Harold Smith (New York: John Wiley and Sons, Inc., 1958), p. 88.

[202]"Agriculture," 1957 Britannica Book of the Year (Chicago: Encyclopaedia
Britannica, Inc., 1957), p. 90.

[203]The Annual America 1958 (New York: Americana Corp., 1958), p. 15.

[204]The 1960 Conservation Reserve, U.S.D.A. (Washington: Government Printing
Office, 1959), p. 1.

conservation are outlined in the Conservation Reserve program. The following are but a few:

1. Planting a permanent cover of grasses and legumes to protect soil or to change land use, including treatment of the land with limes, fertilizer, or gypsum if necessary to establish such cover.
2. Establishing trees or shrubs for erosion control, watershed protection, shelterbelt, or forestry purposes.
3. Constructing dams, pits, or ponds to permit grazing management as a means of protecting vegetative cover on land not placed in the Conservation Reserve. (See Figure 67)
4. Establishing and managing cover specifically beneficial to wildlife.
5. Water impounding to benefit fish and other wildlife. This practice includes the development of shallow water areas to improve habitat for waterfowl, fur animals, and other wildlife. [205]

The Feed Grain Program, although designed essentially to raise farm income and to reduce program costs to tax payers, none-the-less is a significant agriculture conservation measure. The diverted acres may be devoted to the following conservation uses, among others:[206]

1. Permanent type or rotation cover of grasses and legumes.
2. Temporary cover of grasses or legumes.
3. Wildlife food or habitat planting.
4. Trees or shrubs.

The federal government has played a major role in agricultural conservation. Financial assistance, especially for soil conservation measures has been provided by the Federal government through the Soil Conservation Service, the Agricultural and Stabilization and Conservation Service, The T.V.A., and the Farmers' Home Administration. Assistance has been particularly in the form of loans from the F.H.A., in low cost fertilizer from the T.V.A., and as direct cost outlay from other agencies. Over the years, the program of the Agricultural Stabilization and Conservation Service has been the largest source of financial aid for these purposes. [207]

[205]Ibid., p. 10.
[206]The 1964 Feed Grain Program, Agricultural Stabilization and Conservation Service, U. S. Department of Agriculture (Washington: Government Printing Office, 1964), p. 5.
[207]The McGraw-Hill Encyclopedia of Science and Technology, Vol. 12 (New York: McGraw-Hill Book Company, Inc., 1960), p. 449.

Figure 67.   Protection of agricultural areas from future flooding

During the 1955 through 1960 sessions of their legislatures, forty states enacted laws to further cooperation between state and local agencies and the Secretary of Agriculture in activities authorized by the Watershed Protection and Flood Protection and Flood Prevention Act of August 4, 1954, as amended.   In all, 167 such laws were enacted in the forty states during this period.   The Watershed Protection and Flood Prevention Act, as amended, authorizes the Secretary of Agriculture to furnish assistance to state and local agencies

Minnesota Department of Business Development

Figure 68.   Corn cultivation

in developing projects for the following: (1) prevention of erosion, floodwater, and sediment damages; (2) management of water for agriculture, including irrigation and drainage; (3) development of fish and wildlife resources; (4) development of municipal and industrial water supplies; (5) creation of recreation areas; (6) reduction of pollution.   This new project-type approach requires that local people, through their local agencies (organizations), initiate and participate fully in the development of the watershed projects.   Thus, they are local projects with federal participation rather than federal projects with local participation. [208]

The above paragraphs point to the newer phase of agriculture conservation, and conservation in general. This phase extends the ecological or integrated approach to include a more complete acceptance of the force of societal factors -- such as economics, government, and social conditions, in determining resource management. There is also a closer examination of social costs and benefits and of human goals for which resources are employed. [209]

Intimately related to the story of agriculture conservation is the pageant of progress in American farming -- its coming of technological age. In fact, "the change from hand to power methods in American agriculture in little more than a century is one of the most far-reaching transformations in human history."[210] (See Figures 68 and 69) Today, with mounted or semi-mounted disk plows, depth and speed are no longer limited by horse or mule power. Speed of cultivating with the present-day tractor eases the pressure of controlling weeds. Today, one man with a two-row tractor mounted corn picker out-husks a dozen good hand pickers. Milking machines enable fewer men to bring more milk to more people. Portable sprinkler irrigation saves water and can be used on level or sloping land. These are but a few modifications where mechanization has increased farm production.

Scientific mechanized agriculture has not only reduced the grueling types of work in farm production, but it has also resulted in a phenomenal development of food volume, improvement in quality, and decrease in production costs. For example, refrigeration of perishable products -- meats, milk, fruits, and vegetables -- greatly reduces spoilage. The farmer can now raise perishable foods in regions best suited to them with the assurance that they will be delivered in good condition by refrigerator cars or trucks. Thus, the choice of nutritious foods has been greatly widened and the nation's diet has been improved. Thus, the farmer's profit possibilities have increased.

[208]R. Frank Hedges and L. M. Adams, Status of State Legislation Relating to the Watershed Protection Act as Amended, Soil Conservation Service, U. S. Department of Agriculture (Washington: Government Printing Office, 1961), p. 1.

[209]McGraw-Hill Encyclopedia of Science and Technology, Vol. 3 (New York: McGraw-Hill Book Company, Inc. , 1960), p. 410.

[210]Bert S. Gittins, The Land of Plenty (Chicago: Farm Equipment Institute, 1950).

Minnesota Department of Business Development

Figure 69.   A hay baler at work

With the possible exception of proximity to shopping centers, there is little difference today between the farm home
and the city home.   The rural home now may have running
water, electrical appliances, and telephone.   The rural home
has the advantage, in fact, of a yard, a garden plot, and a
ranging area for children or pets.

But, one of the major economic problems of the day is
the economic plight of the farmer.   Needed is an economic
climate -- a set of institutions and operating programs -- in
which a flexible, efficient agriculture can produce abundance
and earn a fair return for the farmer.   The efficient farmer

should be able to earn an income comparable to incomes earned
by similar resources and for similar efforts in non-farm employment.[211] But, such is not the case. Average per capita
income of farm people is low -- $965 compared with $2,216
for non-farm people in 1959. It is also to be noted that large
commercial farms ($5,000 annual sales and above) make 87
per cent of all farm product sales, but they represent only 39
per cent of all farms, and most income farming is earned by
these largers farms.[212] As Orville L. Freeman, Secretary of
Agriculture says, "Agriculture presents a puzzling contradic-
tion -- an outstanding success in terms of efficient production
and in contribution to economic growth, but a serious problem
in terms of farm income and budgetary costs. This riddle
must be solved."[213]

In addition to mechanization, research and education
have been great forces in raising American agriculture. There
are six major functionary groups who devote their energies to
educating and informing the farmers.

I. State agricultural colleges teach efficient, profitable,
and scientific farm methods. These colleges also provide
short courses in addition to four year courses for agriculture
students.

II. High schools in rural areas often teach vocational
agriculture. Federal and state departments of education direct
the programs.

III. State and federal experiment stations breed new
plants, improve livestock, test new machinery, and act as
clearing houses for information regarding farm problems.
(See Figure 70)

IV. County agents through state extension departments
go directly to the farmers to give demonstrations, develop
local leadership, or communicate the latest research. (See
Figure 71)

V. Voluntary organizations such as the Farm Bureau
and National Farmers Organization work to improve the
farmer's income and way of life.

VI. Manufacturers of farm equipment also carry on
extensive research to develop better tools and equipment to

---

[211]Food and Agriculture: A Program for the 1960's, U. S. Department of Agriculture (Washington: Government Printing Office, 1962), p. 14.
[212]Ibid., p. 49.
[213]Ibid., III.

Minnesota Department of Conservation

Figure 70. Experimentation and soil erosion

promote efficiency and economy.[214]

And, interestingly enough, one of the proposals made
for a program for the 1960's by the U. S. Department of Agriculture was that Congress should consider making special provision for improving the educational opportunities and vocational training of youth.[215]

[214]Contribution of Agriculture to Health -- Happiness -- Prosperity (New York:
Bureau of Educational Services in cooperation with International Harvester, 1947), p. 12.
[215]Food and Agriculture: A Program for the 1960's, op. cit. , p. 12.

Minnesota Historical Society

Figure 71.   Contour plowing -- a practical application of agricultural research

In his statement in the booklet *Food and Agriculture: A Program For The 1960's*, Orville L. Freeman said: "On the one hand, more land is being used to produce food and fiber than is needed. On the other hand, there is a growing demand for recreation, wildlife, and simply open space in and around the cities of our increasingly urban nation. This may well be *the critical decade* in determing how wisely our land will be used for generations to come. [216]

[216]Ibid., p. IV.

In summary, agriculture conservation may be thought of as that integrating element in the over-all human, social concern with conservation. It is the ecological rationale which gives coherence to the struggle for better recreational resources -- shot through with aesthetic elements of the landscape: field, stream, mountains, forests, lakes, birds and mammals, fish and reptiles, sun and clouds, and a clear sky. Agriculture conservation is concerned with people: Their economic, social, and political environment. Agriculture conservation is concerned with legislation at the national, state, and local levels which provides the machinery for farm progress. Agriculture conservation is concerned with mechanization, research, and education which provide farmers with better tools and vehicles in making a better life. Agricultural conservation is the ecological cement which ties soil conservation, water conservation, grassland conservation, forest conservation, wildlife conservation into a comprehensive unit for a matrix. And it is out of this over-all format that a philosophy for the future can be developed.

ACTIVITIES

1. Make a report on ten different occupations related to agriculture. Consider: education, salary, skills, future of occupation, etc. **S**
2. Indicate foods raised in the state, but which are often offered in local markets out-of-season. Contrast costs and quality. **E-S**
3. Visit local "freezer," canning factory, or meat packing plant as a class, committee, or individual and report back to class. **E-S**
4. Check a variety of food products to discover how the retail price compares with price paid the farmer and what per cent of the food dollar the farmer received. **E-S**
5. Make a line or bar graph showing the shift of population by decade from the farm to the urban and suburban areas. **E-S**
6. Discuss parity. The definition from the *Congressional Quarterly* may be a beginning: "Parity is a formula to measure the purchasing power of farm prices. If a bushel of corn sells for 100 per cent of parity, the proceeds of that sale will buy the farmer as many Sunday neckties as

the price of a bushel of corn bought during the base period. For commodities subject to old parity the base period is 1910-14, while for modern parity the base is the most recent ten years. Traditional parity gradually bridges the gap between old and modern parity. " **S- C**

7. Collect pictures or photographs for a display showing the mechanization of the modern farm. **E—S**

8. On an outline map of the United States, show per cent of total land area in farms (see Guy-Harold Smith, p. 155) and/or by dots show the area of major concentration of cotton, corn, tobacco, rice, wheat, etc. **E-S**

9. Visit an efficiently operated farm in the community -- especially during planting or harvesting time. Specific objectives should be outlined for the visit. **E-S**

10. Write a research paper, in depth, regarding the dairy industry, poultry industry, cotton industry, or beef cattle and hog industries. **S-C**

11. Make a model of a "good" and a "bad" farm at the rear of the classroom. **E**

12. Brainstorm what research and education will have done to agriculture twenty years from now. **S-C**

13. Have an agriculture conservation fair with a variety of exhibits ranging from machinery and dairy products to wildlife and electricity. **E-S**

14. Have an agriculture conservation field day where students have an opportunity to meet conservationists and share the results of their projects with experts. **S-C**

15. Present an assembly program where students present skits, read poems or essays, or sing songs having to do with agricultural conservation. **E-S**

16. Write a radio or television script for presentation over closed circuit television or local radio station. **S-C**

17. Prepare a series of transparencies for the overhead projector having to do with the various aspects of agricultural conservation. **S-C**

18. Mimeograph a series of descriptions of farmlands in trouble. Ask the students how they would solve the problem. **S-C**

19. Have an exchange program of urban and farm youths for a day. Three students from a city school may exchange places with three rural students for a day. In each instance, the students would be given the opportunity to talk about conservation problems. **S**

20. Organize a workshop or seminar for teachers on agricultural conservation or the whole area of conservation. **C**
21. Make a bulletin board display of the evolution of modern farming. A time line with pictures of specific inventions might be desirable. Brief reports could be correlated with the development of the project such as wooden moldboard vs. cast-iron share, foot-lift sulky, scythe and cradle and treading vs. threshing machine. **E-S**
22. Discuss the proposition that farming has become big business. This may be introduced by a panel of experts such as a farm equipment dealer, U. S. D. A. official, and a practicing farmer. **S-C**
23. Make a large wall chart showing major exports and imports of agricultural products. (Indicate countries from which products come and go -- as well as volume.) **E-S**
24. Relate current events to agriculture conservation. Clip current newspapers for articles and have a round table discussion. Examples: "The Poultry War" involving the Common Market, "The Wheat Sales to U. S. S. R.," "Import of Beef to the U. S." **S-C**
25. Dramatize "The Farmer's Wife." Show the changes that have occurred to make her life better during the last few decades. A visit could be made to grandfather's farm by a city cousin. **E-S**

BIBLIOGRAPHY

Agricultural Conservation Program: Handbook for 1964 (Minnesota).

> Agricultural Stabilization and Conservation Service, U. S. Department of Agriculture. Washington: Government Printing Office, December, 1963. **S-C**

Agriculture: Our Fountain of Life, Bureau of Educational Services. New York: Byron G. Moon Company, Inc., 1947. **E-S**

Black, John Donald. *Introduction to Economics for Agriculture*. New York: The Macmillan Company, 1953. **S-C**

Blanck, Fred C. *Handbook of Food and Agriculture.* New York: Reinhold Publishing Corporation, 1955. **C**

Caldwell, Bailey, and Watkins. *Our Land and Our Living.* Syracuse: L. W. Singer Company, 1947. **S-C**

Contributions of Agriculture to Health-Happiness...Prosperity.. Bureau of Educational Services. New York: Byron G. Moon Company, Inc., 1947. **S-C**

Down On The Farm (commentary by Stewart H. Holbrook). New York: Crown Publishers, Inc., 1954. **E-S-C**

Food and Agriculture: A Program For The 1960's, U. S. Department of Agriculture. Washington: Government Printing Office, March, 1962. **S-C**

Food for the Future -- Through Research, Agriculture Information Bulletin No. 220, U. S. Department of Agriculture. Washington: Government Printing Office, April, 1960. **E**

Gittins, Bert S. *Land of Plenty.* Chicago: Farm Equipment Institute, 1950. **E-S**

Graham, E. H. *Natural Principles of Land Use.* New York: Oxford University Press, 1944. **S-C**

Higbee, Edward. *The American Oasis: The Land and its Uses.* New York: Alfred A. Knopf, 1957. **S-C**

Hilles, Helen Train. *Farm Wanted.* New York: Julian Messner, Inc., 1951. **S**

Howard, Robert West. *The Real Book About Farms.* Garden City: Garden City Books, 1952. **E-S**

Land Facts, Soil Conservation Service, U. S. Department of Agriculture. Washington: Government Printing Office, November, 1953. **S-C**

McWilliams, Cary. *Ill Fares The Land.* Boston: Little, Brown and Company, 1942. **S-C**

Pageant of Progress. Racine: J. I. Case Company, 1951.

Rowan, Carl. "Should The Marginal Farmer Quit The Soil?" *Minneapolis Tribune,* February 8, 1958. **S-C**

Schickele, Rainer. *Agricultural Policy: Farm Programs and National Welfare.* New York: McGraw-Hill Book Company, 1954. **S-C**

Smith, Guy-Harold. *Conservation of Natural Resources.* New York: John Wiley and Sons, Inc., 1958. **S-C**

Status of State Legislation Relating To The Watershed Protection And Flood Prevention Act As Amended, Soil Conservation Service, U. S. Department of Agriculture. Washington: Government Printing Office, January, 1961. **C**

The 1960 Conservation Reserve, Commodity Stabilization Service, U. S. Department of Agriculture. Washington: Government Printing Office, July, 1959. *S-C*

The 1964 Feed Grain Program, Agricultural Stabilization and
Conservation Service, U. S. Department of Agriculture.
Washington: Government Printing Office, January, 1964.
S-C

The Research and Policy Committee. *Economic Policy for
American Agriculture.* New York: The Research and
Policy Committee, January 1956. *C*

"What is Happening to American Farmers?" *Christian Science
Monitor,* March 21, 1958. *S-C*

AUDIO-VISUAL MATERIALS

FILMS:

Agriculture Lifelines - (U. S. D. A.)

The story of food on the move, showing vital steps which
insure quality and quantity of the food we want ... and
get. *S-C*

Agriculture Story, The - (U. S. D. A.)

A summary of the many fields of work done by the U. S.
Department of Agriculture. Accomplishments of U. S. D. A.
are shown. *S-C*

Agriculture, U. S. A. - (U. S. D. A.)

Answers many questions the public is asking today: What
is the place of the farmer in today's society? In the
home, industry, the market place? It surveys the past,
talks of the present and looks toward the future. This
film shows that from research comes knowledge and from
knowledge comes power, the power to meet needs of our
everexpanding population. *S-C*

Atomic Age Farmer - (Handel Films)

Shows how agricultural research is speeded up by using
a radio-active tracer element in livestock feed and fertilizer. *S-C*

Big Harvest - (Industrial Films, Inc.)

Explains the basic service which agriculture has played and must continue to play in the support of our economy and of the kind of life which we lead, and of the strength our nation. *E-S-C*

Comments By Farmers - (U. S. D. A.)

Three mid-American farmers express themselves on current problems of agriculture. *S-C*

Compass for Agriculture - (USDA)

Explains in some detail how U. S. D. A. and state agriculture departments collect data from which crop and livestock reports are made. *S-C*

Corn Farmer, The - (EBF)

Depicts the lot of a typical corn farmer in growing and harvesting his crops. Problems of planting, cultivating, harvesting, crop rotation, haying, hog and cattle raising and marketing are portrayed. The role of the machine in modern farming is given due consideration. *S-C*

Dairy Farm, The - (Cor)

The economic and social importance of the dairy farm in American life is portrayed by a visit to a typical midwest farm. *E-S*

Farmer Don and The City - (Film Associates)

Shows various ways the farmer and city people depend and help each other. *E*

Farmer, The - (EBF)

Varied tasks on a farm are presented -- including the procedure of harvesting. *E*

Farmers of India - (United World Films)

Shows a densely populated, underdeveloped land marked by poverty, crowded living conditions, famine, and disease. *E-S*

Farming in South China - (United World Films)

Farm land is scarce and an intensive subsistence type of agriculture is the characteristic means of livelihood. **E-S**

Helpful Henry - (International Harvester Co.)

A comedy showing the mistakes a city chap makes on his first trip to the farm. **E-S**

It Started With Eve - (Grocery Mfg. of America)

Compares early day and present methods of marketing food. The film breaks down our total food bill into components and shows relative costs of each step in the marketing process. **S-C**

New Man On The Land - (Massey Ferguson)

The film explains how today's management techniques and equipment have put "a new man on the land." **S-C**

New Uses for Farm Products - (USDA)

Review highlights of U. S. D. A. researchers in their constant quest for new uses for farm products. **S-C**

Old MacDonald - (Am. Feed Mfg. Assn.)

Using the Edward R. Murrow television technique, a farmer is called in to tell his story. **E-S**

Production of Foods - (EBF)

This film presents authentic material concerning the technology and geography of food production. Photographic and animation sequences depict the role of land in production; the methods employed in the production of plant and animal products; and the relation of animal food production to plant food. **E-S**

REA Story, The - (USDA)

Recalls the early days of drudgery before rural electricity and indicates how electric power has transformed life in rural America. **S-C**

Science and Agriculture - (EBF)

Presents the soybean as an example of the ever-increasing importance of science and technology in agriculture. **S**

To Market, To Market - (Frith Films Co.)

Shows the flow of commodities from the farm, through the different wholesalers' hands to the retailer. **S-C**

Wheat Farmer, The - (EBF)

Shows the daily life of a wheat farmer and his family in a typical midwestern area. **E**

SLIDES:

America The Beautiful - (USDA)

Slides show a typical conservation practice in each of the fifty states. **E-S-C**

Farm Management - (Hal Routhe)

Illustrates some of the most important principles in planning a farm business. **S-C**

GLOSSARY

Abortion - birth which occurs before the normal time

Absorption - process by which water and dissolved substances pass into cells

Accessible - to easily reach

Acquatic - living or growing in water, as a fresh-water environment

Adiabatic - occurring with loss or gain of heat

Aggregation - collection of many individuals generally of the same species

Algae - water plants that do not have true leaves, stems, or roots -- algae may be one-celled or as large as seaweed

Alluvial - a deposit formed by sand or mud left by flowing water

Anthracite - highest grade of coal, hard and burning with little smoke or flame

Aquifer - a water-bearing bed or stratum of earth, gravel, or porous stone

Argon - chemical element -- colorless and odorless gas that forms a small part of the air

Aromatic - sweet smelling, as to give off such an odor

Atomic energy - energy released when the nuclei of atoms are broken apart or put together

Bacteria - microscopic, one-celled fungus plants -- can be beneficial or harmful

Bare bottom stage - first stage in pond succession -- having a sandy bottom

Bauxite - mineral from which aluminum is obtained

Benefication - process of improving or developing higher quality product from low grade ore

Biome - major world-wide ecological units such as the desert, the tropical forest, or the coniferous forest

Biota - animal and plant life of a region -- the fauna and flora

Bituminous - soft coal, burning with much smoke and flame

Bounty - a sum of money paid by some states for the scalps, claws, or other portions of predatory birds or animals

Capillary - a force causing the rise of a liquid along the surface of a tube or hollow place
Carbon dioxide - a gas -- in expiration animals expel carbon
   dioxide while plants absorb it from the air to use in the
   construction of plant tissue
Carbonate - to charge with carbonic acid gas, as soda water
   is carbonated
Carnivores - animals that eat meat, other animals
Cartilage - gristle, the flexible substance which forms parts
   of the skeletons of vertebrates
Chernozem - rich black soil, especially that across the central
   portion of Europe and Russia
Chernozemic soils - black soils which are formed under sub-
   humid conditions and under grasslands
Coke - fuel made from soft coal used in furnaces for melting
   metal
Commensalism - gains benefit from its host without conferring
   either harm or benefit.
Condensation - the change from a gaseous to a liquid form,
   as from water vapor to rain
Coniferous - refers to a tree bearing seed cones -- usually
   an evergreen
Conservation - the preservation and wise use of natural
   resources
Contour plowing - plowing so that the rows "run around" the
   hill or slope on the same level, rather than up and down
Contraception - the prevention of conception or impregnation
Crustaceans - any of a class of animals, most of which live
   in water, having a hard outside shell such as crabs,
   lobsters, and shrimps
Curie - a unit of mass of radium emanation, being the amount
   in equilibrium with one gram of radium

Deciduous - trees which shed leaves annually
Decompose - to decay or rot
Dehydration - process of taking water away
Deme - particular population in a particular area
Demography - the statistical study of population
Derivatives - obtained from an original source
Desertic soils - red or grayish soils formed under conditions
   where rainfall is very low, generally very rich in
   mineral nutrients
Disintegration - a crumbling or wearing down, as rocks by
   weather

Dispersal - spread of individuals away from their homesites

Distillation - process of separating a liquid from a mixture by heating so as to form a vapor which is carried off and condensed by cooling

Diurnal - occurring daily or belonging to the daytime

Dominance - relative control exerted by organisms over the species composition of the community -- species exerting this important control are called dominants

Ecological succession - sequence of events that follow a pre-dictable pattern given a particular set of physiographic factors and climate as in pond succession from bare bottom, submerged vegetation, emerging vegetation, temporary pond and prairie, to beech and maple forest

Ecology - study of the relationships between living things and their environments

Electrodialysis - relatively new process which has risen to a leading status among the processes designed to de-mineralize brackish water

Electroscope - an instrument for determining when dangerous amounts of radiation are present in the air

Embryo - animal from fertilized egg until it can live inde-pendently -- undeveloped, as a chicken in an egg

Emerging vegetation stage - in pond succession, the stage where scattered vegetation begins to break through the surface of the water

Environment - surroundings of an organism, living and non-living

Eolian - action of wind on the land

Equilibrium - opposite forces seem to balance or equal each other

Erosion - process of topsoil being lost by the action of wind or water

Evaporation - the process during which a liquid changes to a vapor

Evolution - the theory that all present forms of plant and animal life have developed gradually through the ages from lower and simpler forms

Fallout - radioactive particles from an atomic explosion which may be carried in the atomic cloud for long dis-tances from ground zero and then "rained down" to the earth's surface

Feces - solid intestinal waste material

Ferrous - pertaining to or derived from iron

Filter - either apparatus or material such as sand or cloth to
     strain out solid matter from liquids

Fission - splitting of atomic nuclei into two approximately
     equal parts with the release of energy

Flora - plants or plant life

Food chains - members of a community are linked together by
     their eating-eaten relationships

Food web - the total of all the food chains in a community

Forage - food for horses and cattle

Freshets - a rush of water caused by heavy rains or melting
     snow

Fungi - plants without chlorophyll deriving nourishment from
     another organism -- mushrooms and molds are good
     examples of these flowerless, leafless plants

Fusion - combining of small atomic nuclei or particles into
     larger ones with the release of energy

Genetics - science dealing with heredity and differences among
     plants and animals

Geological - having to do with the science of the earth's crust,
     its layers and its history

Glacial - made by the action of ice or glaciers, as during the
     glacial period great ice sheets covered much of North
     America

Gully erosion - an advanced stage of water erosion following
     rill erosion

Gynecology - the the branch of medicine which treats women,
     their diseases, hygiene, etc.

Habitat - home or place of abode

Half-life - a term used to indicate the set rate of speed at
     which a radioactive material disintegrates

Headwaters - the source and upper waters of a stream

Herbivores - organisms that feed on plants

Hibernate - to spend the winter months in an inactive condition

Humidity - moisture in the air

Humus - decayed vegetable matter -- black soil rich in
     vegetable matter

Hybrid - an animal or plant produced from the crossing of
     two distinct varieties or species

Hydration - combination with water

Incapacitation - state of being disabled, no longer having the
    ability or power to do a task
Incubator - apparatus for keeping eggs warm until they hatch
Ingest - to take in for digestion, as into the stomach
Inorganic - the materials of the physical earth, lacking the
    element carbon
Insecticide - an active chemical or formulation used to kill
    unwanted insects
Interdependence - the state of being dependent upon each other
Ion - an atomic particle, an atom, or a molecule which carries
    an electrical charge
Irrigation - diversion of water into an area during dry periods
Isotope - one form of an element -- the isotopes of any element
    behave the same way but differ slightly in weight

Laterite - a residual product of rock decay, red in color and
    having a high content of oxides of iron and hydroxide of
    aluminum and a low proportion of silica
Latosolic soil - develops in humid tropical or semi-tropical
    forested regions. In early stages of its formation the
    soil is neutral or slightly alkaline, but as leaching con-
    tinues, it becomes acid.
Lava - molten rock, as that flowing from a volcano
Leached - loss of soluble soil minerals as the result of the
    movement of ground water
Legumes - plants such as beans and peas which can absorb
    nitrogen from the air
Lichens - alga and fungus living together to their mutual advan-
    tage resembling one plant
Lignite - variety of coal intermediate between peat and
    bituminous coal
Loam - loose, sandy soil rich in plant food
Low prairie stage - in pond succession, the stage in which the
    pond is dry prairie for most of the year; only in spring
    is there water in the pond

Maldistribution -- poorly distributed
Mammal - an animal that suckles its young
Marsh stage - in pond succession, the stage where there are
    no longer any large sized areas of open water because
    pond is chiefly occupied by grasses and sedges
Mesquite - shrub-like tree growing generally in clumps and
    thickets found in the southwestern part of the U. S.

Metabolism - process of building food into living matter and
  using living matter until it is broken down into simpler
  substances or waste matter, giving off energy
Metallic - like metal or consisting of metal
Microorganisms - living animals or plants so tiny as to be
  seen only under a microscope
Migration - seasonal movement of animals
Mimicry - resemble closely or imitate
Molecule - a unit mass of a compound formed by the chemical
  combination of two or more atoms
Mutation - a genetic change, which is transmitted to offspring
  and affects hereditary characteristics
Mutualism - a relationship which is mutually beneficial

Neutrons - one of the two basic particles of which an atom is
  built having no electrical charge
Niche - standard "jobs" which are filled by different species
  in natural communities
Nitrogen - major element of air essential in the growth of
  plants
Nocturnal - of the night or active in the night
Nucleus - an essential part of a cell, plant or animal, without
  which the cell cannot grow or divide
Nutrient - nourishment, as food

Omnivores - organism which eats both plant and animal substances
Ore - rock, dirt, or sand containing some metal, or compound
  of a metal, such as iron, copper, gold
Organic - carbon-containing substances produced by living
  things
Organism - entire body of any living thing
Ornithology - study of birds
Osmosis - the diffusion which proceeds through a semiperme-
  able membrane, typically separating two solutions, or a
  solven and a solution, and tending to equalize their concentrations
Oxidation - to burn or to combine oxygen with another element
  in making new substances
Oxygen - chemical element necessary in water and air, essential to life of plants and animals

Parasite - organism which gets its food entirely from another living organism

Pathogenic - organism capable of causing disease

Peat - partly rotted moss and plant used as a fuel when dried

Permeate - to pass through the pores or crevices, as water permeates sand

Pesticide - any chemical compound effective in killing or controlling pests

pH - a symbol denoting the relative concentration of hydrogen ions in a solution

Podzolic soils - soils, thin and dark, which are formed under a comparatively cool and humid climate, under forest vegetation

Pollen - grains of fine yellowish powder carried from plant to plant, as by insects, to fertilize them

Pollution - any substance which makes air, food, water, or surroundings unhealthy for living organisms

Porosity - quality of being capable of absorbing water - full of pores

Precipitation - movement of water to the earth from the atmosphere

Predators - animals which prey on other animals

Proton - one of the basic particles of which the nucleus of an atom is composed, carrying a positive charge of electricity

Protozoan - one-celled microscopic animal

Pulp - the soft fleshy part of plant stems, fruit, or any soft wet mass such as wood pulp

Radiocactivity - emission of radiant energy, possessed by radium and uranium

Radioisotope - radioactive form of any element

Reclamation - restoration to a useful condition, as reclaiming the land

Reforestation - the propagation of trees by natural and artificial means

Residue - that which remains after a part has been removed by filtration, burning, etc.

Resources - potential or actual wealth of a country -- its coal, iron, water, and trees, for example

Rill erosion - the formation of tiny rills by rain across the surface of the land

Rivulet - a little stream

Resin - solid substance remaining after distilling crude tur-
    pentine
Run-off - rain (or snow) water which runs off the surface in-
    stead of being absorbed by the earth

Sanctuary - a protected place for wildlife -- especially birds
Saprophyte - a plant (or animal) that gets its food from plants
    or animals that have died
Saturate - to fill to the limit of the capacity for absorbing --
    as to saturate the ground with water
Sedimentary - formed by material deposited by water (or some-
    times by wind) such as sedimentary rocks or sands
Sheet erosion - loss of a thin layer of soil due to standing
    water
Silting - the process by which eroded soil is deposited by
    waters in river beds and reservoirs
Smog - combination of smoke and fog in the air
Solubility - quality of dissolving or being dissolved easily
Smelting - process of melting ore to obtain metal
Spawn - fish eggs ready for hatching
Splash erosion - the very beginnings of erosion as that caused
    by the splashing of raindrops
Steppe - vast treeless plains area, especially in southeast
    Europe and in Asia
Sublethal - a little less than lethal, not causing death
Submarginal - in reference to land which is not productive
    enough to be worth developing into farming land
Submerged vegetation stage - in pond succession, the stage
    where humus has accumulated on the bottom of the pond
    and green algae begin reaching for the surface of the
    water
Substratum - surface or medium such as the earth, water,
    and the air, or the bodies of other plants and animals
    upon which organisms live
Subterranean - below the surface of the earth
Synthetics - artificially made products

Taconite - flint-hard, iron ore-bearing rock found near the
    surface of the ground
Technological - having to do with the science of industry
Temporary pond stage - in pond succession, the stage in
    which the pond is wet in early spring only to become
    dry prairie the rest of the year

Tendon - band of fibrous tissue attaching a muscle to a bone, to another muscle, or to an organ of the body

Terrestrial - belonging to or living on the ground or earth

Thinning - removing inferior trees from a stand to provide for better development of crop trees

Toxin - poison produced by certain microorganisms

Tracer - a radioactive isotope whose location can be detected by Geiger counter

Transpiration - the loss of water from plants

Tributaries - streams that flow into a larger body of water

Tundra - zone below polar region which is characterized by absence of trees, a short growing season, and frozen ground during much of the year

Ultraviolet rays - are invisible to the human eye, but affect some photographic plates, and are useful in the treatment of diseases

Uranium - a heavy, white, radioactive metal which is the principal source of fuel for nuclear reactors

Watershed - a drainage area, as a hilly region which conducts surface water to streams

Wilderness area - a region or territory maintained or found in its original condition

Zonation - state of being where a region or area is characterized by uniform or similar animal and plant life

Zoologist - a scientist who studies animal life and the relation of animals to other living things

INDEX

Date Due

DEC 19 1966		
MAY 14 1967		
JAN 8 1968		

Demco 293-5